INTRODUCTION TO
VERTEBRATE
EMBRYOLOGY

By

WALDO SHUMWAY

PROFESSOR OF ZOOLOGY
UNIVERSITY OF ILLINOIS

FOURTH EDITION
FOURTH PRINTING

NEW YORK: JOHN WILEY & SONS, Inc.
LONDON: CHAPMAN & HALL, Limited

FOURTH EDITION
Fourth Printing, March, 1947

To E. S. S. and F. S. S.

PREFACE

The fourth edition of *Vertebrate Embryology* has been so extensively rewritten as to require a new preface. I shall both restate some of the features of the book which have been retained and outline the changes introduced.

In the first place, this edition, like the others, is organized on a comparative basis. By this I mean that the successive stages in vertebrate development, as well as the developmental anatomy of the different organ systems, are considered from the comparative point of view. This is in contrast to another sort of treatment which may be designated as sequential or chronological, in which the complete embryology of one vertebrate is considered before that of another is commenced. The plan here adopted is to describe, for each stage or each organ system, the common vertebrate plan of development, and then to point out the specific details in each of the types selected for study. These types are four in number: amphioxus, because of the diagrammatic simplicity with which its early embryology may be followed; the frog (*Rana pipiens*)[1], unexcelled as an example of development in a small-yolked aquatic embryo; the chick, which is the basic form for all laboratory courses; and, finally, man, for human embryology is the topic in which the student, quite rightly, has the greatest interest.

This organization makes the book available for the premedical student, especially since in this edition the amount of space devoted to human embryology has been greatly increased. The teacher who wishes to devote the greater part of the course to human embryology may easily omit the sections dealing specifically with the frog in the chapters on organogeny. Similarly, the teacher who wishes to emphasize the development of the frog may omit the sections on human organogeny. The recasting of the vertebrate organogeny into separate chapters for the different organ systems has made it possible to set off these sections more distinctly.

In the second place, the treatment of the material is both morphological and physiological. In the opinion of many teachers embryology is no longer a purely anatomical subject, and the student finds that the best way to learn the structures of the embryo is through the study of the dynamic aspects of development. In this edition the chapter on

[1] See Note on page 270.

experimental embryology has been transferred to a position immediately following the chapters on organogeny, and it may be omitted by those who prefer to leave the latest advances of embryology to more advanced courses.

In the third place, an attempt has been made to bring all the different topics treated up to date. The literature of the subject is truly enormous. Elsewhere (*Science*, 1940) I have written that between 1927 and 1936 3469 abstracts in vertebrate embryology were printed in *Biological Abstracts*. These and later abstracts have been considered in preparing this revision, and the reader will find included much new material such as the data made available through the publications of the Carnegie Institution of Washington on primate and particularly human development. The results obtained through the use of vital stains by Vogt, Pasteels, and many others have been incorporated in the chapter on early embryology. Particular attention may be called to the photographs of frog embryos during gastrulation and neurulation and the interpretative drawings which accompany them. I believe that this account of gastrulation in the frog is as accurate as can be given at the present time.

These changes, including an increase in the proportion of the book devoted to organogeny from one quarter of the total to one third, have necessitated certain condensations elsewhere. The chapter on chromosomes and genes has been shortened by eliminating the description of inheritance in *Drosophila* which is now adequately treated in most introductory textbooks of zoology. The chapters in earlier editions dealing with the anatomy of vertebrate embryos have been condensed into an atlas (Chapter 18), and some of the descriptive matter has been worked into the chapters on organogeny. Since the appearance of a laboratory manual prepared with my colleague, Dr. F. B. Adamstone, covering the anatomy of these embryos, the descriptions in the textbook have no longer been necessary to our students, but the illustrations have continued to be very useful as a preview or review of the work in the laboratory. I should stress the fact that these illustrations are intended to be faithful representations of typical laboratory preparations such as the student may expect to encounter in his own laboratory work. Elsewhere in the text, to be sure, diagrams, smoothed drawings, and reconstructions have been employed where teaching experience has shown their desirability. In our laboratory, my colleagues and I make much use of such models as Ziegler's, the excellent frog models of Müller, the chick models of Jewell and Patten, and wax reconstructions prepared for our own use.

The chapter on vertebrate life histories has proved very useful as a general introduction to the comparative chapters which follow and has been retained. In this revision the illustrations of frog embryos originally published in the *Anatomical Record* (1940) have been used with the permission of that journal.

The pages devoted to the preparation and study of embryological material have been condensed into a single chapter. It has long been my experience and that of my associates that the study of serial sections is facilitated greatly if the student is given opportunity to prepare at least one set of slides in the laboratory. Where this is not practicable, he may derive some benefit from reading an account of the method by which such material is prepared.

Space has also been saved by eliminating the chapter references and substituting a classified working bibliography. The glossary has been compared carefully with other glossaries, particularly the one in Rugh's *Experimental Embryology*. The terminology has been checked against Webster's *New International Dictionary*, and I hope that it now conforms to the best American usage.

The most pleasant task in preparing a new edition is to review the contributions made by the author's friends. Of the new illustrations the great majority are prepared by the artist of the earlier editions, Mrs. Katharine Hill Paul. The photographs are the work of my student, George Svihla. Most of the wax reconstructions illustrated have been prepared by the students named in the figure legends, and I am happy to acknowledge their enthusiasm and skill. A number of figures have been borrowed from other publications, and I am indebted to the courtesy of the copyright holders for permission to republish them. I take this opportunity to thank Drs. W. C. Curtis, Mary J. Guthrie, L. B. Arey, W. F. Windle, A. T. Hertig, and John Rock, as well as their respective publishers, John Wiley and Sons, W. B. Saunders, and the Carnegie Institution of Washington. I am grateful also to Dr. E. A. Boyden and the *Anatomical Record* for permission to republish the plates of my normal stages of *Rana pipiens*.

To Dr. J. H. McGregor, teacher and friend, I owe a debt of gratitude for his stimulating instruction and his encouragement and advice in the preparation of the original edition of this book. I have been very fortunate while preparing this edition to have the advice of my colleague, Dr. C. G. Hartman, who was kind enough to read the first six chapters in proof. To my friend and colleague, Dr. F. B. Adamstone, I am indebted for many suggestions based on the continuous use of the textbook for fifteen years and for invaluable assistance in correcting proof sheets. Special thanks are due my publisher, John Wiley and Sons, who has taken as much interest in the contents of the book as in its external appearance, and to the many teachers who have made me their debtor by suggestions

for making the book more useful.   The errors which must have persisted,
however, are my own, and I shall be grateful to all friends who call my
attention to them.

WALDO SHUMWAY

URBANA, ILLINOIS
December, 1941

CONTENTS

CONTENTS

CHAPTER 1

THE STUDY OF EMBRYOLOGY

Embryology may be defined as that division of biological science which deals with the development of the individual organism. It is concerned with the orderly series of changes in form and function through which the initial germ of the new individual is transformed into a sexually mature adult. Among vertebrate animals, at least, the germ with which development commences is normally an egg that has been fertilized by a sperm. The sexually mature adult is an individual which has developed to a point where it can produce mature eggs if a female, or sperms if a male. Sometimes the word ontogeny is used as a synonym for embryology, but more often it is defined to include the entire life history of an individual from its origin to its death.

Early embryologists. The earliest treatise on embryology which has been preserved is Aristotle's (384–322 B.C.), entitled " De Generatione Animalium " — concerning the generation of animals. This work describes the reproduction and development of many kinds of animals. Another treatise of his, " De Historia Animalium," contains the first account of the development of the hen's egg. Comparing the different types of reproduction, Aristotle placed the mammals first, for, being unable to discover the egg, he thought that their young arose from a mixture of male and female fluids and were " born alive." Sharks, on the other hand, arose from eggs which were retained within the body of the mother and so were also born alive. Next he placed the type of reproduction shown by reptiles and birds in which the egg is " complete," that is to say, furnished with albumen and a shell. Lowest among the vertebrates were the amphibians and bony fish with " incomplete " eggs. His account of development showed great powers of observation, skill in comparison, and imagination in interpretation. Notable among his speculations is one which has been given the name " epigenesis." From his observations on the development of the hen's egg he concluded that development always proceeds from a simple formless beginning to the complex organization of the adult.

1

Another famous name in embryology is William Harvey (1578–1657). His book, "Exercitationes de Generatione Animalium," is based largely on the development of the chick, which he described in great detail, although he too was limited by the fact that the microscope had not yet come into general use. One of his contributions was a careful study of the development of the deer, which he compared with the chick. From purely theoretical considerations he came to the conclusion that mammals also formed eggs. The dictum " Ex ovo omnia " — all animals arise from eggs — is found on the frontispiece of the first editions of his book.

After the invention of the microscope, Marcello Malpighi (1628–1694) published an account of the development of the hen's egg, " De Ovo Incubato," illustrated with excellent figures of development from the 24-hour stage of incubation on. His work was responsible for a theory of " preformation " as opposed to Aristotle's epigenesis. On theoretical grounds, he held that the various parts of the embryo were contained in the egg and became visible as they increased in size. The enthusiasm resulting from the remarkable discoveries made with the newly invented microscope led to many later and wholly imaginative accounts of homunculi — miniature adults — in eggs or sperms, respectively.

Caspar Friedrich Wolff (1733–1794), in a highly theoretical treatise, " Theoria Generationis," attacked the theory of preformation on logical grounds. A more important contribution on the development of the intestine in the chick demonstrated that the tubular intestine arose from the folding of a flat layer in an earlier stage of incubation. This was a direct refutation of the preformationist idea that the intestine was tubular from the beginning.

Comparative embryology. Karl Ernst von Baer (1792–1876) is known as the " father of modern embryology." He discovered the egg of mammals in 1827 and published a book on animal development (1828 and 1837) in which he compared in detail the development of different animals. From these he drew four important conclusions, known as von Baer's laws.

" 1. The more general characteristics of any large group of animals appear in the embryo earlier than the more special characteristics.

" 2. After the more general characteristics those that are less general arise and so on until the most special characteristics appear.

" 3. The embryo of any particular kind of animal grows more unlike the forms of other species instead of passing through them.

" 4. The embryo of a higher species may resemble the embryo of a lower species but never resembles the adult form of that species."

From the time of von Baer up to the present the history of embryology has been marked by increasing specialization. Thus there is a comparative embryology of the vertebrates and a comparative embryology of the invertebrates. There are also other divisions of embryology which will be indicated briefly in the following paragraphs.

Cellular embryology. Soon after the first volume of von Baer's treatise appeared, Schleiden and Schwann (1838, 1839) announced the cell theory, namely that all living things are composed of, and arise from, living units known as cells. This resulted in an intensive study, commencing in the latter part of the nineteenth century, of the germ cells, their origin and fertilization, which led Sutton in 1901 to the chromosomal theory of inheritance. In 1878 Charles Otis Whitman (1842–1910) traced for the first time the detailed history of the cells formed by the dividing egg (in the leech, *Clepsine*), thereby initiating the study of cell lineage. Cellular embryology is a subject which unites embryology with cytology, the study of the cell and its activities.

Genetics and embryology. In 1866, Gregor Mendel (1822–1884) first carried on successfully experiments in breeding plants to discover the laws by which individual characteristics are inherited from one generation to another. His contributions were long unrecognized, but in 1900 they were rediscovered and in the following year Sutton first suggested that the behavior of the chromosomes afforded a mechanical explanation of these laws. This has led to the theory of the gene, a name proposed for the unit of heredity by Johannsen (1911). This theory in the hands of T. H. Morgan has assumed great importance to the embryologist, for, to quote from Brachet, " Embryology is fundamentally the study of heredity in action."

Phylogeny and embryology. In 1866, Ernst Haeckel (1834–1919) published a theory which he believed supported Darwin's theory of evolution. He called it the " fundamental biogenetic law." It is more often known as the recapitulation theory. This theory states that ontogeny is a brief and incomplete recapitulation of phylogeny, or that an animal passes through stages in its development comparable to those through which its ancestors passed in their evolution. So far as the vertebrates are concerned, this would mean that a mammalian embryo should pass through stages which are definitely fish-like and later through stages which are essentially reptilian. The fact is that, although there are individual characteristics which at times are reminiscent of fish-like or reptilian ancestors, there is never a time in the development of a mammal when it could be mistaken for a fish or a reptile. There are evidences that the vertebrates do retain in development certain features which also appeared in the development of their ancestors. For example, clefts appear in the pharynx of the embryos of birds and mammals, opening to the exterior just as they do in the embryos of fish. In the adult fish these clefts contain the gills, but this is not true of adult reptiles or birds. It has been found very difficult, if not impossible, to draw up a genealogical tree of the vertebrates based solely on embryological data, and the recapitulation theory is not so widely accepted as in former times.[1]

Experimental embryology. Among Haeckel's contemporary opponents was Wilhelm His (1831–1904), who directed attention to the physiology of the embryo. Denying the theory of recapitulation,

SOME IMPORTANT EVENTS IN THE HISTORY OF EMBRYOLOGY UP TO 1900

Embryology in the classic period

| 4th century B.C. | Aristotle | |

Embryology in the Renaissance period
(Before the general use of the microscope)

| 1651 | Harvey | Epigenesis |

(After the general use of the microscope)

| 1672 | Malpighi | Preformation |
| 1768 | Wolff | Epigenesis |

Embryology in modern times

1828	von Baer	Comparative embryology
1839	(Schleiden and Schwann announced cell theory)	
1859	(Darwin announced theory of natural selection)	
1866	Haeckel	Biogenetic law
1866	(Mendel announced laws of inheritance)	
	(Microscopic technique being developed)	
1874	His	Experimental embryology
1878	Whitman	Cell lineage
1883	Roux	Mechanics of development
1891	Weismann	Theory of the germplasm
1899	Loeb	Artificial parthenogenesis
1900	(Rediscovery of Mendel's laws)	

[1]Shumway. 1932. "The Recapitulation Theory." *Quart. Rev. Biol.* 7:93–99.

There are two different ways of approaching the subject of vertebrate embryology, when more than one type of development is to be studied. By the first method the different types of development are taken up one after another, e.g., amphioxus, frog, chick, man. The second method consists of discussing the different topics of embryology in turn and comparing the conditions found in each of the types. In this book, the second, or comparative, method is employed. But before taking up the first topic in comparative embryology, it is helpful to examine, very briefly, the life history of each of the types to be used in the later discussion. This will serve to introduce the main stages of embryology, and to point out the different conditions under which development takes place.

SUMMARY

The history of embryology has passed through three phases. First came the period of fact-finding or description. The first name associated with this period is Aristotle's. Before the invention of the microscope, Harvey, and, after its invention, Malpighi, made careful studies of the development of the hen's egg.

The second period is comparative embryology, commencing with von Baer. Comparative embryology has been influenced in the past by Haeckel's theory of recapitulation, which was supposed to support the Darwinian theory. With this period we associate also the subject of cellular embryology growing out of Schleiden and Schwann's cell theory. This subject is now closely linked with genetics, for the gene, or unit of genetics, is located in the nucleus of the cell.

The present period may be called experimental embryology, foreshadowed by His and put on a firm basis by Roux.

The study of embryology is of value in understanding the relationships of the parts of the adult body and the homologies of adult organs in different groups of animals. But its immediate aim is to discover the nature of developmental processes. Its methods are observational and experimental. It is concerned both with the behavior of the cells of the embryo and with the activities of the embryo as a whole.

CHAPTER 2

VERTEBRATE LIFE HISTORIES

The general pattern of development is essentially the same in all vertebrate animals. In the different classes of vertebrates, to be sure, there are many individual departures from this general plan. Nevertheless, a more accurate picture of vertebrate embryology can be obtained from a study of the details of development in several well-known forms than in one. Of all the vertebrates the four which have been studied most intensively are the amphioxus, the frog, the chick, and man. In order to compare the details of development in these vertebrates it is helpful to have a general picture of the life history of each. Before continuing with a brief account of the life history of these vertebrates it is advisable for the student to recall the list of terms which will be used in the descriptions following.

SOME EXPRESSIONS COMMON IN DESCRIBING EMBRYOS
(Synonyms in parentheses)

Anterior (cephalic, cranial, rostral) — head end.
Posterior (caudal) — tail end.
Dorsal — back surface.
Ventral — belly surface.
Lateral — either right (dextral) side, or left (sinistral) side.
Mesial (median, medial) — middle.
Proximal — nearer the point of reference.
Distal — farther from the point of reference.
Transverse — a plane intersecting the anteroposterior axis at right angles, dividing anterior portion from posterior.
Sagittal — the mesial plane of the body or any plane parallel to it, dividing right portion from left.
Frontal (coronal) — any plane at right angles to both transverse and mesial planes dividing dorsal portion from ventral.
Primordium (anlage, Ger.; ébauche, Fr.) — the first recognizable stage in the development of any new part of the embryo.
Invagination — the growth of a surface in (toward the point of reference).
Evagination — the growth of a surface out (away from the point of reference).

AMPHIOXUS

The amphioxus (*Branchiostoma lanceolatum*) is not really a vertebrate, for it lacks a skull and vertebral column. But because it has a notochord and other chordate structures it is a relative of

8

the vertebrates, a protochordate. Some believe that the structures peculiar to the amphioxus are more primitive than those seen in the vertebrates; others hold that they are degenerate and due to the mode of life adopted by this curious animal.

Spawning. Amphioxus is found in many localities. In the Bay of Naples, where the development of the amphioxus has been carefully studied, its breeding season takes place in late spring and summer. During the late afternoon the males and females emerge from the sands in which they burrow normally, and swim about in the shallow waters, shedding sperms and eggs respectively. The eggs are quite small (0.1 mm. in diameter) and contain little yolk.

Fertilization. The sperms swim to the eggs, one sperm normally entering each egg, about which a membrane — the fertilization membrane — appears. Before fertilization each egg gives off a very small cell — the first polar body. After fertilization a second polar body is formed (Fig. 1*A*).

Cleavage. About an hour after fertilization the fertilized egg divides into two equal parts. This is called the first cleavage or 2-cell stage, and each of the cells is called a ½-blastomere (Fig. 1*B, C*). The second cleavage follows in about three-quarters of an hour to bring about the 4-cell stage with its ¼-blastomeres. Later cleavages occur more rapidly. It will be noticed that the cells near the point at which the polar bodies (animal pole) were given off are a little smaller than those in the opposite (vegetal) hemisphere (Fig. 1*D, E*).

Blastula. Four to six hours after fertilization it is seen that the blastomeres have arranged themselves in the form of a hollow sphere. This is called a blastula (Fig. 1*F*), and the enclosed cavity, which is due to the rounding up of the inner surfaces of the blastomeres and the formation of a jelly between them, is called the blastocoel (Fig. 1*G*).

Gastrula. Six to seven hours after fertilization it will be observed that the larger blastomeres are moving into the blastocoel just as if that side of the blastula were collapsing inward. This is called invagination, and when the process is complete the hollow sphere has been transformed into a two-layered cup, the gastrula (Fig. 1*H*). The blastocoel has been pushed out of the picture, and a new cavity, the gastrocoel (or archenteron), has taken its place. This new cavity opens to the exterior by means of a large aperture, the blastopore, which later narrows as the gastrula increases in length (Fig. 1*I*).

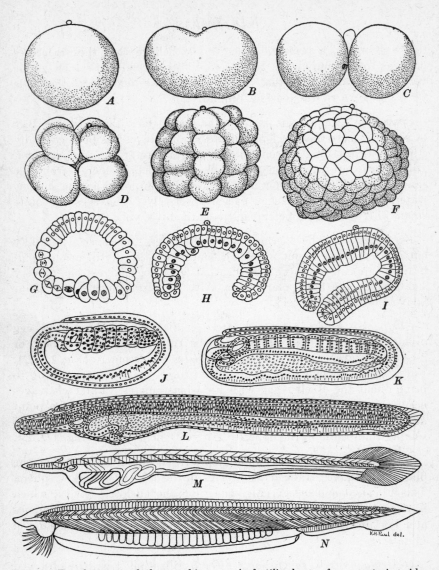

FIG. 1. Development of the amphioxus. *A*, fertilized egg, from posterior side. *B*, beginning first cleavage, from posterior side. *C*, first cleavage complete, from vegetal side (note extruded jelly). *D*, third cleavage, from right side. *E*, fifth cleavage (32 cell stage), from side. *F*, blastula (256 cell stage), from right side. *G*, blastula, sagittal section. *H*, gastrula, sagittal section. *I*, late gastrula, sagittal section. *J*, early embryo of seven somites, optical section from left side. *K*, embryo of ten or eleven somites, optical section from left side. *L*, embryo of 48 hours, optical section from left side. (*A–L*, ×166, after Conklin, 1932.) *M*, larva with three gill slits, from left side, ×60 (after Lankaster and Willey). *N*, adult, from left side, ×2 (after Lankaster).

The germ layers. The outer layer of the gastrula is known as the ectoderm; the inner one is frequently called the endoderm. It really includes not only the endoderm proper, which is to become the lining of the digestive tube, but also the middle germ layer or chorda-mesoderm, which now forms the roof of the gastrocoel. The notochord and mesoderm are separated from each other about 11 or 12 hours after fertilization. The mesoderm gives rise to a series of pouches or enterocoels which are metamerically arranged on either side of the notochord. The endoderm from either side grows up under the mesoderm and unites under the notochord so that the cavity is completely lined with endoderm.

The ectoderm immediately overlying the chorda-mesoderm is the neural plate. At its margin lateral folds arise and arch towards the midline to meet and form a neural tube. Ectoderm from the ventral lip of the blastopore fuses with them about 15 hours after fertilization, forming a neurenteric canal by which neural tube and gut are connected (Figs. 1*J*, 1*K*).

Hatching. The embryo escapes from its egg envelopes at this time, if not indeed a little earlier. It is now cylindrical in form, flattened on the dorsal surface, its length about twice its diameter. It appears to be about twice the volume of the original egg, owing to the large digestive cavity arising from the gastrocoel.

The larva. After hatching, the embryo still subsists on the remainder of its yolk until the mouth opens, about the fourth day after fertilization. It is then about 1 mm. in length, very slender, and probably of no greater volume than the original egg (Fig. 1*L*). As soon as the mouth opens and the embryo is able to ingest food from external sources it is called a larva. By now all the organ systems except those connected with reproduction are functioning. For about three months the larva leads a free-swimming existence, making its way to deeper waters (Fig. 1*M*).

Metamorphosis. At the end of three months, roughly speaking, the larva has increased in length to an average of 3.5 mm. It now gives up its free-swimming life to burrow in the sands and slowly assume its adult characteristics (Fig. 1*N*). The ability to produce mature germ cells is first manifested when the animal is about 20 mm. long.

THE FROG

The frog (*Rana pipiens*) is one of the anuran amphibia. It is selected as a type of ichthyopsid (fish and amphibia) or anamniote (developing without an amnion). It has been a favorite object of embryological observations and experiments for centuries, and its development is better known than that of any other vertebrate except the chick.

Spawning. The breeding season of the frog is in the early spring, soon after the ice is off the ponds. The males, emerging first from hibernation, make their way to the breeding grounds, where they congregate and sing in chorus while awaiting the coming of the females. On arrival, each female is seized by a male who grasps her for long periods (amplexus). In the early morning both individuals discharge their germ cells, so that fertilization is external. The egg, about 1.7 mm. in diameter (Fig. 2*A*), is surrounded with a layer of albumen which swells rapidly, causing the eggs, in masses of 3500 to 4500 (Wright), to adhere to vegetation or to rest on the bottom in shallow water. The yolk, present in the form of platelets, is concentrated largely in the lower hemisphere of the egg.

Fertilization. Fertilization is external, but the close contact of the individuals during amplexus ensures that the sperm enters the egg before the swelling of the egg jelly prevents it. The first polar body is formed before fertilization, the second afterwards.

Cleavage. The rate of cleavage depends upon the temperature, but the first division (Fig. 2*B*) may occur one to two hours after fertilization, earlier at high temperatures, later at low ones. Cleavage divides the egg completely, but the third cleavage is unequal so that the four ⅛-blastomeres of the animal hemisphere are markedly smaller than the four of the vegetal hemisphere (Fig. 2*D*). After the third cleavage, the pattern becomes more irregular.

Blastula. The presence of the large yolk-laden blastomeres in the vegetal hemisphere results in an eccentrically placed blastocoel. Furthermore, cleavage planes tangential to the surface of the blastula produce a layer of blastomeres several cells in thickness.

Gastrula. The presence of great amounts of yolk prevents any invagination, and gastrulation takes place by overgrowth instead. Commencing from a shallow groove just below the equator (Fig. 2*F*), the smaller cells grow down over the larger ones. The down-growing cells form a two-layered fold because the cells at the margin are turned in as the fold grows down. As this overgrowth and tucking-in continues, the fold extends at its two extremities to become crescent-shaped (Fig. 2*G*). Finally the two ends of the crescent meet to form a circle, which rapidly diminishes in circumference until finally only a small plug of the larger yolk-laden cells protrudes (Fig. 2H). The circle is known as the blastopore, and the groove with which it commenced is known as the dorsal lip of the blastopore.   A gastrocoel

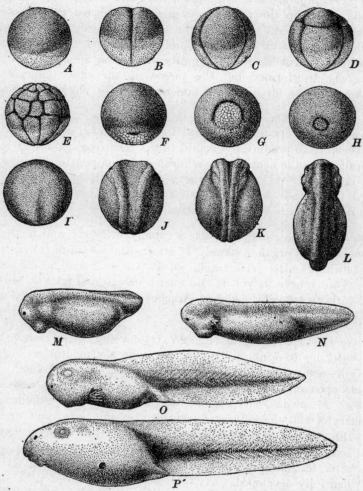

Fig. 2.   Development of the frog, *Rana pipiens*.   *A*, fertilized egg, from left side. *B*, first cleavage, from posterior side.   *C*, second cleavage, from left side.   *D*, third cleavage, from side.   *E*, fifth cleavage, from side.   *F*, early gastrula (dorsal lipstage), from posterior side.   *G*, midgastrula (lateral lips), posterior side.   *H*, late gastrula (yolk plug stage), posterior side.   *I*, neurula, dorsal side.   *J*, neural folds open, dorsal side.   *K*, neural folds closed, dorsal side.   *L*, tail bud stage, dorsal side. (*A–L*, ×10.)   *M*, stage of muscular response.   *N*, hatching stage.   *O*, opercular fold stage.   *P*, tadpole after closing of operculum.   (*M–P*, ×7½.)   (From Shumway, *Anatomical Record* 78:139–147, rearranged.)

is formed between the large yolk-laden cells and the smaller cells turned in at the lips of the blastopore.

The germ layers. The cells which were left on the exterior of the gastrula make up the ectoderm, while the inturned cells make up the chorda-mesoderm or roof of the gastrocoel formed at the dorsal lip and mesoderm at the lateral and ventral lips. The yolk-laden cells which were overgrown in the process become the endoderm. No enterocoels are formed but the mesoderm on either side of the notochord breaks up into a metameric series of block-like somites.

The neurula. The neural plate lies over the roof of the gastrocoel. It forms around its margin neural folds (Fig. 2*I*), which will later grow together to produce the neural tube. The frog embryo is called a neurula when the neural plate is formed (50 hours after fertilization, when kept at 18° C.). While the neural tube is being formed the embryo increases in length to about 2.5 mm. This length is attained, ordinarily, 72 hours after fertilization (Fig. 2*K*).

Hatching. The embryo increases rapidly in length and in the development of its organ systems. It attains the length of 6 mm. (Fig. 2*N*), 140 hours after fertilization (at 18° C.) and wriggles out of its jelly. The embryo as yet has no mouth or external gills but is provided with a sucker by which it attaches itself to the egg jelly while these organs are forming.

The larva. External·gills (Fig. 2*N*, *O*) develop on the embryo soon after hatching (6–7 mm.), but, by the time the mouth has formed, these gills are covered over by a fold of skin, the operculum. This remains open on the left side by means of an aperture called the spiracle. Meantime, clefts have opened between the endoderm of the pharynx and the ectoderm just back of the head, and in these clefts the internal gills are formed. By now the embryo may be called a larva. It is 11 mm. in length (Fig. 2*P*) and its age is 284 hours after fertilization (at 18° C.). The tadpole is about 84 mm. long when fully developed.

About a month after hatching, the legs develop: first the fore-legs, concealed by the operculum; later the hind-legs. The lungs are now developing, and the tadpoles frequently come to the surface to breathe.

Metamorphosis. About 3 months (90 to 100 days) after the egg is laid, the larva undergoes a rapid change into the adult condition (Fig. 2*N*). If food is scanty or prolonged cool weather prevails, this metamorphosis may be held over until the following spring. The animals become sexually mature in the second spring following metamorphosis.

THE CHICK

The domestic fowl (*Gallus domesticus*) develops under conditions widely removed from the two types preceding, for the egg is laid on land. This type of development is characteristic of the sauropsids (reptiles and birds) and of the egg-laying mammals (monotremes). We have observed that most of the early embryologists worked with the hen's egg, for it may be procured in abundance at all seasons of the year and is easily incubated. The development of the hen's egg is studied in almost every embryological laboratory and is better known than that of any other vertebrate.

Fertilization. The egg is fertilized within the oviduct of the female after copulation with a male. The sperms make their way to the upper portion of the duct and retain their vitality for at least three weeks. The egg forms two polar bodies, but it is not known whether the sperm enters the egg before or after the formation of the second polar body. In the pigeon's egg the sperm enters while the first polar body is being formed.

The egg itself is extremely large, at the time of fertilization consisting of an enormous mass of yolk about 40 mm. in diameter. On this rests a tiny disc of protoplasm, the blastodisc, about 3 mm. in length. All is enclosed by a vitelline membrane (Fig. 3*A*).

As the egg makes its way down the oviduct (a process requiring about 24 hours), albumen or egg white is deposited around it, shell membranes are laid down enclosing the albumen, and finally calcium salts are deposited on the membranes. These harden about 13 hours after ovulation.

Cleavage. This process also takes place as the egg is traversing the oviduct. In the hen's egg, cleavage affects only the blastodisc and the yolk is entirely undivided (Fig. 3*B, C*). Furthermore, the blastomeres are not at first divided completely from each other but remain connected below and at the margin of the disc.

Blastula. Tangential cleavage planes, at about the 64-cell stage, cut off the central cells from the undivided protoplasm beneath them, thus forming a blastocoel. The marginal cells are still united beneath the blastocoel and at their margin by the undivided protoplasm or periblast. Central and marginal cells together make up the blastoderm, which expands rapidly as new cells are added at its periphery

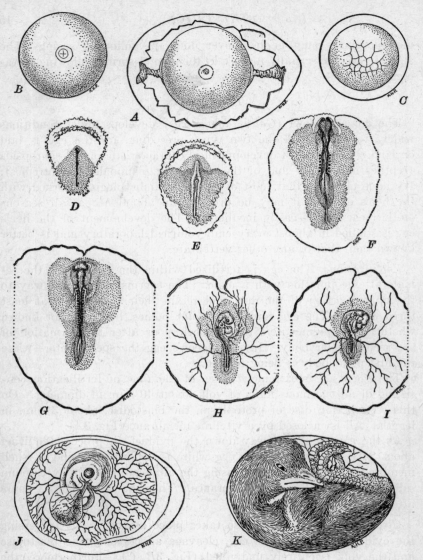

FIG. 3. Development of the hen's egg. *A*, fertilized egg, with shell partly broken away to show interior, ×¾. *B*, second cleavage, shell and albumen removed, from above, ×¾. *C*, later cleavage stage, germinal disc only, from above, ×4. *D*, blastoderm at 15 hours of incubation, ×7. *E*, blastoderm at 20 hours of incubation, ×7. *F*, blastoderm at 25 hours of incubation, ×6. *G*, blastoderm at 38 hours of incubation, ×5½. *H*, blastoderm at 48 hours of incubation, ×2¼. *I*, blastoderm at 68 hours of incubation, ×2¼. *J*, embryo and yolk sac at sixth day of incubation, ×¾. *K*, embryo at nineteenth day of incubation, ×¾. (All after Duval; *K* modified.)

and cut off from the periblast. The central portion of the periblast is soon consumed, and the central portion of the blastoderm lies directly above the yolk. The original blastocoel thus is enlarged by the addition of space resulting from the liquefaction of the yolk. When viewed by reflected light, the area over this cavity appears more transparent and is called the area pellucida, and the denser area surrounding it is called the area opaca.

Gastrula. The blastoderm grows out over the yolk all around its periphery, but in one area cells migrate beneath the surface, converting the area pellucida into a two-layered structure which may be called the gastrula. The underlying cavity is the gastrocoel, and the area where the ingrowth took place represents the blastopore.

Laying and incubation. It is during gastrulation that the eggs are usually laid (Fig. 3A). After the eggs are laid, the hen broods them for about three weeks. This process keeps the eggs at a temperature of about 38°–39° C.

Germ layers. The two layers of the gastrula are usually called the ectoderm and the endoderm. The cells which will later migrate beneath the surface to form the chorda-mesoderm are still in the outer layer. Early in the first day of incubation an axial area, which is known as the primitive streak (Fig. 3D), appears in the area pellucida. Here it will be sufficient to note that the notochord grows forward from the anterior end of the streak, while the mesoderm grows out from its sides and posterior end (Fig. 3E).

Formation of the body. The embryo is still a flat disc, so the neural folds, somites, etc., take their origin during the first day in a manner which differs from that of the frog much as a flat map differs from a globe (Fig. 3F). Later a series of folds cuts off the embryo (Fig. 3G, H, I) in the pellucid area while the area opaca is growing down around the yolk to form a yolk sac. To this the embryo is attached by a yolk stalk. In the wall of the yolk sac there develops an extensive circulatory system which conveys food digested by the wall of the sac to the rapidly growing embryo.

Amnion and allantois. Other folds grow up from the area pellucida to form a second sac, the amnion, which encloses the embryo. In this a fluid is formed so that the chick really develops in a watery medium, or " private pond," as it has been called (Fig. 3J). In connection with the growth of the amnion a third sac, the chorion, is formed, enclosing a cavity known as the exocoel or extra-embryonic coelom.

Still another sac grows out from the body of the chick which serves in the first instance to receive the waste products of metabolism while the chick is still within the shell. This sac, the allantois (Fig. 3*J*), later develops a network of blood vessels which come in close contact with the shell and serve as a respiratory device whereby oxygen is obtained and carbon dioxide given off. Finally this sac encloses the albumen, which is also utilized as food and a source of water.

Hatching. On the twentieth day (Fig. 3*K*) the chick punctures the shell, the remains of the yolk sac are drawn back into the body, and the lungs are put to work. The following day it makes its way out of the shell, leaving amnion, chorion, and allantois behind. Sexual maturity is attained at the age of 4 or 5 months in the male, and 4 to 10 months in the female.

MAN

The development of man (*Homo sapiens*) has been a subject of study and speculation since long before the time of Aristotle, particularly among students of medicine. But although much is known concerning the later stages of development, the earliest stages remain almost entirely unknown, and our account must be supplemented from observation of other placental mammals.

Fertilization. Fertilization is internal and probably takes place in the upper part of the oviduct, after the first polar body is formed and before the formation of the second (Fig. 4*A*).

Cleavage. The human egg has not been observed in cleavage stages, but in the monkey (Fig. 4*B, C, D*) it is known that cleavage is complete and the first blastomeres are approximately equal in size. There is so little yolk in the egg that the blastomeres round up and slip about on each other, giving rise to a solid mass of blastomeres called a morula.

Blastula. The human blastula is also unknown, and there is some difficulty about homologizing the early embryos of other mammals. Some authorities consider the morula a solid blastula. Others, and these are in the majority, believe that the blastula stage of other vertebrates is represented by a form known as the blastocyst. This is derived from the morula by the formation of a cavity, filled with a liquid, which gradually separates an outer layer of cells, the trophoblast, from an inner mass of cells, the embryonic knob (Fig. 4*E*).

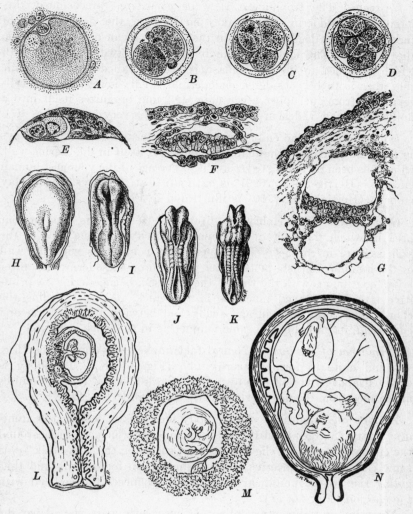

Fig. 4. Development of man. *A*, mature egg, unfertilized, from uterine tube, section, ×250 (after Allen). *B, C, D*, cleavage in the monkey egg, first, second, and third cleavages, ×112 (after Lewis and Hartman in Arey). *E*, section of monkey egg before implantation, ×250 (after Streeter). *F*, section of human ovum, after implantation, ×150 (after Hertig). *G*, section of human embryo, 15 days old, ×100 (after Brewer). *H*, primitive groove stage ×20 (Heuser). *I*, three somites and neural folds ×18 (Ingalls). *J*, seven somites ×15 (Payne). *K*, ten somites ×15 (Corner). (*I–K*, redrawn from Streeter.) *L*, diagram of uterus and embryo at about one month, ×½ (after Arey). *M*, embryo of eleven millimeters (about six weeks) with its membranes, chorion opened, ×1 (after Arey). *N*, fetus, near term, (diagrammatic after Ahlfeld).

Gastrula. The trophoblast may be considered precociously differentiated ectoderm which takes no part in the development of the embryo but does take part in the making of an outer membrane, the chorion. The embryonic knob consists of two regions, one of which, attached to the trophoblast, is usually called ectoderm, while the other is to be considered endodermal. This lower layer of cells separates from the upper layer (Fig. 4*F*) and organizes itself into a hollow yolk sac, which in the human embryo is very small (Fig. 4*G*).

Implantation. The embryo reaches the uterus after about 3½ days in the tube and about the tenth day implants itself in the uterine wall, which has been preparing to receive it. The age of the youngest human embryo (Hertig-Rock 7699) is estimated at 11 days. A 12-day embryo (Hertig-Rock 7700) is illustrated in Fig. 4*F*.

Germ layers. The embryonic disc (Fig. 4*H*) consists of a circular area in which the floor of the amniotic cavity and the roof of the yolk sac are in contact. The upper layer, continuous with the wall of the amnion, consists of ectoderm and chorda-mesoderm; the lower layer, continuous with the wall of the yolk sac, is endoderm. A primitive streak is formed much as in the chick. Along this line the chorda-mesoderm turns in and swings out between the ectoderm and endoderm, in probably the same manner as in the chick embryo.

Formation of the body. Neural folds make their appearance (Fig. 4*I*) and unite to form a neural tube (Fig. 4*J, K*). The body is elevated above the yolk sac by head, lateral, and tail folds. Somites are formed from the mesoderm next the notochord (Fig. 4*J, K*).

Amnion and allantois. As the body increases in length, the amniotic cavity enlarges until the anterior and posterior ends arch around the embryo to meet on the ventral side, enclosing the yolk stalk (plus some embryonic connective tissue formed from mesoderm) and thus giving rise to the umbilical stalk, which connects the embryo with the chorion (Fig. 4*L, M*).

Meantime a rudimentary allantois has grown part way down the umbilical stalk. The allantoic blood vessels, however, continue all the way to the chorion, where they branch out to form a vascular area.

Placenta. As the embryo enlarges, its membranes also increase in size, and soon the embryonic complex bulges out from the uterine wall (Fig. 4*L*). It is still covered with a thin layer of uterine cells and remains attached to the uterine wall by a circular area known as the placenta (Fig. 4*L, N*). It is this area which is supplied by the allantoic (umbilical) blood vessels. Here the maternal and embryonic blood streams are brought close together and substances diffuse from one to the other. This is the region where oxygen and carbon dioxide are interchanged, and here the embryo receives its food, predigested by the mother.

Fetus. By the end of the second month the embryo has quite definitely taken on the characteristics of the human species and is known hereafter as the fetus. From this time on, its developmental history is mainly one of growth while the final details of development proceed (Fig. 4N). At the tenth lunar month (280 days) the intra-uterine development is completed and the fetus is delivered from the body of the mother (parturition or birth).

Extra-uterine development. Like all mammals, the human infant is still dependent upon the mother for nourishment after birth. It is in the human species, moreover, that parental care is carried to the greatest extreme. Development continues long after birth, e.g., the replacement of the teeth and the " knitting " of the bones. Sexual maturity (puberty) is not attained until the age of 12–15 in females, and 13–16 in males. Growth continues into the third decade.

SUMMARY

The egg of the amphioxus is small and contains a small amount of yolk which is evenly distributed. The egg is fertilized externally and develops entirely in a watery medium. The embryo hatches at a very early stage in the life history, and spends a considerable time in a form and mode of life unlike those of the adult. This larval period is succeeded by a slow metamorphosis.

The egg of the frog is larger than that of the amphioxus, contains relatively a large amount of yolk concentrated in the lower hemisphere, and is protected by egg envelopes. Fertilization is external but controlled through a sexual embrace. The embryo develops in water and after hatching soon assumes an appearance and activities quite unlike those of the adult. This larval period is terminated by a sudden metamorphosis associated with a change to terrestrial conditions.

The egg of the chick is enormous because of the great amount of yolk and the albumen enclosed within the shell. Fertilization is internal and prior to the formation of the albumen and shell. Development is very rapid and accompanied by the development of an amnion or water bath, and an allantois which serves as an extra-embryonic bladder, lung, and albumen sac. These features are correlated with the terrestrial environment of the developing egg. Eggs of this type are termed " cleidoic " or enclosed (Needham).

The human egg is very small owing to the small amount of contained yolk. Fertilization is internal, and the developing egg soon implants itself in the wall of the uterus where its later development takes place. The early stages of development are passed through very rapidly, and the blastula and gastrula are quite unlike any seen in other classes of vertebrates. An amnion is formed around the developing embryo, and this structure is concerned in the formation of an umbilical cord connecting the embryo to the placenta, a disc-shaped organ of maternal and fetal origin. The placenta serves as an organ of interchange between mother and young up to the time of birth. Development continues long after this event.

Chapter 3

GERM CELLS

The germ with which the development of the vertebrate commences is the fertilized egg, or zygote. Before discussing the development of the zygote, it is advisable to examine the gametes, egg and sperm, whose union results in its existence.

THE GAMETES

Vertebrates are characterized by the bisexual method of reproduction, in which there are two distinct sexes: the female, or egg-producing individuals, and the male, or sperm-producing individuals. Among the protochordates (tunicates) we find groups in which the same individual produces both eggs and sperms. Such individuals are called hermaphrodites. This phenomenon is rare among the vertebrates and is not typical of any species.

The two kinds of gametes, eggs and sperms, differ from each other in appearance, size, and structure. These differences will be more apparent after a brief review of cell structure in general.

STRUCTURE OF THE CELL

A. Nucleus (composed of karyoplasm).
 1. Reticulum (composed of chromatin).
 2. Karyolymph (nuclear sap).
 3. Nucleolus (plasmasome).
 4. Nuclear membrane.
B. Cytosome (composed of cytoplasm).
 1. Hyaloplasm (ground protoplasm).
 2. Centrosomes (centrioles).
 3. Mitochondria (chondriosomes).
 4. Golgi bodies (dictyosomes).
 5. Plastids (*not found in animal cells*).
 6. Metaplasm (relatively lifeless accumulations).
 7. Plasma membrane.
C. Envelopes or matrix (cell wall).

The cell. The familiar definition of a cell (Fig. 5) is " a mass of protoplasm, containing a nucleus, both of which have arisen by the division of the corresponding elements of a pre-existing cell." Proto-

23

plasm in this sense refers to the living substance of the cell, including the material both inside the nucleus and in the cell body or cytosome. It is customary to use the term karyoplasm (nucleoplasm) for the nuclear protoplasm and the word cytoplasm for the protoplasm of the cell body. Some writers employ only the words nucleus and cytoplasm to distinguish between nucleus and cell body.

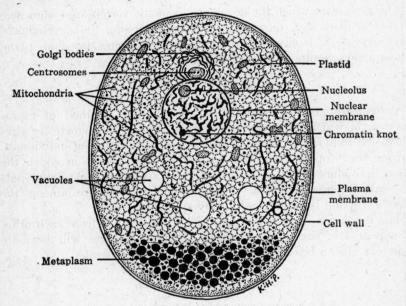

Golgi bodies

Centrosomes

Mitochondria

Vacuoles

Metaplasm

Plastid

Nucleolus

Nuclear membrane

Chromatin knot

Plasma membrane

Cell wall

FIG. 5. Diagram of a composite cell.   (After Wilson.)

The nucleus. The cell nucleus is generally a rounded body separated from the cytosome by a delicate nuclear membrane. Within this is a transparent ground substance known as the karyolymph or nuclear sap. But the characteristic substance of the nucleus is its chromatin, a substance staining sharply with basic dyes, and arranged usually in a network of threads called the reticulum (Sharp). Sometimes swellings, chromomeres, are apparent at the nodes of the network. The nucleus usually contains a smaller body known as the nucleolus, a droplet of some material heavier than the nuclear sap, but staining with acid dyes. Its staining properties alter during cell division.

The nucleus may fragment to form polynuclear cells. It may also divide, often many times, while the cell body remains undivided, resulting in the formation of a syncytium. Sometimes the nucleus may be ejected to leave enucleate cells such as the red blood corpuscles of mammals. But in general every cell has one nucleus.

The type of nucleus here described is known as the vesicular type. There is distinguished also the massive or compact type of nucleus, in which the chromatin forms apparently a solid mass, as in the sperm cell. Then there is a diffuse type, in which the nuclear membrane is absent and the chromatin is scattered through the cell body in granules called chromidia.

The cytosome. The cytoplasm of the cell body includes an outer delicate semipermeable membrane known as the plasma membrane. This is the surface at which the protoplasm of the cell is in contact with its environment. Within this is the liquid ground substance or hyaloplasm, in which are distributed a number of differentiated bodies. Of these cytoplasmic inclusions the more important seem to be the centrosomes, mitochondria, and Golgi bodies, all of which appear to have the properties of independent growth and division.

The centrosomes (centrioles), small spherical bodies, one or two in number, lie near the nucleus. They seem to be concerned in the process of cell division. In cells with locomotor organs, like the tail of the sperm, the centrosomes are connected with the contractile element of the cell.

The mitochondria (chrondriosomes) are small rods, or granules, very numerous and scattered through the cytoplasm. They are dissolved by many common methods of preparing cells for observation, but can be demonstrated in the living cell by a stain called Janus Green B. They are preserved by special chemicals, e.g., osmium tetroxide.

The Golgi bodies (dictyosomes) are sometimes scattered through the cytoplasm but often aggregated into a network, the Golgi apparatus. Some authors deny that there is a real structure of Golgi bodies and speak therefore of the Golgi material or the Golgi zone. Other investigators have sought to identify these bodies with the plastids and other cytoplasmic elements which are found in plant cells. Golgi bodies are hard to identify in living cells but can be demonstrated by special techniques involving the use of osmium tetroxide or silver nitrate. Their function is doubtful, but there is some reason to believe that they are concerned with the elaboration of substances within the cell such as enzymes.

Still another type of inclusion in the cytosome is represented by the plastids. These bodies, e.g., chloroplasts, the chlorophyll bodies, which appear to have the capacity of independent growth and division, are found in plant cells.

Metaplasm is the name given to all those bodies in the cytoplasm which clearly do not possess the properties of independent growth and division. These may be aggregated in vacuoles or distributed in tiny droplets, granules, etc. Among these are such bodies as secretory granules, intermediate stages in the production of cell secretions (enzymes, etc.). Storage granules are end stages in the accumulation of such reserve food materials as yolk, oil, and starch. Here also we may include the minute pigment granules. Embryologists sometimes use the term deutoplasm for reserve food materials in the cell.

The cell wall. In concluding this brief review of cell structures we must recall that the cell may secrete a wall around itself such as the vitelline membrane. In some tissues the individual cells form a common matrix such as the intercellular substance of cartilage or bone.

The sperm. The male germ cell of vertebrates is a very minute flagellate cell ranging in size from 0.020 mm. (crocodile) to more than 2 mm. (*Discoglossus,* an amphibian). The general shape is that of a tadpole with an excessively long tail, but there are sufficient differences among these tiny cells for them to be identified by specialists.

The sperm (spermatozoon) consists of a head and a tail (Fig. 6). Some sperms, e.g., human, have a short neck between the head and tail. The head contains the nucleus, which is compact and stains very deeply with basic dyes. Here also is the acrosome, usually at the apical end, originating from Golgi bodies, possibly connected with the production of some secretion involved in fertilization. The head is surrounded with a delicate plasma membrane.

The tail consists of three divisions: middle piece, main piece and end piece. The middle piece contains two centrosomes; the one nearer the head is called the proximal centrosome, the one farther from the head the distal centrosome. These bodies are so minute that great differences of opinion have been expressed as to their number and position in the various types of sperm. They have also been confused with other small bodies such as the " neck bodies " of the human sperm. The axial filament arises in the middle piece of the sperm apparently from the proximal centrosome and passes through the ring-shaped distal centrosome. Surrounding the axial filament in the middle piece are granules of mitochondrial origin. Outside all these is a plasma membrane. The main piece, as the name implies, is the longest part of the tail and consists of the axial filament and plasma membrane. The end piece is the terminal region in which the naked axial filament projects beyond the limits of its sheath.

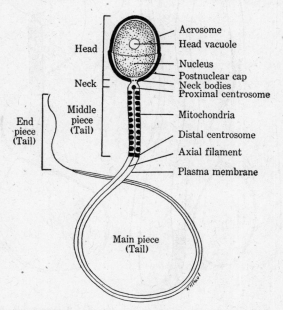

Fɪɢ. 6.   Diagram of a human sperm.   (After Gatenby.)

Abnormal giant or dwarf sperms occur in some individuals. Later we shall see that there are always (except in birds and some fish) two classes of sperms, which are respectively male-producing and female-producing. These are not visibly different as a rule.

SPERM OF THE AMPHIOXUS

The sperm of the amphioxus (Fig. 7A) is the smallest recorded among chordate animals. Its total length varies from 0.016 to 0.021 mm. (Sabotta). The spherical head is not more than 0.001 mm. in length, the size of a yolk granule. There is a minute bead-like acrosome. What appears to be a rounded middle piece pressed against the head is followed by a very slender main piece. The end piece is not distinguishable. The length of life of the sperm has not been recorded.

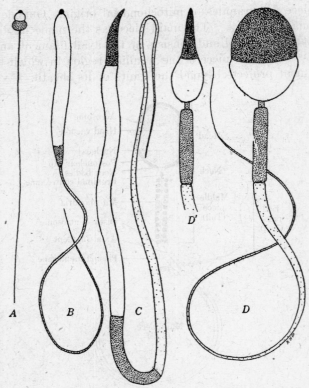

Fig. 7. Typical sperms. *A*, amphioxus. (After Ballowitz.) *B*, frog. *C*, fowl.
D, man. ×4000.

SPERM OF THE FROG

The sperm of *Rana pipiens* (Fig. 7*B*) averages about 0.03 mm. in
length after fixation. The head is long and cylindrical, surmounted
by a bead-like acrosome. The tail originates in a short middle piece,
and has a long main piece indistinguishable from the end piece. No
records on the length of life for sperm of this species have been discovered.

SPERM OF THE FOWL

The sperm of the domestic fowl (Fig. 7*C*) averages approximately
0.05 mm. in length after fixation. The head is long and cylindrical
and surmounted by a sharp recurved acrosome. Adamstone has
described the presence of lipoidal bead-like structures in the head of
the sperm which he considers to be in the nature of reserve food

supply. The middle piece is long and merges into the main piece, which is relatively stout and terminates in a short end piece.

The sperms of the fowl retail their fertilizing power in the oviduct of the hen for about two weeks on the average, with a maximum recorded life of a month.

HUMAN SPERM

The human sperm (Figs. 6, 7D, 7D1), studied by many investigators, contains ten parts (Gatenby and Aykroyd, 1940). It averages 0.055 mm. in length. The acrosome, fitting over the nucleus like a cap, is flattened to a shovel shape at the anterior end. The nucleus is oval and contains a small vacuole. At its posterior end it is covered by a postnuclear cap which joins the acrosome to surround the nucleus completely. The short, constricted neck contains two or more neck bodies. The middle piece is well developed, with a centrosome at either end, and contains mitochondrial granules. A long main piece and short end piece are present.

Recent investigators conclude that the length of life of the sperms in the oviducts does not exceed a week, with an even shorter period of fertilizing capacity. In the monkey (*Macacus*) Hartman has shown that the sperms survive for but a few days.

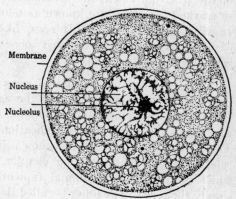

Membrane

Nucleus

Nucleolus

FIG. 8. Egg of the cat (after Dahlgren and Kepner.)

The egg. The female germ cell (Fig. 8) is extremely large, protected by envelopes of various kinds, containing reserve food material, and without power of locomotion. The size range in vertebrates lies between 0.06 mm. (mouse) and 85 mm. (ostrich). The latter figure is the diameter of the egg without shell or albumen, which are egg envelopes. Even larger eggs existed in the past; e.g., in an extinct species of birds (*Aepyornis*) the fossil eggshells are 13 by 9 inches and have a capacity roughly of a gallon. The shape of the egg varies from spherical to oval.

Prior to its maturation the egg contains a large vesicular nucleus. The cytoplasm often appears to be even larger in proportion, but this is due to the great amount of metaplasm present. Centrosomes are present before maturation. Mitochondria and Golgi bodies have also been identified. The color of the egg is caused by the presence of pigment granules in the cytoplasm.

Yolk. The bulk of the egg is due to the presence of metaplasm in the form of yolk. This substance contains the principal foodstuffs for the developing embryo. Studies on the yolk of the hen's egg indicate that it contains water (50 per cent), proteins, fats, carbohydrates, inorganic salts, vitamins, pigments, and enzymes (Needham).

The yolk is present in the form of spheres, ovoids, or discs, which stain usually with basic dyes. The yolk tends to accumulate in one hemisphere of the egg, forcing the nucleus into the other. Since the yolk is heavier than the other constituents of the egg, the yolk-laden hemisphere is the lower one when the egg is suspended in water. In large-yolked (macrolecithal, megalecithal) eggs, such as those of the frog and chick, the accumulation of the yolk in one region is so marked that they are known as telolecithal eggs. In small-yolked (microlecithal, oligolecithal) eggs, like those of the amphioxus and of man, the yolk is distributed more generally and they are called isolecithal (homolecithal).

Polarity. Even in isolecithal eggs there is a visible distinction between the two hemispheres of the egg, so that an axis exists from the center of one hemisphere to that of the other. This, known as the polar axis, is the earliest indication of a differentiation in the egg. The two ends of the axis are known as the poles. The polar bodies, referred to in the preceding chapter, are formed at one of these which is known as the animal (apical) pole. It is sometimes called simply the pole. The other is called the vegetal (vegetative, abapical) pole, sometimes the antipole. The nucleus always lies in the polar axis, more or less towards the animal pole. The yolk shows a gradation from the animal towards the vegetal pole. We shall observe in later chapters that the animal pole often marks the anterior end of the developing embryo and in these cases the vegetal pole marks the posterior end. There is also reason to believe that the polar axis, in addition to being the first expression of symmetry in the egg, marks a gradient of metabolism (Child). By this is meant that metabolic processes are accelerated at the animal pole and progressively retarded towards the vegetal pole.

A considerable body of evidence shows that the animal pole of the egg is the one which was most active in physiological exchange with its environment while still in the ovary. It is the pole of the egg which is attached to the ovary in the amphioxus (Conklin) and the chick (Conklin).

Egg envelopes. The egg usually possesses, in addition to the plasma membrane, a variety of protective envelopes which are divided into three classes according to the mode of their formation. Primary envelopes are those formed by the egg itself, such as the delicate vitelline membrane. The secondary envelopes are those formed by

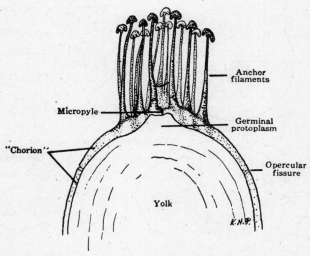

Fig. 9. Egg of *Myxine*, showing " chorion " and micropyle (after Dean).

the follicle cells which immediately surround the egg in the ovary. A good example is the so-called chorion of one of the cyclostomes, *Myxine* (Fig. 9). It is usually quite difficult to distinguish primary from secondary envelopes, and it is probable that many vitelline membranes are compound in origin. In those vertebrates in which fertilization is external, such as the cyclostomes and bony fish, the primary and secondary envelopes are often perforated by openings called micropyles, through which the sperm may have access to the egg. The tertiary envelopes include all those formed by the walls of the oviduct during the passage of the egg. Examples are the egg albumen, shell membranes, and shells of such groups as the reptiles, birds, and the egg-laying mammals; the egg capsules of the elasmo-branchs, and the egg jelly of the amphibia and many bony fish. These envelopes are not formed until after fertilization, except in the case of the egg jelly, which does not attain its final thickness until after the entrance of the sperm, when it swells by the absorption of water.

THE EGG OF THE AMPHIOXUS

The eggs (Fig. 10A) are 0.1 mm. in diameter. Before maturation the large nucleus is roughly 0.05 mm. in diameter displaced well towards the animal pole. The cytoplasm consists of a thin outer layer

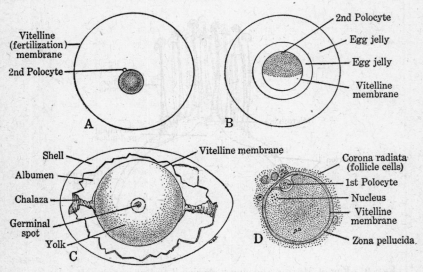

FIG. 10. Typical eggs. A, amphioxus, approx. ×70 (after Wilson in Willey). B, frog ×8. C, hen ×¾ (after Duval). D, human ×250 (after Allen in Arey).

relatively free from yolk and probably containing mitochondria. The rest of the cytoplasm contains yolk. There are no egg envelopes except perhaps a vitelline membrane. The egg is classed as isolecithal.

THE EGG OF THE FROG

The diameter of the egg (Fig. 10B) is 1.7 mm. (R. pipiens, Wright), with a large nucleus before maturation. There is a thin outer layer of cytoplasm, containing granules of pigment in the animal hemisphere. Pigment is also found around the nucleus. The yolk is distributed with fewer and smaller platelets in the animal hemisphere, grading down to more and larger platelets in the vegetal hemisphere. There are a vitelline membrane (primary), "chorion" (secondary),

and one to three layers of egg jelly (tertiary). The eggs are discharged in large masses which adhere to each other by means of this
jelly. The eggs are classified as telolecithal.

THE EGG OF THE CHICK

The hen's egg (Fig. 10C) is extremely telolecithal. The cytoplasm,
with the nucleus in its center, forms a small germinal disc upon the
great mass of yolk. This yolk is arranged in concentric layers of
yellow and white material around a central mass of white yolk,
called the latebra (Fig. 11). From this latebra a stalk of white
yolk (the neck of the latebra) extends upward and spreads outward
as the isthmus of Pander. The germinal disc rests on this isthmus.
The yolk and germinal disc are surrounded by a delicate vitelline

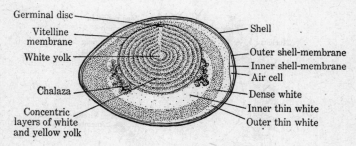

Germinal disc —
Vitelline membrane —
White yolk —
Chalaza —
Concentric layers of white and yellow yolk —
Shell
Outer shell-membrane
Inner shell-membrane
Air cell
Dense white
Inner thin white
Outer thin white

FIG. 11. Diagram of hen's egg sectioned (after Adamstone).

membrane (primary). This in turn is surrounded by the albumen,
a viscous tertiary membrane twisted spirally from left to right, starting from the broad end of the egg. The albumen next to the vitelline
membrane is denser than the outer layers and is prolonged into two
spirally twisted cords, the chalazae, one at either end of the yolk.
The albumen is in turn surrounded by two parchment-like shell
membranes, of which the inner one is the thinner. These two are
separated at the blunt end of the egg, thus forming the air chamber.
The egg shell is a calcareous deposit upon the outer shell membrane.
Its color is due to bile pigments of the hen. The germinal disc is
about 4 mm. in diameter, the yolk about 40 mm. The size of the
egg as a whole varies largely, depending on the amount of albumen
deposited around the yolk.

Giant and dwarf eggs are sometimes recorded. In the hen's egg,
double- and triple-yolked eggs are known, as well as those which
have no yolk at all. A very strange abnormality is known as the
" ovum in ovo," where one egg is formed around another. The eggs

of birds are either male-producing or female-producing, a statement based solely on the evidence of genetics as no visible differences have been observed.

THE HUMAN EGG

As in all placental mammals, the human egg (Fig. 10*D*) is very small, its diameter being about 0.13 mm. No yolk is demonstrable in the egg (Gatenby and Aykroyd, 1940). There is a delicate vitelline membrane surrounded by a rather thick zona pellucida, which is, at least in part, a secondary envelope. When the egg is first discharged from the follicle, the zona pellucida is still surrounded by a layer of follicle cells which make up the corona radiata. The

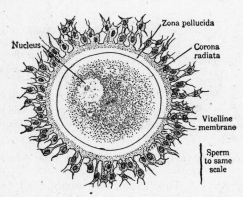

FIG. 12. Human egg (ovarian) ✕200 (after Waldeyer).

corona soon disintegrates or is stripped off the egg. The work of Hartman indicates that the life of the egg, or at least the period in which it can be fertilized, does not exceed three days in the monkey.

Eggs and their environment. Needham has recently pointed out that eggs differ from one another in respect to the physicochemical constitution of the unfertilized egg and the possibility of obtaining necessary material from the environment. The marine egg, exemplified by the amphioxus, develops in a medium containing oxygen and inorganic salts. The egg is organized in such a manner as to facilitate the exchange of materials with the environment. The yolk is small in amount and (to judge from analyses made on marine fish) relatively poor in fats and inorganic salts. Development is rapid up to the hatching stage, but thereafter the larva takes a long time to attain its full size and sexual maturity.

The egg which develops in fresh water, like that of the frog, does not have a medium so rich in salts as the marine egg. It is therefore originally equipped with a larger store of this material. But the aqueous medium still affords facilities for the exchange of carbon dioxide and oxygen and for the disposal of nitrogenous wastes. The jelly with which the frog's egg is provided consists almost entirely of protein and water. Diffusion takes place through it readily, and it affords protection against mechanical injury and bacterial infection, and also furnishes a source of nourishment immediately after hatching.

The terrestrial (cleidoic) egg, such as the hen's, stands easily first in respect to the amount of yolk present. The ratio of fat to protein in the yolk is also the highest. It is obvious that the egg must contain all the material necessary for growth except free oxygen and water, for these are the only substances passing from the atmosphere through the protective envelopes of the egg. Hence, as pointed out by Milnes-Marshall, except in the earliest stages the chick develops more rapidly than the amphioxus and attains its adult form in a much shorter time. The egg albumen, also a source of food, is a watery solution of protein with some carbohydrates. As we shall see in later chapters, the relative isolation of the embryo in the cleidoic egg is correlated with the development of its extra-embryonic sacs, i.e., the amnion, or water bath, and the allantois which serves in the first instance to store nitrogenous wastes.

The intra-uterine egg, typical of the mammals, is characterized by little yolk, for, from a very early period, its nourishment is derived exclusively from the body of the mother. Accordingly there is a precocious separation of a special layer, the trophoblast, concerned with implantation, and later the development of a special organ of interchange, the placenta.

Comparison of the egg and the sperm. Both gametes are morphologically complete cells. Each has a nucleus and a cytosome containing representatives of the centrosomes, mitochondria, and Golgi bodies. Each has a plasma membrane. Yet neither is capable of independent, continued existence, for physiologically they are unbalanced. The egg is large, inert, contains a vast store of metaplasm, is protected by egg envelopes, and has lost the power of continued division. The sperm is small, highly motile, contains little cytoplasm and no metaplasm, is devoid of protective membranes, and in itself has lost the power of continued division. We shall now turn to the study of the development of the germ cells and see how the structural differences, at least, arise.

COMPARISON OF THE VERTEBRATE EGG AND SPERM

Ovum	Cell structures	Sperm
Large amount	Cytoplasm	Small amount
One, disappears in maturation	Centrosomes	Two, retained in maturation
Diffuse	Mitochondria	In middle piece
Diffuse	Golgi bodies	Acrosome
Present	Plasma membrane	Present
Vesicular	Nucleus	Compact
Present	Nucleolus	Indistinguishable
Present	Nuclear membrane	Present

	Other differences	
Large	Size	Small
Quiescent	Movement	Swims actively
None	Motile organs	Flagellum
Egg envelopes	Protection	None
Spheroid	Shape	Tadpole
Few to many	Numbers produced	Very many

GAMETOGENESIS

Gametogenesis is the term applied to the history of the gametes — their origin and development (Fig. 13). The special history of the male gametes is called spermatogenesis, of the female gametes, oögenesis.

The origin of the germ cells. Weismann is responsible for a theory that the germ cells separate completely from all the other cells of the body (soma cells) at a very early stage in development. There is some evidence for this in the embryology of a few invertebrate animals such as *Ascaris,* a parasitic roundworm. In the very first cleavage of the fertilized egg, the two daughter cells show a striking difference, for when one of the daughter cells divides it retains all the chromatin of its nucleus, whereas the other gives up a portion of this material to the cytosome. This phenomenon has been called

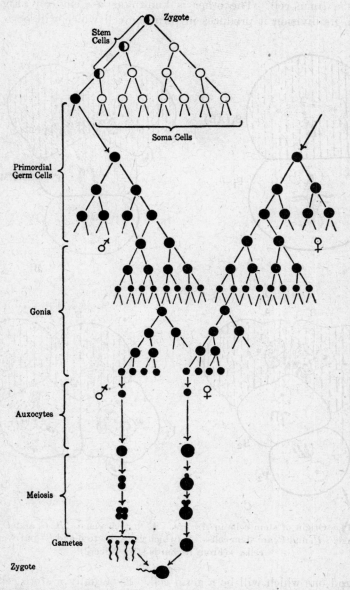

FIG. 13. Diagram of gametogenesis: male on left, female on right (after Wilson).

chromatin diminution, and the cell showing this characteristic becomes a soma cell. The other is known as a stem cell (Fig. 14), and in its division it produces in turn one cell which will be a soma

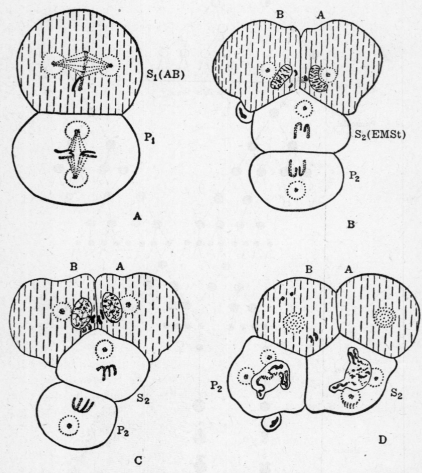

Fig. 14. Origin of stem cells in *Ascaris*. *A*, first cleavage. *B*, *C*, and *D*, second cleavage. P_1 and P_2 are stem cells. S_1 (which gives rise to *A* and *B*) and S_2 are soma cells. (From Richards after Boveri.)

cell and one which will be a germ cell. Eventually a stem cell gives rise to two identical cells, both of which are germ cells. These are known as primordial germ cells, and, from this time on, they and their descendants produce germ cells only.

This theory of the distinction between germ cells and soma cells has held an important place in the history of biology because it seemed to deny the possibility of the inheritance of characteristics acquired after fertilization. In other words, the characteristics would be acquired by the soma cells, whereas inheritance is a function of the germ cells which are entirely distinct, according to the theory of Weismann. This argument has been weakened by the evidence that the nuclei of all cells are identical, at least in early cleavage, and the belief of many investigators that in the mammals, at least, the primordial germ cells degenerate without leaving descendants, and that the functional germ cells arise from epithelial cells of the gonads.

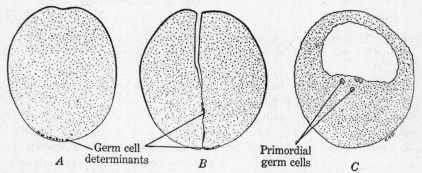

Germ cell determinants — Primordial germ cells

A   B   C

FIG. 15. Germ cell determinants and primordial germ cells in the frog. *A*, fertilized egg. *B*, four-cell stage. *C*, blastula. (After Bounoure, 1939.)

Primordial germ cells. Bounoure (1939) claims to have identified stem cells in cleavage stages of the frog (Fig. 15), but in all other vertebrates the germ cells are first recognizable in the lining of the gut at a very early stage of development. These primordial germ cells, as they are called, are distinguishable by their large size, clear cytoplasm, and heavily staining nucleus (Fig. 16). From the gut wall they migrate into the mesentery suspending the gut from the roof of the coelom, and thence to the wall of the coelom. Here they multiply rapidly and produce two longitudinal ridges, which are the primordia of the sex glands, or gonads.

The gonia. There are two opinions concerning the fate of the primordial germ cells in vertebrates: one that they give rise to all the later generations of germ cells; the other that they degenerate and the later germ cells arise independently from the tissue of the gonads. In any case, the germ cells which continue to multiply actively in the gonads are known as gonia: spermatogonia if they are to give rise to sperm, oögonia if they give rise to eggs.

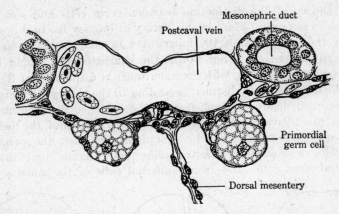

FIG. 16. Primordial germ cells in the frog (*Rana sylvatica*). Part of transverse section through 10-mm. larva, showing coelomic roof, ×375. (After Witschi.)

The cytes. When the individual becomes sexually mature, individual gonia undergo a period of growth, after which they are known as cytes (auxocytes, meiocytes): spermatocytes if male, oöcytes if female. The cyte (Fig. 17) is a large cell with a vesicular nucleus, two centrosomes surrounded by a clear area sometimes known as the idiosome, which is in turn surrounded by a layer of Golgi bodies, and a cloud of mitochondria.

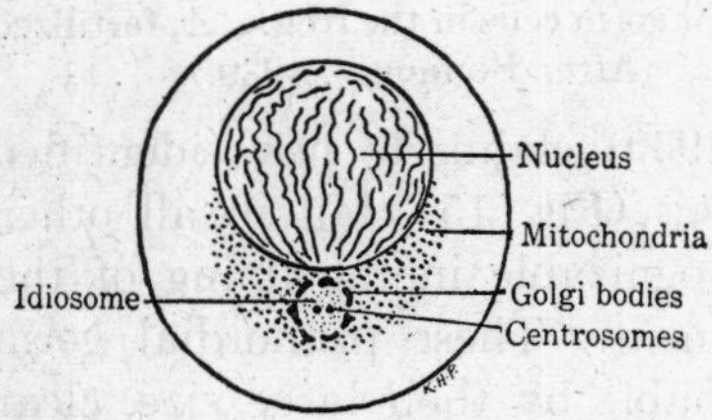

FIG. 17. Diagram of an early cyte (auxocyte). (After Wilson.)

The maturation divisions. Each cyte gives rise to four daughter cells by means of two cell divisions. These divisions are unique because of certain internal phenomena and are known as the maturation divisions. The nature of these divisions will be discussed in more detail in later pages. Meantime we note that the spermatocyte gives rise to four cells of equal size, the spermatids, each of which will be transformed into a sperm. The oöcyte, on the contrary, gives rise, by the first maturation division, to two cells, one of which is very minute, the first polar body (polocyte I). The larger cell undergoes a second unequal division, resulting in the production of a second polar body (polocyte II) and the mature egg or ovum. Sometimes the first polar body also divides, in which case four cells (oötids) may be produced by the oöcyte.

STAGES IN GAMETOGENESIS

Spermatogenesis	General	Oögenesis
	(Stem cells)	
	Primordial germ cells	
	Period of migration and multiplication	
Spermatogonia	Gonia	Oögonia
	Period of growth	
Spermatocytes	Cytes	Oöcytes
	Period of maturation	
Spermatids		Ovum and polocytes (Oötids)
Period of metamorphosis		
Sperms		

Spermatogenesis. The male cyte (primary spermatocyte) is a large cell containing a large vesicular nucleus, more or less excentric. In the human spermatocyte (Fig. 18*A*), according to Gatenby and Beams, the idiosome and Golgi bodies form a complex body lying next to the nucleus. This Golgi-idiosome complex consists of an inner chromophobic mass, surrounded by an outer chromophilic layer. Within the chromophobic mass are the two centrosomes, and a number

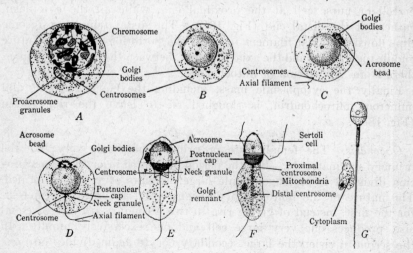

FIG. 18. Transformation of the spermatid into the mature sperm. *A*, spermatocyte. *B*, *C*, *D*, *E*, spermatids. *F*, immature sperm. *G*, mature sperm. (After Gatenby and Beams, 1935.)

of proacrosomic granules, each in a tiny vacuole. Throughout the cytoplasm are numerous granular mitochondria.

At the end of the two maturation divisions the mitochondria and Golgi bodies are diffuse (Fig. 18*B*). Soon the proacrosomic material is condensed to form a proacrosome bead in a vacuole surrounded by a chromophilic sheath (Fig. 18*C*). The centrosomes are near the plasma membrane at first. They give rise, apparently together, to the axial filament which penetrates the plasma membrane of the spermatid. Thereafter they separate, and the distal centrosome forms a ring around the axial filament. A little later they move towards the nucleus, which now shows the beginning of the post-nuclear cap (Fig. 18*D*) on the side opposite the Golgi-idiosome complex. The mitochondria are thickest in the centrosomal side of the spermatid.

In a later stage in the transformation of the spermatid (spermiogenesis, spermioteleosis), the nucleus condenses (Fig. 18*E*), the acrosomal bead spreads over its anterior surface to form the acrosome. The remainder of the Golgi complex drifts down the side of the nucleus to form the Golgi remnant. Meantime the postnuclear cap is enlarging, the distal or ring centrosome has enlarged, the axial filament is greatly lengthened, and the cell has become an elongate body with the nucleus at the proximal end.

The immature sperm, as we may now call it, attaches itself to a Sertoli or nurse cell at the proximal end, while all the cytoplasm gathers at the distal end (Fig. 18*F*). The distal (ring) centrosome slips down the axial filament to mark the posterior end of the future middle piece. Around the axial filament, between the two centrosomes, there is an aggregation of mitochondria.

Finally the cytoplasmic mass, including the Golgi remnant and numerous mitochondria, is sloughed off to leave the ripe sperm (Fig. 18*G*).

Oögenesis. The female cyte or primary oöcyte is very like the primary spermatocyte. But the period of growth prior to the maturation divisions is prolonged while large amounts of yolk are formed. The nature of the maturation divisions (Fig. 19) also is different, for the first, instead of giving rise to two secondary oöcytes of equal size, produces one very large cell and one excessively minute. In the second division the large secondary oöcyte again divides into one large cell and one tiny cell, while the small secondary oöcyte may or may not divide into two equal cells. In this way four (or three, if the smaller secondary oöcyte fails to divide) oötids are produced, of which the single large cell is the ovum, the smaller ones being known as polocytes. They are incapable of fertilization and degenerate. As they are formed at the animal pole of the egg, they are often known as the polar bodies and are of practical value in orienting the egg.

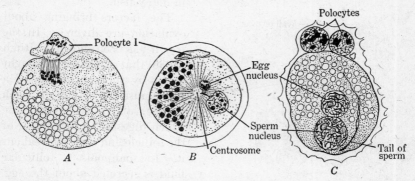

FIG. 19. Maturation divisions in egg of guinea pig. *A*, first maturation division. *B*, fertilization. *C*, second maturation division. (After Lams.)

We shall defer to a later section an account of the details of the maturation divisions, remarking here only that the principal nuclear result is that the chromatin is sorted out into unlike nuclei. The centrosomes are often difficult to find in the primary oöcyte and have not been found in the ovum. The idiosome and the mass of mito- chondria are often associated in a yolk-nucleus-complex. During the maturation divisions a large amount of nuclear material is cast out into the cytoplasm.

Unlike the male gametes, whose maturation is completed within the testis, the oöcytes do not complete their maturation until after leaving the ovary, and, in vertebrates at least, the second division is not completed until after the entrance of the sperm.

FERTILIZATION

The union of the two gametes, egg and sperm, to form a fertilized egg (zygote) is known as fertilization (syngamy). Prior to the actual union of the gametes are two preliminary processes, the dis- charge of the egg from the ovary (ovulation) and the discharge of the sperms (ejaculation).

Ovulation. Within the ovary the vertebrate egg is surrounded by nurse cells which make up a nest or follicle (Fig. 20). Within this it enlarges and may undergo its first maturation division. Peri-

odically, varying from once a year in most vertebrates to once a
month in the human species, or daily in the domestic fowl, eggs are
discharged from the ovary. In numbers this discharge varies from
a single egg as in man or the fowl to thousands in the frog or millions
in many fish.

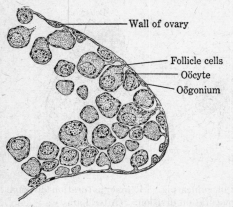

Wall of ovary

Follicle cells
Oöcyte
Oögonium

FIG. 20.   Transverse section through part
of frog ovary.   ×95.

The factors bringing about
ovulation are diverse. In the
frog it has been shown by Rugh
(1935) that ovulation is brought
about by the contraction of a
thin muscular layer in each
follicle, aided by an enzyme
which digests the outer wall of
the follicle and thereby weakens
it. In mammals a follicular
fluid is secreted about the egg,
enlarging the follicle until it
protrudes from the surface.
Finally the outer wall of the
follicle, now very thin, ruptures,
owing perhaps to factors similar to those acting on the frog's egg. It
has been shown in many vertebrates that ovulation can be induced at
any time by means of a hormone secreted by the anterior lobe of the
pituitary gland.

Oviposition. From the ovary the eggs are caught up in the open
end of the oviduct, down which they pass to the exterior. In many
aquatic forms they are discharged directly. In others they accumulate
in an enlarged portion of the oviduct known as the uterus, awaiting
discharge from the body; such animals are known as oviparous (amphioxus, frog, chick). In still others the egg remains in the uterus
until development has reached an advanced stage; these are the
viviparous animals (man, etc.).

Many zoologists use the term ovoviviparous for such vertebrates
as certain snakes, in which the egg remains for some time in the
uterus while the young develop within the egg envelopes. The young
snakes hatch from the egg while still inside the body, from which they
are discharged at a later date.

Ejaculation. This term is applied to the discharge of the sperms.
These cells remain in the testis (Fig. 21) until mature, often attached to nurse cells. When discharged they pass through tubules
of the testis which lead directly to a sperm duct. They become

motile upon reaching the medium in which fertilization takes place. Enormous numbers are produced at a single discharge (over 200,000,-000 in man).

In aquatic animals such as the amphioxus and fish the two sexes congregate together at the breeding season, and eggs and sperms are discharged together. Some aquatic animals even have copulatory organs which introduce the sperms into the oviduct, bringing about internal fertilization. In the frog, the males and females unite in

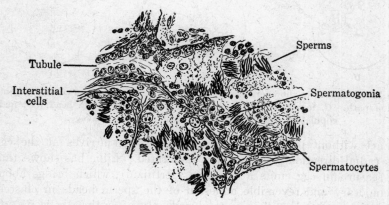

FIG. 21. Section through part of frog testis. ×200.

pairs (amplexus), thus ensuring that the sperms are discharged simultaneously with the eggs so that fertilization, although external, is regulated. In all terrestrial vertebrates fertilization is internal.

Fertilization. The actual fertilization of the egg (syngamy) has been observed in the amphioxus and the frog, but our detailed knowledge of the process is obtained from the study of such marine invertebrates as the sea urchin. The essential feature of fertilization is the entrance of a single sperm into the egg and the coming together of the two nuclei (pronuclei) (Fig. 22). But this phenomenon is preceded by other events concerned in bringing the sperm to the egg.

Attraction. One of the factors believed to bring the sperm towards the egg is an attraction (chemotaxis) caused by the emission of some chemical substance by the egg or the female sex organs. It is known also that sperms swim in a spiral path, and that when they come in contact with a solid object they remain in contact with it (thigmotaxis). If the spiral brings a sperm obliquely towards the egg the contact flattens out the spiral, causing the sperm to remain in

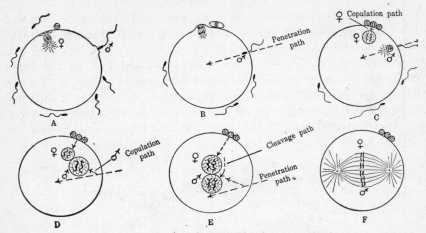

Fig. 22. Diagram to show fertilization of the egg. *A*, fertilization cone. *B*, penetration path. *C*, female copulation path and rotation of sperm head. *D*, male copulation path. *E*, cleavage path. *F*, first cleavage.

contact without penetration. But if the sperm arrives at the egg in a radial direction penetration is facilitated. Lillie has shown that the sea-urchin egg emits a secretion (fertilizin), which brings about a temporary and reversible adhesion of the sperm heads in clusters (agglutination). Fertilizin is produced only after the egg is mature and before it is fertilized.

Penetration. The sperm bores its way through the egg envelopes but then apparently comes to rest against the plasma membrane. In the eggs of some invertebrates there has been observed at the surface of the egg a cone or even a long filament of cytoplasm which comes in contact with the sperm head. It then retracts, drawing the sperm to the egg and engulfing it (Fig. 22*A*, *B*). Thereafter, and commencing at the point where the sperm head was engulfed, a thin membrane, known as the fertilization membrane, is formed, apparently from the outer surface of the vitelline membrane. In older days, when it was thought that the sperm bored its way into the egg, it was believed also that the fertilization membrane acted as a bar to other sperms. Apparently the elevation of the membrane is due to the secretion of some fluid from the egg, which decreases in diameter at the same time. Okkelberg describes a loss of 14 per cent in the volume of the egg of the brook lamprey. The formation of this membrane with its perivitelline fluid underneath marks the successful fertilization of the egg. For example, the fertilized frog's egg will rotate within this membrane.

The pronuclei. After the second maturation division, which does not take place in vertebrates until after the entrance of the sperm, the nucleus of the ovum (female pronucleus) is near the periphery at the animal pole, while the nucleus of the sperm (male pronucleus) is at the periphery near the point of penetration. The sperm head rotates 180° so that the male pronucleus now lies distal to the middle piece containing the centrosome (Fig. 22C). The two pronuclei come together (Fig. 22D, E) by a route which may be analyzed into the following components: (1) the sperm penetration path, which is usually the radius of the egg at which the sperm entered; (2) the sperm copulation path, which is directed towards the point at which the pronuclei will meet and is often at a considerable angle to the penetration path; (3) the egg copulation path, along which the female pronucleus moves towards the meeting point; and (4) the cleavage path (Fig. 22E), along which the two pronuclei move to their final position on the egg axis, often slightly nearer the animal pole. The two pronuclei may unite to form a common cleavage nucleus, or they may remain close together and contribute independently to the first nuclear division of the zygote (Fig. 22F). See also Chapter 17.

The centrosome of the egg disappears after the second maturation division. The centrosome of the zygote, therefore, is either the centrosome of the sperm or, as it is believed in some cases, a new one developed in the egg cytoplasm near the engulfed sperm head.

The mitochondrial material of the sperm fragments and is distributed throughout the cytoplasm of the zygote. The later history of the acrosome has not been followed.

There is much divergence among different kinds of animals with respect to those parts of the sperm which are actually engulfed in the egg. In some, it is the entire sperm; in others, only the sperm head.

Organ-forming areas. In many different kinds of eggs, the student of cellular embryology has been able to recognize different regions by differences in the cytoplasm, such as the presence or absence of pigment, mitochondria, yolk, etc., and to trace the distributions of these materials into the different daughter cells as cleavage takes place. These organ-forming areas, as they may be called, are usually more easily demonstrated after fertilization. For example, before fertilization the living egg of the tunicate *Styela* (Fig. 23), according to Conklin (1905), has yellow pigment granules uniformly distributed in its outer layer of cytoplasm. During fertilization, following an intricate series of stream movements, the yellow pigment is concentrated in a crescentic area at what will later be the posterior surface. On the opposite side of the egg at what will become the anterior surface is a gray crescent. Below these crescents the vegetal hemisphere is marked by the presence of yolk granules. In later cleavage, the yellow crescent will be distributed to the cells which form the mesoderm of the tail, the gray crescent to the cells which form the notochord and the neural plate, the yolk to the cells of the endoderm, and the remainder of the egg goes to the cells of the

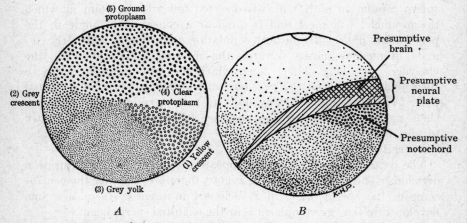

FIG. 23. Organ-forming areas in tunicate eggs. *A*, fertilized egg of *Styela*, from left side (after Conklin). *B*, unfertilized egg of *Ascidiella*, from right side. (After Vandebroek in Dalcq.) Approximately ×250.

epidermis. These results have been confirmed and extended by Vandebroek (1937) through the use of vital stains applied to the unfertilized egg (Fig. 23*B*).

Parthenogenesis. This term is applied to the development of a new individual from an unfertilized egg. It does not occur naturally among the vertebrates but may be illustrated by the honey bee, in which the unfertilized egg develops into a male (drone) and the fertilized egg becomes a female (either queen or worker according to the type of food supplied).

Artificial parthenogenesis has been induced in the eggs of many invertebrate animals by various means. Among vertebrates, fish, amphibia, and mammals have been the objects of successful experiments. The frog's egg has been used by a number of investigators. Parmenter (1940), who induced development by smearing the egg with frog's blood and then pricking it with a fine needle, reports on 619 pricked eggs. Of these 546 formed the second polar body, 63 underwent cleavage, and 4 developed to the tadpole stage. A few parthenogenetic eggs have been reared to the adult stage (Loeb), out of many thousands experimented upon. Pincus (1940) has induced development in the rabbit's egg by the use of very low temperatures.

FERTILIZATION OF THE AMPHIOXUS EGG

In the amphioxus, fertilization is external. The males and females leave the sands to swarm in the shallow waters during late afternoons of spring and summer. Eggs and sperms are discharged, from the

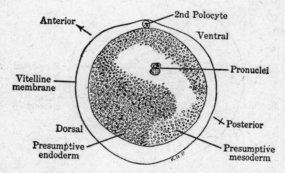

FIG. 24. Organ forming areas in egg of the amphioxus, one hour after fertilization. Sagittal section, approx. ×220. (After Conklin 1932.)

segmental gonads in which they develop, into the cavity of the atrium, and escape to the exterior through the atriopore. The first polocyte is given off before fertilization. Immediately after fertilization the vitelline, now the fertilization, membrane expands greatly, leaving the egg in a large perivitelline space (Figs. 24 and 10*A*). The second polocyte given off after the formation of the fertilization membrane remains attached to the egg while the first is usually lost to view.

The fertilized egg of the amphioxus (Conklin, 1932) shows in sections (Fig. 24) a crescent of more deeply staining protoplasm on the side of the egg which will give rise to the posterior part of the body. This crescent will form the cells of the mesoderm (compare the yellow crescent of *Styela*). Opposite this is a less clearly defined crescentic area from which the cells of the notochord and neural plate will be formed (compare the gray crescent of *Styela* and of the frog). The material of the vegetal hemisphere, bounded above by these crescents, will form the endoderm; the material of the animal hemisphere above the crescents will form the epidermis.

FERTILIZATION OF THE FROG'S EGG

The fertilization of the frog's egg is external, but the sperms are brought into close proximity to the eggs during the sexual embrace or amplexus. During the breeding season the males embrace the females with the fore-legs, at which time the germ cells of each are extruded. The sperms make their way through the layers of egg

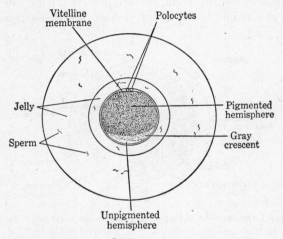

FIG. 25. Diagram of frog's egg after fertilization to show gray crescent. The line immediately external to the vitelline membrane and polocytes represents the " chorion." ×10.

jelly before these envelopes have attained their final thickness. The first sperm coming into contact with the vitelline membrane enters the egg, usually within 40° of the animal pole. The vitelline membrane is elevated to become the fertilization membrane, leaving a perivitelline space within which the egg may rotate. The second maturation division then occurs, followed by the conjugation of the pronuclei. The penetration and sperm copulation paths are marked by a trail of pigment dragged in with the sperm head. The tail is left near the surface. Immediately upon fertilization the cortical cytoplasm of the egg rushes towards the point of penetration, carrying with it the black pigment (melanin) of the animal hemisphere. Upon the side of the egg opposite the point of penetration there appears a crescent-shaped area in which the pigment is less dense and which is therefore known as the gray crescent (Fig. 25). This area gives rise later to the notochord and mesoderm, or chorda-mesoderm, and is especially significant in the later organization of the embryo (Chapter 5). It is sufficient at this point to indicate that the appearance of the gray crescent gives the egg a bilateral symmetry.

FERTILIZATION OF THE HEN'S EGG

In the fowl, fertilization is internal. The sperms, introduced into the cloaca of the female during copulation, make their way to the upper end of the oviduct, where they may remain for two weeks or more. As each egg, i.e., the yolk with its germinal disc of protoplasm surrounded by a vitelline membrane, escapes from its ovarian follicle and enters the oviduct, five or six sperms enter the germinal disc, where they remain inactive until after the second maturation division. One of them then moves inward until it comes in contact with the female pronucleus, which has itself moved downward from the surface of the germinal disc. The supernumerary sperms move outward to the border of the disc, where, after a few divisions, they degenerate. The fertilized egg moves slowly down the oviduct while the tertiary envelopes are forming about it.

FERTILIZATION OF THE HUMAN EGG

Fertilization is internal and occurs at the upper end of the oviduct (Fallopian tube). It is probable that a single sperm enters the egg after the first maturation division as in the guinea pig (Fig. 19B). Further details are lacking, as no direct observations have been recorded. Clinical evidence, supported by the work of Hartman on Macacus, indicates that ovulation usually takes place between the eleventh and fourteenth day of the menstrual cycle, and that, if not fertilized in a day or two, the egg soon undergoes degenerative changes.

SUMMARY

The gametes are atypical cells, the egg and sperm differing both from each other and from a composite cell. The egg most resembles a composite cell, from which it differs in the absence of a centrosome after it has become mature. It is large, quiescent, and protected by envelopes. The sperm, almost devoid of cytoplasm, is small, active, and naked.

The origin of the germ cells among vertebrates is still uncertain. After the formation of the gonad, ovary or testis, the germ cells, then known as gonia, undergo a period of multiplication. This process is periodical in some vertebrates, continuous in others. It is followed by a period of growth in which some gonia are enlarged to become cytes. The spermatocyte gives rise to four spermatids, each of which will be transformed into a sperm. The oöcyte, on the contrary, gives rise to an ovum and two or three polocytes.

The zygote, or fertilized egg, arises from the union of an egg and a sperm. This union is preceded by the discharge of eggs from the ovary (ovulation) and sperms from the testis. The sperm enters the egg through the mutual action of the two gametes, and the nuclei of the two gametes come together, each to contribute to the first division of the fertilized egg.

After fertilization, and sometimes even before, it can be seen that the egg has a definite organization, manifest in its polarity (seen even in ovarian eggs) and, in especially favorable material, evident in organ-forming areas.

CHAPTER 4

CHROMOSOMES AND GENES

The germ cells are really cells detached from the bodies of the parents. When they unite in fertilization they bring together material from both parents. Herein lies the explanation of the inheritance of parental characteristics, of the fact that the fertilized egg develops in a way characteristic of the species, and the fact that individuals differ from one another. In the following paragraphs we shall review the theory that the individual units of heredity are the genes, borne in the chromosomes, distributed in the maturation divisions, and brought together in fertilization.

THE CHROMOSOMES

It will be necessary first to describe the chromosomes as they behave in ordinary (somatic) cell division, then to point out the peculiar features of the maturation (meiotic) divisions and of fertilization, and finally to indicate how this behavior of the chromosomes affects the distribution of the genes.

The chromosomes in mitosis. The division of most cells is accompanied by the formation and longitudinal division of threads of chromatin, called chromosomes, in the nucleus. This type of cell division is known as mitosis (Fig. 26). Some cells, however, divide without the appearance of chromosomes (amitosis), and the daughter cells are thereafter incapable of mitotic division. For the sake of convenience we may use the terms karyokinesis for the division of the nucleus in mitosis and cytokinesis for the division of the cytosome.

Karyokinesis. Before cell division the metabolic ("resting") nucleus is a reticulum of chromatin lying in the fluid karyolymph with a nucleolus, the whole surrounded with a nuclear membrane (Fig. 26A). In mitosis we distinguish four stages, prophase, metaphase, anaphase, and telophase.

In the prophase the reticulum separates into its constituent threads, chromonemata, by the breaking down of the smaller threads connecting them. Very early it can be seen that these threads are

53

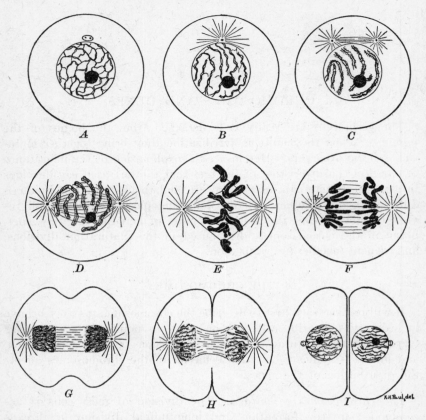

Fɪɢ. 26. Diagrams of somatic mitosis. *A*, metabolic (" resting ") stage. *B*, early prophase showing chromonemata and attachment points. *C*, middle prophase, matrix appearing. *D*, late prophase, chromonemata obscured. *E*, metaphase. *F*, anaphase. *G*, early telophase, matrix disappearing. *H*, middle telophase, nuclear membrane forming. *I*, late telophase, reticulum developing. (Based on a diagram by Sharp.)

double or split longitudinally (Fig. 26*B*). Soon thereafter a matrix is visible about the two chromonemata. This compound structure, consisting of the two chromonemata and the surrounding matrix, is a chromosome (Fig. 26*C*). The number of chromosomes so formed is the same in every cell of every individual belonging to any particular species. (This statement is subject to exceptions. See pages 62 ff.) Towards the end of the prophase the chromonemata are usually invisible. Finally the nuclear membrane disappears, and the karyolymph assumes the form of a double cone or spindle (Fig. 26*D*).

In the metaphase (Fig. 26E), the chromosomes line up in an equatorial plane through the spindle. Each has a definite attachment region (centromere) lying in the equatorial plane even though the ends of the chromosomes may lie outside the plane.

In the anaphase (Fig. 26F), the chromosomes separate into two longitudinal portions, each containing one of the original chromonemata with surrounding matrix. Preceded always by its attachment region, each daughter chromosome moves towards a pole of the spindle. Carothers (1934) describes the growth of a fiber from the attachment region of each daughter chromosome to the nearest pole of the spindle. Eventually two equivalent sets of chromosomes are formed, one in the vicinity of either pole, each set containing a daughter chromosome from each of the original chromosomes formed in the prophase.

In the telophase (Fig. 26G, H, I), each set of chromosomes assumes the metabolic condition. The matrix loses its staining capacity and the chromonemata reappear, often already split longitudinally. The nuclear membrane is formed about each group, the chromonemata are united by tiny cross-strands, the nucleolus reappears, and the nucleus is seen to be filled with karyolymph. The cell now contains two daughter nuclei, each identical with the other and with the parent nucleus.

Cytokinesis. Other striking events are taking place in the cytosome during mitosis. During the prophase the centrosome, if not already divided, separates into two daughter centrosomes which move apart. About each of them is a spherical mass of protoplasm, often containing radial striations, known as the aster. Between them is a central spindle apparently containing fibers. Cytologists distinguish three types of fibers: (1) primary or continuous fibers extending from centrosome to centrosome, (2) half spindle components extending from chromosome to centrosome, and (3) interzonal connections extending between the separating daughter chromosomes (Schrader). The centrosomes reach the opposite sides of the nucleus just as the nuclear membrane disappears. The karyolymph apparently unites with the material between the two centrosomes to form the mitotic spindle along which the chromosomes move in the anaphase. In the telophase, asters and spindle disappear and the centrosomes alone remain in the positions they occupied at the poles of the mitotic spindle. Sometimes they divide in anticipation of the next mitosis.

The mitochondria usually divide en masse (Fig. 27A). This division of the mitochondria is approximately an equal one, and some investigators believe that the individual mitochondria divide during mitosis or just prior to it.

The Golgi bodies, even when aggregated into a Golgi apparatus, separate during mitosis and are segregated into the daughter cells, usually associating themselves with the two centrosomes (Fig. 27B). It is uncertain whether each Golgi body divides individually at mitosis, but some evidence has been brought forward to support this contention.

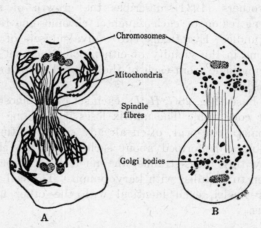

FIG. 27. The mitochondria and Golgi bodies in mitosis. A, mitochondria. B, Golgi bodies. (After Bowen.)

In animal cells the cytosome as a whole divides by constriction. In this process the cell elongates in the direction of the spindle during the anaphase and telophase. Following the reconstruction of the daughter nuclei in the telophase, a furrow appears at the periphery of the cell, around the equatorial belt, and at right angles to the axis of elongation. This furrow advances towards the center of the cell until the cell is completely divided.

Distribution of the chromosomes. Each daughter cell has approximately half of the cytoplasm proper, half of the mitochondria and Golgi bodies, a centrosome derived from that of the parent cell, and a nucleus built up from a set of chromosomes, each of which was produced by the division of a chromosome in the parent cell. It is apparent from the foregoing account that the key to the complexities of mitosis is the division of the chromosomes. The achromatic figure is the framework upon which this division takes place. The division of the mitochondria and Golgi bodies is still too little understood.

But the chromosomes, appearing in the prophase, halved with such accuracy in metaphase and anaphase, and disappearing again in the telophase, are characterized by a constancy in number, an individuality evinced in form and behavior, and a persistence from generation to generation. In some favorable material it has even been possible to demonstrate that the chromonemata arise in the prophase exactly as they merged into a reticulum in the previous telophase. From the statements above, it is not unreasonable to draw the conclusion that the chromosomes are directly concerned with inheritance in cell reproduction.

The chromosomes in meiosis. During the two maturation divisions by which the gametes are formed, the number of chromosomes is reduced to one-half the number characteristic of the species. Since in the ordinary somatic mitosis the number of chromosomes given to each daughter cell is exactly the same as that to the parent, it is evident that we are dealing with a peculiar type of mitosis (Fig. 28). The name meiosis is frequently applied to the maturation divisions.

First meiotic division. The essential feature in which the first meiotic division differs from the ordinary (somatic) mitosis is that during the prophase the chromosomes unite in pairs (Fig. 29, 2). This is synapsis and occurs only in the first meiotic division. Since each of the chromosomes always divides during the prophase also (Fig. 29, 4), the net result is that at the end of the prophase there are only half the number of chromosomes seen in somatic mitosis, but each of these consists of four parts (chromatids) instead of two (Fig. 29, 5). These compound bodies consisting of four chromatids are called tetrads (Fig. 29, 6). The quadripartite nature of the tetrad may be expressed by the formula $\frac{A : a}{A : a}$, where A represents one of the synaptic mates and a the other.

In the anaphase (Fig. 29, 7), each of the daughter chromosomes possesses two chromatids and is known as a dyad. But there are two different ways of dividing a tetrad. In one case the two chromatids derived from one of the synaptic mates $\left(\frac{A}{A}\right)$ might be separated from those derived from the other mate $\left(\frac{a}{a}\right)$ in a reduction (disjunction) division. In the other, each dyad might contain one chromatid from each of the synaptic mates $(A : a)$ as the result of an equation division. Recent evidence (based on the study of the fruit fly, *Drosophila*, and of maize) indicates that the first meiotic

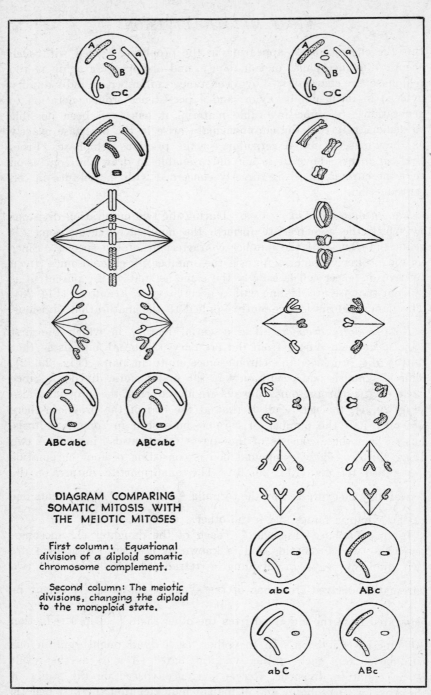

DIAGRAM COMPARING SOMATIC MITOSIS WITH THE MEIOTIC MITOSES

First column: Equational division of a diploid somatic chromosome complement.

Second column: The meiotic divisions, changing the diploid to the monoploid state.

FIG. 28. Comparison of somatic and meiotic mitosis. (From Sharp.)

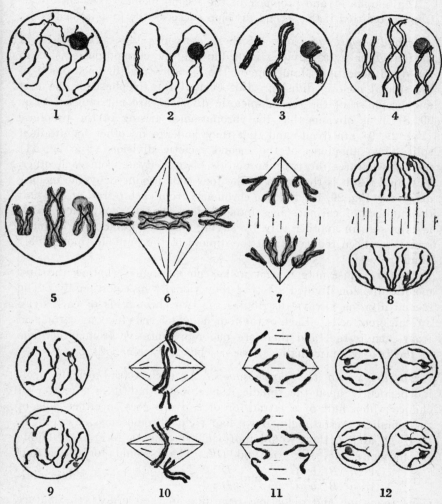

FIG. 29. Diagram of meiosis. *1*, first meiotic division, prophase (leptonema stage). *2*, do., showing synapsis (zygonema stage). *3*, do., showing thickening of the chromosomes (pachynema stage). *4*, do., showing formation of tetrads (diplonema stage). *5*, do., showing condensation of matrix (diakinesis stage). *6*, metaphase I. *7*, anaphase I, showing dyads. *8*, telophase I. *9*, second meiotic division, prophase showing dyads united at attachment points. *10*, metaphase II. *11*, anaphase II, showing the separation of the chromatids which composed the dyads. *12*, telophase II. Each of the four germ cells now has the haploid number of chromatids (chromosomes). (From Sharp.)

division is reductional, at least in the region of the centromere. The telophase (and prophase of the second meiotic division) sometimes is omitted if the second division succeeds the first immediately.

Second meiotic division. If these omissions take place, each of the daughter cytes divides immediately, the chromosomes, still in the dyad condition, lining up on the spindles for the metaphase of the second meiotic division. But even if the telophase of the first and prophase of the second meiotic divisions are not omitted (Fig. 29, 8), it is obvious that the chromosomes arising in the prophase (Fig. 29, 9) are dyads and that they undergo no other longitudinal split. The anaphase of the second meiotic division (Fig. 29, 11) merely separates the two chromatids of each dyad from each other. The final result is that each of the four cells produced by the meiotic divisions (Fig. 29, 12) has one chromatid from each tetrad or one-half the number of chromosomes found before meiosis took place. This is expressed in another way by saying that the number of chromosomes has been reduced from the diploid to the haploid (monoploid) number.

Here we must note that it makes no difference whether the first meiotic division divided a tetrad reductionally or equationally. The second division always distributes the two chromatids of each dyad into different cells. Each of the four daughter cells has one chromatid from each tetrad, and therefore one representative from either one of the two synaptic mates (A or a), but not from both.

Distribution of the chromosomes. As each tetrad orients itself independently upon the spindle it is evident that it is a matter of chance which half of a tetrad, or of a dyad, goes to either pole of the spindle. Accordingly, if we had eight chromosomes, A, a, B, b, C, c, D, and d, they would unite in synapsis to form four double chromosomes, Aa, Bb, Cc, and Dd. These would form the four tetrads, $\dfrac{A:a}{A:a}$, $\dfrac{B:b}{B:b}$, $\dfrac{C:c}{C:c}$, and $\dfrac{D:d}{D:d}$. After the two meiotic divisions (equation and reduction, regardless of their order), the mature germ cells would have four chromosomes (the haploid number), but only one representative of each synaptic pair. The possible combinations are 2^4 or 16, namely, $ABCD$, $ABCd$, $ABcd$, $Abcd$, $ABcD$, $AbCD$, $AbCd$, $aBCD$, $aBCd$, $aBcd$, $abcd$, $aBcD$, $abcD$, $abCD$, $AbcD$, and $abCd$. Accordingly the number of different types of gametes which may be formed can be determined from the formula 2^n when n is the haploid number of chromosomes characteristic of the species.

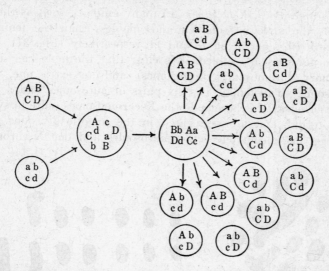

FIG. 30. Diagram showing the distribution of the chromosomes in fertilization and the following meiotic divisions. (After Wilson.)

The chromosomes in fertilization. Evidently when the egg and sperm unite in fertilization, the pronucleus contributed by each contains the haploid number of chromosomes. In this way the diploid number characteristic of the species is restored. It is obvious that, unless the number had been reduced by meiosis, it would be doubled in each new generation.

In the second place, it is clear that each germ cell contributes a homologous set of chromosomes, and that in synapsis the chromosomes unite in homologous pairs. In the example referred to above, chromosomes *A, B, C, D* came from one parent and *a, b, c, d* came from the other. We can now visualize each synaptic pair as consisting of one paternal and one maternal chromosome.

During meiosis the paternal and maternal chromosomes are sorted out into different assortments in the different germ cells. During fertilization these different assortments are brought together in random recombinations. We have said that in an animal with 8 chromosomes we might have 2^4, or 16, different classes of gametes. In random fertilization this number would be squared, so that there would be 4^4, or 256, possible combinations. Many of these would be duplicates, so that the exact number of different (genotypic) classes of zygotes, according to their assortment of chromosomes would be 3^4, or 81.

Sex chromosomes, X-O type. In many animals, such as the insect *Protenor*, the male has one chromosome less than the female, the numbers in *Protenor* being 13 and 14, respectively (Fig. 31). If the synaptic pairs are assembled, it is clear that the male has six pairs of ordinary chromosomes (autosomes) and an extra one, the X-chromosome. The female has six pairs of autosomes and a pair of X-chromosomes. In the female the X-chromosomes unite in synapsis, form a tetrad, and are segregated in the meiotic divisions so that every egg has a complete set of autosomes and one X-chromosome

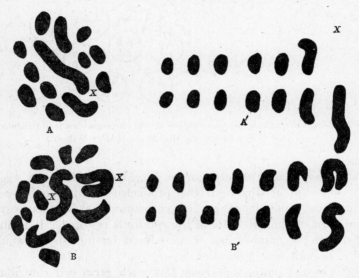

Fig. 31. Chromosomes of *Protenor*. A, A′, male diploid group. B, B′, female diploid group. The X-chromosomes are indicated by *X*. (After Wilson.)

$(A + X)$. In the male, on the other hand, the single X-chromosome has no synaptic mate and so goes on the spindle of the first meiotic division as a dyad, which is carried to one pole of the spindle entire. In the second meiotic division the dyad is divided as usual. The end result is that only half the spermatids receive an X-chromosome, and two classes of sperms are formed, either with or without an X-chromosome $(A + X$ or $A + 0)$. If a sperm with an X-chromosome fertilizes the egg, the female combination $(2A + 2X)$ is restored. If a sperm without the X-chromosome penetrates the egg, the male combination $(2A + X)$ is formed (Fig. 32).

Sex chromosomes, X-Y type. But the sexes do not always differ in chromosome number, for in many animals, like the insect *Lygaeus*

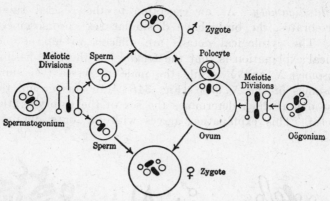

Fig. 32. Diagram showing history of the X-chromosome during meiosis and fertilization. (After Wilson.)

(Fig. 33), the X-chromosome of the male is furnished with a synaptic mate which differs from it in size, form, and probably composition, and is therefore known as the Y-chromosome. The male forms a tetrad $\dfrac{X:Y}{X:Y}$, and the sperms therefore have either an

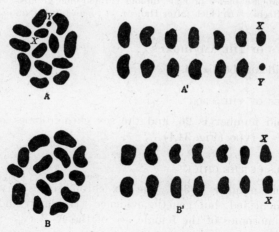

Fig. 33. Chromosomes of *Lygaeus*. A, A', male diploid group. B, B', female diploid group. X and Y indicate the X- and Y-chromosomes respectively. (After Wilson.)

X-chromosome or a Y-chromosome. Fertilization by a sperm bearing the X-chromosome results in the development of a female $(2A + 2X)$, whereas if a sperm bearing a Y-chromosome enters the egg the embryo will give rise to a male $(2A + XY)$.

Female digamety. As an exception to the general rule among the vertebrates, the birds have dissimilar sex chromosomes in the female. The cytological details are difficult to interpret but the theoretical explanation is that the female has the two dissimilar sex chromosomes X and Y, while the male possesses two similar sex chromosomes of the X type (Fig. 34B). In this group, therefore, it is the ovum which determines the sex of the embryo rather than the sperm. This explanation agrees with the data obtained from genetics.

Fig. 34. Metaphase plates of male diploid chromosome groups. A, frog (after Witschi). B, chick (after Hance). C, man (after Painter).

CHROMOSOMES OF THE AMPHIOXUS

The diploid number is 24.

CHROMOSOMES OF THE FROG

The diploid number is 26, and the sex chromosomes of the male are of the X-Y type (Fig. 34A).

CHROMOSOMES OF THE CHICK

The diploid number is 36. The sex chromosomes have not been positively identified, but genetic evidence (Haldane) indicates that the sex chromosomes of the female are of the X-Y type (Fig. 34B).

CHROMOSOMES OF MAN

The diploid number, according to the most recent researches, is 48. The sex chromosomes are of the X-Y type (Fig. 34C). It is interesting to note that with 48 chromosomes the possible types of gametes number 2^{24} or 16,777,300, and that from these 3^{24} zygote recombinations are possible.

THE GENES

It has already been said that the behavior of the chromosomes itself might suggest that these bodies are concerned with the transmission of hereditary characters. However, since the number of hereditary characters usually far outnumbers the chromosomes, smaller units than the chromosomes must exist.

The unit of genetics is the gene. These genes are arranged in linear order in the chromosomes. They exist in great numbers; in the fruitfly *Drosophila* it is estimated that there are between 2000 and 3000. The genes are known by the effects their presence induces, and named according to the most obvious of these effects.

Since each chromosome contains a large number of genes it follows that many of them remain in groups during meiosis and fertilization. The number of these linkage groups, as they are called, corresponds to the haploid number of chromosomes. But there are enough exchanges of genes between chromosomes so that percentage values of these crossovers can be determined. On the hypothesis that the percentage value of crossing over corresponds to the distance between the genes concerned, chromosome maps (Fig. 35) have been constructed.

The work of Painter, Bridges, and others has demonstrated that in *Drosophila* and other Diptera the exceptionally long and stout chromosomes in the cells of the salivary glands (Fig. 36) are marked by swellings, constrictions, and transverse markings. Painstaking studies of these chromosomes has led to the identification of the regions in which the genes are located. Whether or not the markings correspond to the genes themselves is still debatable.

The question naturally arises as to the origin of the genes which are allelic to the so-called normal genes. In *Drosophila* the abnormal genes, or mutants as they are called, arose in laboratory cultures. It has been discovered that the rate of mutation, i.e., the number of mutants arising in a given number of flies, may be increased by high temperatures (Plough) and by irradiation (Müller). When one of these genes is altered in any way to become a mutant, the course of development is disturbed. Most mutant genes disturb the course of development so greatly as to cause death (lethal mutants). A smaller number produce visible changes when present in each chromosome of the synaptic mates (recessive mutants). A few produce visible changes if contained in a single chromosome (dominant mutants). Accordingly, every species of animals contains a certain number of mutant genes (500 in *Drosophila*). As these enter into

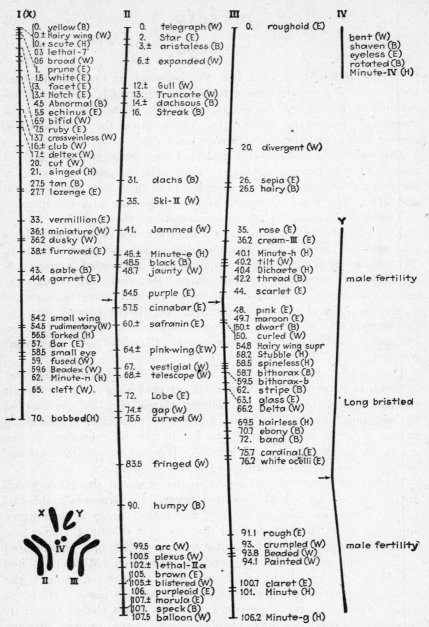

Fig. 35. The chromosomes of *Drosophila melanogaster* and map showing the positions of many genes as determined from cross over ratios. Letters in parentheses indicate part of body affected: *B*, body; *E*, eye; *H*, hair; *W*, wing. Arrows indicate position of attachment point. All genes in IV are closely linked. The exact position of genes in *Y* still undetermined. (From Sharp after Morgan *et al.*, 1925, and Stern 1929.)

new genetic combinations according to the behavior of the chromosomes in meiosis and fertilization, they give rise to individual differences in development. But the greater number of stable or nonmutant genes holds development true to the specific type.

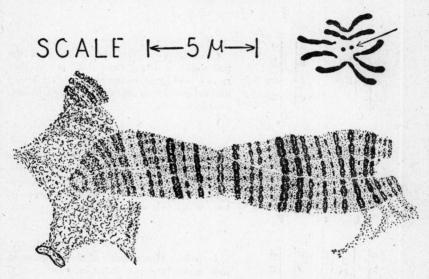

F<small>IG</small>. 36. Chromosomes of *Drosophila.* Above, metaphase of oögonium, arrow pointing to pair of chromosomes IV. Below, pair of chromosomes IV in salivary gland. Both to same scale. (From Curtis and Guthrie after Bridges.)

Chromosomal aberrations. Of particular interest to the student of embryology are the new types of individuals arising from disturbances in the usual course of meiosis. Some of these chromosomal aberrations are shown graphically in Fig. 37. One of the most striking types of aberration is known as non-disjunction, which may affect one to all of the chromosomal pairs during meiosis. In total non-disjunction, the members of each synaptic pair fail to separate during a meiotic division so that one daughter cell gets a double set of chromosomes while its sister cell receives none. As a result there will be one gamete with the diploid number of chromosomes. If such a gamete with the diploid number $(2A + 2X)$ is fertilized by another with the haploid number $(A + X)$, the zygote will have $3A + 3X$, the triploid number. Such a fly is a female and her progeny will show many interesting characters due to the chromosomal aberrations involved, as shown in the table on page 69.

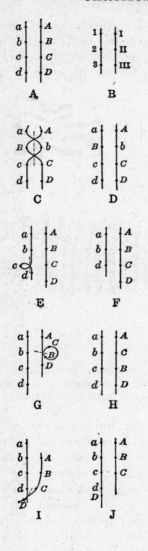

Two pairs of homologous chromosomes showing positions of allelic genes.

Crossing over: The chromosomes of the pair shown in *A* may twist about one another as in *C* and break in the plane of the dotted line so that comparable sections are exchanged as shown in *D.*

Deletion: One member of the chromosome pair shown in *A* may twist on itself as in *E* and break in the plane of the dotted line so that an internal section containing gene *c* is lost, or deleted, as shown in *F.*

Inversion: One member of the chromosome pair shown in *A* may twist on itself as in *G* and break in the plane of the dotted line so that the section containing genes *B* and *C* is inverted as shown in *H.*

Duplication and *Deficiency:* If one member of the chromosome pair shown in *A* comes to lie across the other as shown in *I* and a break occurs in the plane of the dotted line, the chromosome on the left in *J* will have a duplication and contain both gene *d* and gene *D*, while the chromosome on the right will have a deficiency of the section containing gene *D.*

Translocation: One member of the chromosome pair shown in *A* may come to lie across one member of the chromosome pair shown in *B*, as seen in *K.* If a break occurs in the plane of the dotted line, sections of non-homologous chromosomes are exchanged, or translocated, as shown in *L.*

FIG. 37. Diagrams to show crossing over and various chromosomal aberrations.
(From Curtis and Guthrie.)

SEX AND GENIC BALANCE

Egg formula	Sperm formula	Zygote formula	Ratio X/A	Sex
$A + 2X$	$A + X$	$2A + 3X$	1.5	Superfemale (Fig. 38C)
$2A + 2X$	$A + X$	$3A + 3X$	1.0	Triploid Female
$A + X$	$A + X$	$2A + 2X$	1.0	Diploid Female
$2A + X$	$A + X$	$3A + 2X$	0.67	Intersex
$A + 2X$	$A + Y$	$2A + 2X + Y$	1.0	Diploid Female
$2A + 2X$	$A + Y$	$3A + 2X + Y$	0.67	Intersex
$A + X$	$A + Y$	$2A + X + Y$	0.5	Male
$2A + X$	$A + Y$	$3A + X + Y$	0.33	Supermale (Fig. 38D)

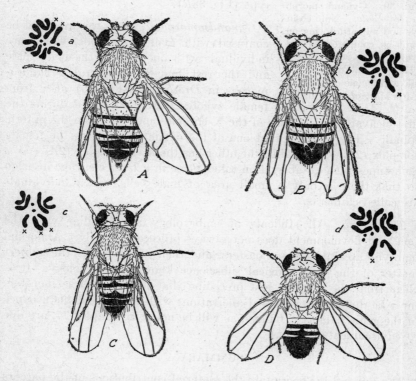

Fig. 38. Intersexes and supersexes in *Drosophila*, occurring in the progeny of triploid females. *A*, female-type intersex. *B*, male-type intersex. *C*, superfemale. *D*, supermale. *a, b, c* and *d* are the chromosome groups characteristic of *A, B, C* and *D* respectively. (From Curtis and Guthrie, after Morgan *et al.*)

Examination of the ratio between the X-chromosomes and other chromosomes (autosomes) suggests that the determination of sex depends on some sort of ratio between the genes in the X-chromosomes and the autosomes. Bridges (1921) has formulated a theory of genic balance to account for the observed results. In the development of the intersexes, the individuals commence as males but at a particular time shift to the type of development characteristic of females. The characters determined before the shift are male, those after it are females. As the time at which the shift takes place is variable the intersex may be of the female type (Fig. 38*A*) or of the male type (Fig. 38*B*).

Fig. 39. Gynandromorph in *Drosophila*. Note eosin eye and miniature wing on right as compared to red eye and long wing on left. This fly is male on the right side and female on the left. (After Morgan and Bridges.)

Gynandromorphs. Intersexes must not be confused with gynandromorphs, which are individuals with one part of the body male and the rest female. Bilateral gynandromorphs in *Drosophila* (Fig. 39) arise from female zygotes (2*A* + 2*X*), but during the first cleavage division one of the X-chromosomes is lost on the mitotic spindle. The result is that one of the daughter cells has the female complex (2*A* + 2*X*) while the other has the male complex (2*A* + *X*). Sometimes such an aberration takes place in a later cleavage division so that there is only a small area of male cells. Such individuals are called chimeras.

Teratology. All students of embryology are familiar with the fact that development does not always proceed normally. Abnormal embryos are known as monsters, and their study forms the subject matter of the embryological subscience known as teratology. It is clear from the sections just preceding that many of these monsters must be due to chromosomal aberrations with consequent disturbance of the genic balance. Others, as will be noted in Chapter 17, are due to environmental factors.

SUMMARY

The egg and the sperm are the material contributions of the parents to the new individual. The equivalent structures of the egg and the sperm are their nuclei. Each nucleus contains the haploid number of chromosomes. The fertilized egg has two haploid sets, or the diploid number. In somatic mitosis the chromosomes are split longitudinally and divided equally among the daughter cells, so that each daughter cell contains an assortment precisely equivalent to that of its sister cell and the mother cell. In the course of the meiotic divisions the diploid number of chromosomes is reduced to one haploid set. This is accomplished through the union of the homologous members of the two sets in synapsis. Each synaptic pair forms a tetrad of four chromatids, the members of which are distributed independently among the mature germ cells. In this way different classes of gametes are formed with varying chromosomal complexes.

The chromosome is built up from a thin thread, the chromonema, which binds together the genes, the units of heredity. These genes, ordinarily ultramicroscopic, are self-reproducing units which seem to accelerate definite chemical reactions without losing any of their own substance in the process. The course of development is largely controlled by the activities of these genes. These activities may be disturbed during meiosis by chromosomal aberrations, thus altering the genic balance and modifying the course of development, in some cases so much as to cause death. The genic balance may also be altered by point mutations or changes in the constitution of an individual gene recognizable through the effects produced.

Either aberrations or point mutations when not lethal may be transmitted in heredity. The distribution of these aberrant chromosomes or mutant genes in meiosis and fertilization is the material basis for heritable differences arising in the course of development of individuals belonging to the same species.

One of the outstanding problems in experimental embryology still awaiting solution is how the genes actually determine the course of development. But the modern student of embryology accepts the general theory that it is the complement of genes, from the egg and sperm respectively, which initiates and largely controls the development of the individual.

CHAPTER 5

EARLY EMBRYOLOGY

The fertilized egg (zygote) is a complete and balanced cell. It has two entire sets of chromosomes, each with a full complement of genes, one set from each parent. These nuclear elements are contained in a cell body whose cytoplasm is principally maternal in origin and which has a definite organization as indicated by its polarity. We are now to examine the way in which the embryo develops from the fertilized egg.

It is convenient to distinguish three steps in the early development of the embryo. First is the period of cleavage in which the egg undergoes a number of mitotic cell divisions, at each of which the number of cells (blastomeres) increases while the size of the cells decreases. The period ends with the embryo in the form of a blastula, a stage in which the blastomeres are not stratified into different layers.

Second comes the period of gastrulation, in which the blastomeres arrange themselves into the three germ layers, ectoderm, mesoderm, and endoderm (entoderm). In many vertebrates one of these layers may be segregated while the other two are still associated so that a two-layer stage consisting of ectoderm and mesendoderm, or of mesectoderm and endoderm, may intervene between the blastula and completed gastrula. As we shall see on later pages, the notochord is associated with the mesoderm to form a chorda-mesoderm area in gastrulation.

The segregation of the germ layers is hardly complete, particularly in amphioxus and the frog, before the neural plate becomes distinguishable from the surrounding ectoderm. The embryo in the neural plate stage is known as the neurula, and the period during which this plate invaginates to form the neural tube is conveniently termed the period of neurulation.

CLEAVAGE

As there are different types of eggs according to the amount and distribution of the yolk, so there are different types of cleavage according to the pattern formed by the dividing egg.

Rules of cleavage. Certain rules have been formulated to express the simpler geometrical relationships of the blastomeres. The first are Sachs's: (1) Cells typically tend to divide into equal parts. (2) Each new plane of division tends to intersect the preceding one at right angles. Sachs's rules are supplemented, and to some extent explained, by Hertwig's: (1) The typical position of the nucleus (and hence of the mitotic figure) tends towards the center of its sphere of influence, i.e., of the protoplasmic mass in which it lies. (2) The axis of the spindle typically lies in the longest axis of the protoplasmic mass, and division therefore tends to cut this axis transversely.

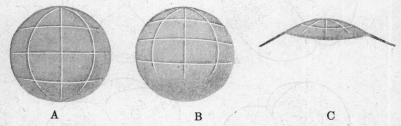

A   B   C

FIG. 40.   Diagram to show main types of cleavage in vertebrates. *A*, equal holoblastic. *B*, unequal holoblastic. *C*, meroblastic.

Types of cleavage. The rate of division is governed by the rule of Balfour: the rate of cleavage is inversely proportional to the amount of yolk present. This leads to a distinction between two types of cleavage. In the first type the cleavage planes divide the egg completely into separate blastomeres. This, known as holoblastic cleavage, is characteristic of isolecithal and moderately telolecithal eggs. In the second type the cleavage planes do not pass through the yolk and so the separate blastomeres come to lie upon a mass of undivided yolk. This, known as meroblastic cleavage, is typical of extremely telolecithal eggs. It is generally true that isolecithal eggs have equal holoblastic cleavage (Fig. 40*A*). Moderately telolecithal eggs have unequal holoblastic cleavage (Fig. 40*B*), and extremely telolecithal eggs have meroblastic cleavage (Fig. 40*C*).

Cell lineage. It must not be thought that cleavage results in a mass of identical blastomeres. Painstaking examination of dividing eggs has shown that in the normal development of favorable material the origin and fate of every blastomere can be determined accurately. The genealogical history of the blastomeres is known appropriately as cell lineage. One of the most clean-cut examples, in forms allied to the vertebrates, is the cell lineage of the tunicate *Styela* (*Cynthia*), worked out by Conklin in 1905.

The student should understand the system used in naming the blastomeres, which is illustrated most easily by means of the 8-cell stage (Fig. 41). The blastomeres on the right side of the embryo have underlined exponents. After the third division blastomeres formed

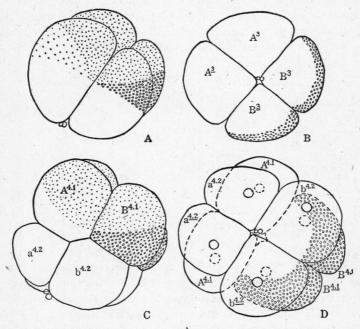

FIG. 41. Cleavage of *Styela* egg. *A,* 4-cell stage from left side. *B,* same stage from animal pole. *C,* 8-cell stage from left side. *D,* same stage from animal pole. For explanation of lettering, see text. (From Richards, after Conklin.)

at the animal hemisphere are in lower-case letters; those at the vegetal hemisphere are in capital letters. Those formed at the anterodorsal side of the embryo are given the designation a, at the anteroventral side A; those at the posterodorsal side are named b; those at the posteroventral side B. The first exponent is the number of the cell generation, counting the fertilized egg as the first generation, the blastomeres of the first cleavage as the second generation, etc. The exponent after the decimal point indicates whether the cell is in the first, second, third, etc., row from the vegetal pole. Thus the cell labeled $A^{4.1}$ is anteroventral, left side, vegetal hemisphere, of the fourth generation, and in the row next to the vegetal pole.

The first cleavage is bilateral; i.e., it divides the egg, with its presumptive organ regions, into a right blastomere (AB^2) and a left blastomere (AB^2). At the second cleavage each of these is divided into an anterodorsal blastomere (A^3 and A^3) and a postero-ventral blastomere (B^3 and B^3). The third cleavage plane (Fig. 41*C*, *D*) separates the smaller cells of the animal hemisphere ($a^{4.2}$, $b^{4.2}$, $a^{\underline{4.2}}$, $b^{\underline{4.2}}$) from the larger cells of the vegetal hemisphere ($A^{4.1}$, $B^{4.1}$, $A^{\underline{4.1}}$, $B^{\underline{4.1}}$).

CELL LINEAGE OF STYELA

(First three cleavages)

$$\text{Egg}^1 \begin{cases} AB^2 \text{ (left)} \begin{cases} A^3 \begin{cases} a^{4.2} \\ A^{4.1} \end{cases} \\ B^3 \begin{cases} b^{4.2} \\ B^{4.1} \end{cases} \end{cases} \\ AB^{\underline{2}} \text{ (right)} \begin{cases} A^{\underline{3}} \begin{cases} a^{\underline{4.2}} \\ A^{\underline{4.1}} \end{cases} \\ B^{\underline{3}} \begin{cases} b^{\underline{4.2}} \\ B^{\underline{4.1}} \end{cases} \end{cases} \end{cases}$$

By the sixth generation (32-cell stage) the organ-forming regions have been segregated into different blastomeres as follows:

Animal hemisphere:

    14 Ectoderm, epidermis.
    2 Ectoderm, neural plate.

Vegetal hemisphere:

    4 Ectoderm and mesoderm, chorda-neural plate.
    4 Mesoderm, gray crescent.
    2 Mesoderm, yellow crescent.
    6 Endoderm cells.

    ——

    32

The cell lineage of many types of invertebrates has been investigated in a similar manner, but the only vertebrate form in which the cell lineage has been reported is the minnow, *Fundulus* (Oppenheimer, 1936). In *normal* development it may be concluded that during cleavage the successive generations of blastomeres show a progressive differentiation. Earlier or later, the organ-forming areas of the fertilized egg are segregated into different groups of blastomeres, which are the organ-forming areas of the blastula.

Later (Chapter 17), experiments will be described which indicate that individual blastomeres may, under *different* conditions, give rise to parts of the embryo other than those which they produce in the normal course of development.

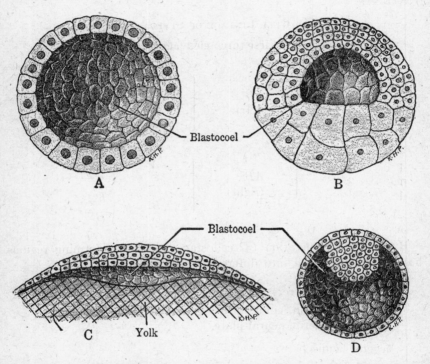

FIG. 42. Diagrams of vertebrate blastulae. *A*, coeloblastula following holoblastic equal cleavage (amphioxus). *B*, coeloblastula following holoblastic unequal cleavage (frog). *C*, discoblastula following meroblastic cleavage (chick). *D*, blastocyst (mammals).

The blastula. The period of cleavage terminates in the appearance of the blastula, but this does not mean that cell division comes to an end. The blastula is generally defined as a hollow sphere of blastomeres surrounding a cavity, the blastocoel. But this definition does not fit the blastulae formed by meroblastic cleavage. So we shall distinguish three classes of blastulae. The first is of the hollow sphere type (coeloblastula) and is the result of holoblastic equal cleavage (Fig. 42A). A variety of this type, in which the blastocoel is displaced towards the animal pole, is the result of holoblastic unequal cleavage (Fig. 42B).

The second type of blastula (discoblastula) is the result of meroblastic cleavage in which the blastomeres rest in a flat disc, the blastoderm, on the undivided yolk mass (Fig. 42C). A segmentation cavity later combines with a yolk cavity, formed by the digestion of the yolk underlying the blastoderm, to form a blastocoel. Such a blastocoel is roofed with cells but has a floor of yolk.

The third type of blastula is found only in mammals and is called a blastocyst (Fig. 42D). The solid morula forms a blastocoel which enlarges until it almost separates an outer layer of cells (trophoblast) from an inner cell mass (the embryonic mass).

Presumptive organ regions of the blastula. As might be inferred from the results of cell-lineage studies, the regions of the blastula will give rise to different parts of the embryo in normal development. In the tunicate and amphioxus, Conklin has mapped out the presumptive organ regions of the blastula, and Vogt and his students, by means of a most ingenious technique, have accomplished the same result for the amphibian blastula. Experimental evidence (Chapter 17) indicates that in the tunicate and amphioxus the organ-forming regions are definitely determined whereas, in amphibians, the regions have a greater plasticity and may give rise to parts of the embryo quite different from those formed in normal development.

CLEAVAGE: THE AMPHIOXUS

In the egg of the amphioxus (Fig. 43), which is isolecithal, cleavage is holoblastic and almost equal. The first cleavage commences as a depression at the animal pole, which later assumes a groove-like form and elongates until it becomes a wide meridional furrow extending around the egg. This constriction deepens until the two hemispheres are completely divided, when each blastomere rounds up into a spherical shape. The second cleavage also commences at the animal pole and is meridional but at right angles to the first, following Sachs' second rule. The third plane of cleavage is at right angles to both the first and second and hence would be equatorial if the egg were completely isolecithal. But as the yolk is a little concentrated at the vegetal pole, the nucleus, following Hertwig's first rule, is in the center of the cytoplasm, i.e., on the egg axis slightly nearer the animal pole. So the third cleavage plane is nearer the animal pole and accordingly is latitudinal. The quartette of cells in the animal hemisphere is there-

fore smaller than those in the vegetal hemisphere.   The smaller cells
are called micromeres; the larger ones, macromeres.   The fourth
division divides each of the eight existing blastomeres in two.   There
are two planes of cleavage, each meridional, at right angles to the
third, and also at right angles to each other.   Sometimes the cleavage
planes of the fourth division are parallel to each other instead of being

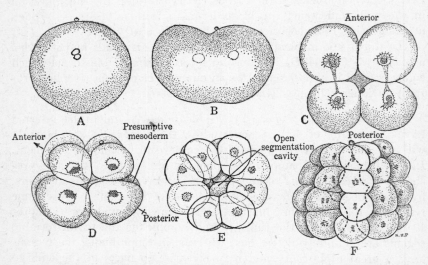

Fig. 43.   Cleavage of the amphioxus egg.   *A*, before cleavage.   *B*, commencing first
cleavage, from posterior side.   *C*, second cleavage, from vegetal pole.   *D*, third
cleavage, from left side.   *E*, fourth cleavage, from vegetal pole.   *F*, fifth cleavage,
side view, segmentation cavity indicated by dotted lines.   ×166.   (After Conklin,
1932.)

at right angles.   This makes the bilateral symmetry of the dividing
egg quite obvious.   In the fifth cleavage 32 cells are produced, again by
two planes of cleavage, at right angles to the planes of the fourth, but
this time latitudinal and parallel to each other.   From this time on
cleavage becomes more and more irregular.   The early cleavages have
been fairly regular; each has divided the entire egg mass; and the
blastomeres, with the exceptions noted, have been almost equal.   The
blastomeres round up as each cleavage is completed, and a jelly is
secreted between them.   In this way a small cavity called the segmentation cavity or blastocoel is formed.

   Conklin (1933) states that comparison of the cleavage of the amphioxus with that of the tunicates shows a general resemblance between
the two in the distribution of the organ-forming substances to the

blastomeres, in the generally bilateral type of cleavage, and the order of division; but in all respects the tunicate egg is the more precise and the more precocious in differentiation.

In the development of the amphioxus we find a good example of the coeloblastula (Fig. 44). The blastomeres are arranged in a single layer around the enlarged blastocoel which is entirely cut off from the exterior. The blastomeres at the animal pole are micromeres; those at the vegetal pole are macromeres; the cells at the equatorial belt are transitional in type.

The cells which are to form the mesoderm are rounded and in active mitosis. They are arranged in a crescent on one side of the egg while those which will form the chorda-neural plate make up a corresponding crescent on the other. The endoderm cells are the larger cells of the vegetal hemisphere.

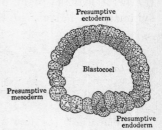

Fig. 44. Blastula of the amphioxus. Sagittal section. ×110. (After Conklin.)

CLEAVAGE: THE FROG

The frog's egg (Fig. 45) is telolecithal with holoblastic unequal cleavage. Here the first division commences as a depression at the animal pole, which elongates and extends around the egg as a shallow furrow until the ends meet at the vegetal pole. The constriction also extends inwards, most rapidly at the animal pole, and eventually bisects the egg into two blastomeres which round up very slightly. The plane of the second division is also meridional and through the animal pole but at right angles to the first. The first two cleavage planes intersect each other at the animal pole. As the blastomeres round up, however, two of them are pushed away from the point of intersection by the two others which flatten against each other to form a short polar furrow. The third cleavage is latitudinal, about 45° from the animal pole, and the micromeres are considerably smaller than the macromeres. Theoretically the fourth and fifth planes of cleavage bear the same relationships to the earlier ones as do those of amphioxus but actually they are more irregular. The two planes of the fourth cleavage often fail to pass through the vegetal pole and hence become vertical rather than true meridional planes. As these planes originate in the animal hemisphere, the micromeres are divided before the macromeres, so that a 12-cell stage intervenes between the 8-cell and 16-cell stages. Similarly, following Balfour's rule, the latitudinal cleavage plane in the animal hemisphere of the fifth division appears

before the corresponding plane in the vegetal hemisphere, so that there
is a 24-cell stage before the 32-cell stage is attained.

The cell lineage of the frog's egg has not been followed in detail as
has that of the tunicate or amphioxus. It is known, however, that
the first cleavage plane ordinarily divides the gray crescent into two
symmetrical halves, so that cleavage is normally bilaterally sym-

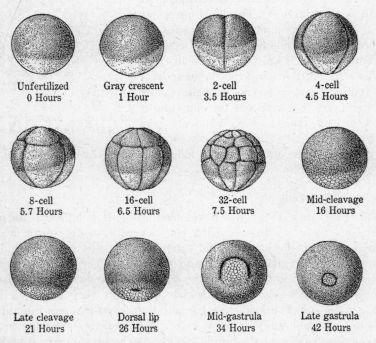

Unfertilized 0 Hours	Gray crescent 1 Hour	2-cell 3.5 Hours	4-cell 4.5 Hours
8-cell 5.7 Hours	16-cell 6.5 Hours	32-cell 7.5 Hours	Mid-cleavage 16 Hours
Late cleavage 21 Hours	Dorsal lip 26 Hours	Mid-gastrula 34 Hours	Late gastrula 42 Hours

Fig. 45. Cleavage and gastrulation in the frog, *Rana pipiens*. Ages given are at a
temperature of 18° C. ×10. (Rearranged from Shumway, *Anatomical Record*
78 : 143.)

metrical from the outset. The segmentation cavity, visible from the
third cleavage on, is displaced toward the animal pole and toward the
gray crescent side of the cleaving egg.

The blastula of the frog (Fig. 46) resembles that of the amphioxus
in all essential characters, but shows minor differences due largely to
the greater amount of yolk present. In the first place, the blastoderm
is no longer one layer of cells in thickness. Tangential divisions have
increased the number of cells so that at the animal pole the blastoderm
may be three or four cells deep. Furthermore, the greater difference in

size between the micromeres of the animal pole and the macromeres of the vegetal pole result in the blastocoel occupying an eccentric position entirely within the limits of the animal hemisphere.

The blastula of the frog shows certain regional differentiations. Thus the cells of the animal hemisphere are smaller than those of the vegetal hemisphere, and contain pigment granules. Between the micromeres of the animal pole and the macromeres lies a band of cells of intermediate size, known as the marginal belt or germ ring. This region corresponds to the region of the gray crescent.

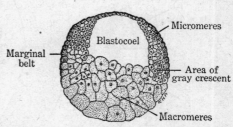

FIG. 46. Blastula of the frog. Sagittal section, ×16.

Vogt has demonstrated the fate of different regions of the amphibian blastula in normal development by marking them with such harmless dyes as Nile blue and neutral red. The stain persists long enough so that the migration of the dyed cell groups can be traced through gastrulation and even later. He has succeeded in mapping out the surface of the blastula into presumptive organ regions, as seen in the diagram (Fig. 47), which represents the organ-forming areas of the fire-toad (*Bombinator igneus*). Another anuran (*Discoglossus*) has been studied by Pasteels (1936) with similar results.

CLEAVAGE: THE CHICK

In telolecithal eggs with meroblastic cleavage, such as that of the fowl, only the protoplasm of the egg, i.e., the blastodisc, is divided, and the cleavage planes do not segment the yolk (Fig. 48). The first furrow commences at the animal pole and extends outwards towards the edges of the blastodisc. The second is formed by two furrows, at right angles to the first, one in each blastomere, which grow towards the first furrow and also towards the edge of the blastodisc. They may join the first furrow at approximately the same point or at separate points, in which case a polar furrow is formed. These four cells are incomplete, as the furrows do not extend all the way to the yolk nor to the edge of the blastodisc, but remain connected both below and at their margins. From this point on, cleavage is irregular. Some cleavage planes are circular and cut off central cells from marginal. These may be compared with the latitudinal planes of the holoblastic type. Others are radial, like the first and second. Still others are tangential and divide the central cells into upper and lower layers, as in the frog's egg.

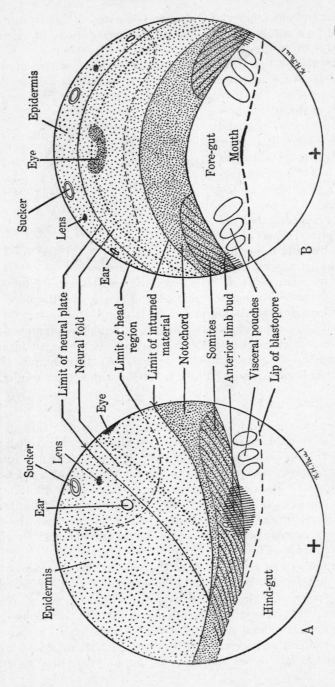

FIG. 47. Diagrams to show presumptive organ regions of the *Bombinator* blastula. *A*, from left side. *B*, from dorsal surface. The cross indicates the position of the vegetal pole. (After Vogt.)

The blastula of the chick is a discoblastula. The blastoderm consists of an inner mass of micromeres completely separated from one another by cleavage planes, and an outer ring of macromeres which are partially separated from one another by incomplete radial cleavage planes only. These latter cells are in direct protoplasmic continuity

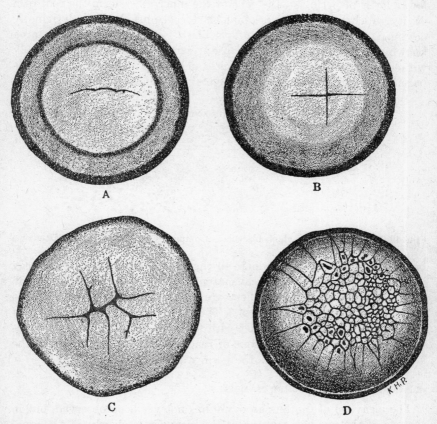

A   B

C   D

FIG. 48. Cleavage of the hen's egg. *A*, first cleavage. *B*, second cleavage. *C*, third cleavage. *D*, later cleavage. All from animal pole. Approx. ×12 (*A, B, D,* after Kölliker; *C*, after Patterson.)

by means of an outer ring of undivided cytoplasm and a thin lower layer of undivided cytoplasm passing beneath the inner mass (Fig. 49). This undivided cytoplasm is called the periblast. The micromeres of the inner mass are separated from the underlying undivided periblast by means of a thin cleft which is the original blastocoel.

The blastoderm expands over the yolk, new cells being added to the inner cell mass from the outer ring of cells. The periblast, contributing its cytoplasm to the formation of new cells in the outer ring, soon uses up all the material contained in the thin lower layer. Meantime its outer ring grows out over the yolk. With the disappearance of the lower layer of periblast, the cells of the inner mass form the roof of a cavity which includes the original blastocoel plus the space originally occupied by the lower layer of periblast. These cells form an area known as the area pellucida because it can be detached from the yolk without carrying any yolk particles and hence appears more transparent. The cells of the outer ring make up the area opaca, so-called

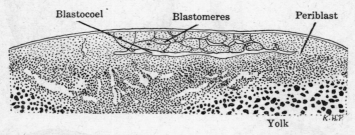

FIG. 49. Section of early chick blastula. Compare Fig. 48D. (After Patterson.)

because particles of yolk adhere to them when removed from the egg and render the region less transparent. As the ring grows outward, the cells at the extreme periphery are lifted slightly above the yolk to form the margin of overgrowth. The cells just inside the margin of overgrowth, and still in contact with the yolk, form the zone of junction. Those just inside the zone of junction and recently added to the area pellucida are known as the germ wall (Fig. 73).

CLEAVAGE: MAN AND OTHER MAMMALS

The cleavage of the human ovum has not yet been observed, but in the egg of the monkey and rabbit the cleavage is clearly of the equal holoblastic type (Fig. 50). In the rabbit the first cleavage takes place about 22½ hours after coitus. It is equal and complete. The second cleavage follows in about 3 hours. Here the two cleavage spindles frequently lie at right angles to each other so that the four blastomeres assume the form of a cross. Cleavage is now irregular, 5-, 6-, 7-, and 8-cell stages appearing in order. The 8-cell stage is attained about 32 hours after coitus. There is now considerable difference in size, the largest blastomere being almost twice the size of the smallest. The 16-cell stage is reached in another hour and a half. In reaching this

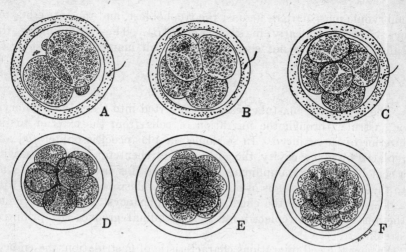

FIG. 50. Cleavage in mammalian egg. *A*, first cleavage. *B*, second cleavage. *C*, third cleavage. *A, B, C*, monkey. ×170. (After Lewis and Hartman in Arey.) *D*, third cleavage. *E*, fourth cleavage. *F*, fifth cleavage. *D, E, F*, rabbit. ×180. (After Gregory.)

stage the cleavage of one blastomere is tangential so that there is always one cell completely enclosed. In later cleavages more tangential cleavages occur, and this, with the shifting of the blastomeres upon each other, results in a solid mass of cells called a morula.

No human embryo in the blastula stage has been recorded, so a description of the blastocyst of the rabbit will be given in its place. About 75 hours after coitus and while the egg is still in the oviduct, a cleft, the blastocoel, appears in the morula apparently due to the accumulation of fluid. This

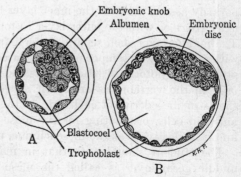

FIG. 51. Sections of rabbit blastocysts. ×200. (After Gregory).

cavity extends rapidly until the trophoblast is separated from the embryonic mass. The separation is almost complete (Fig. 51*A*), extending about 270° of the possible 360°. By this time the blastocyst has reached the uterus and the amount of fluid has greatly increased, expanding the blastocoel and stretching the trophoblast cells. The

embryonic mass flattens against the trophoblast, and the entire blastocyst increases greatly in size (Fig. 51*B*). This flattening of the
embryonic mass is not characteristic of all mammalian blastocysts.

GASTRULATION

The vertebrate blastula becomes converted into a stratified embryo,
or gastrula, through the migration of cells from the exterior to the
interior of the embryo. In so doing the blastocoel is obliterated and
replaced by a new cavity, the gastrocoel (archenteron). In forms with
a coeloblastula like amphioxus and the frog, this cavity communicates
to the exterior by means of an opening, the blastopore. In forms with
a discoblastula, like the chick, or with a blastocyst, like the mammal,
the blastopore is replaced by a longitudinal groove, the primitive
streak.

During the cell migrations characteristic of gastrulation, the embryo
frequently appears to have two layers. The cells left on the exterior
form the outer germ layer commonly known as ectoderm (ectoblast,
epiblast). Those on the inside, lining the gastrocoel, form the inner
germ layer, usually called the endoderm (entoderm, entoblast, hypoblast). It is now generally recognized, since the presumptive germ
layers have been identified in the blastula stage, that cells which will
give rise to the middle germ layer, the chorda-mesoderm, consisting of
the mesoderm (mesoblast) and notochord (chorda dorsalis) are temporarily associated with the inner layer to form mesendoderm (amphioxus, frog) or with the outer layer to form mesectoderm (chick, man).
The middle layer soon separates itself from the endoderm or ectoderm
with which it was temporarily associated. It is then seen to be composed of the notochord (chorda dorsalis), an axial supporting rod found
only in the vertebrates and their allies the protochordates, and two
sheets of mesoderm on each side of the notochord. Later wandering
ameboid cells, originating for the most part from the mesoderm, and
known collectively as the mesenchyme, make their appearance.

The student should note that in many elementary textbooks the
middle germ layer is called the mesoderm and that the notochord
is variously derived from mesoderm, endoderm (amphioxus and frog),
and ectoderm (chick and mammals). This terminology dates back
to the phylogenetic period of embryology (Chapter 1), when it was
supposed that a blastula composed of undifferentiated blastomeres
gave rise to a gastrula with two separate (primary) layers, and that
the mesoderm and the notochord arose separately from one or the
other of the so-called primary layers, primitively from the endoderm.

Today it is generally recognized that the notochord arises in the same manner and at the same time as the mesoderm. To avoid the clumsy phrase, mesoderm and notochord, many writers are now employing the term chorda-mesoderm for the middle germ layer, and restricting the term mesoderm to the middle germ layer exclusive of the notochord, a usage employed in this book.

In collateral reading the student will sometimes encounter the word endomesoderm used in connection with mesoderm " originating from " endoderm. Similarly the word ectomesoderm is sometimes employed to designate mesoderm " originating from " ectoderm. Still other writers use the terms " peristomial " mesoderm, meaning mesoderm appearing in the region of the blastopore, and " gastral " mesoderm for mesoderm appearing to arise from the invaginated endoderm. But inasmuch as the material for the middle germ layer can be located at the blastula stage and sometimes traced to definite blastomeres during early cleavage, this distinction is of small importance.

GASTRULATION IN THE AMPHIOXUS

The first indication of gastrulation is a flattening of the macromeres of the vegetal hemisphere (Fig. 52*A*). These cells divide less frequently and become more columnar, while the others divide more frequently and become more cubical or spherical in shape. This change in the shape and rate of division, says Conklin (1932), is apparently the principal cause of invagination (Fig. 52*B*), although it may be due also in part to the resorption of material from the blastocoel jelly, or to exosmosis, for the contents of the blastocoel become less viscous as gastrulation proceeds.

In later stages of gastrulation the gastrula increases in length, owing to the backward growth of the lips of the blastopore (Fig. 52*C*). While this process is taking place cells are being rolled from the exterior to the interior (involution). The lips of the blastopore grow unevenly, the ventral lip finally turning upward to reduce the blastopore to a very small opening (Fig. 52*D*). Conklin expressly denies that this narrowing of the blastopore is caused by the growing together of the right and left halves of the dorsal lip (concrescence). The cells left on the exterior after gastrulation is complete are ectoderm. Those which have been carried to the interior are endoderm, and presumptive chorda-mesoderm. In late gastrulation the cells of the ectoderm develop cilia, by means of which the embryo rotates within its fertilization membrane. The cells of the mesoderm and notochord form the lip of the blastopore, the notochord cells at the dorsal lip, mesoderm at the ventral and lateral lips. As the lips of the blastopore grow backward, these cells are carried to the interior by involution.

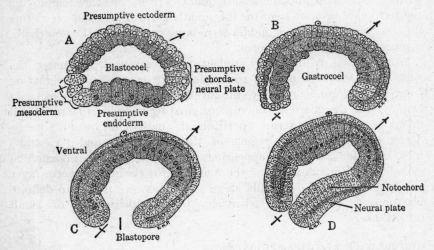

FIG. 52. Sections of amphioxus embryos during gastrulation. *A*, blastula (6 hours after fertilization). *B*, gastrula (9½ hours). *C*, gastrula (12 hours). *D*, gastrula (14 hours). Animal pole indicated by presence of polocyte. Anteroposterior axis shown by arrow. All sagittal sections. ×180. (After Conklin.)

When the ventral lip grows upward, the mesodermal crescent is tilted up behind so that its arms run in an anteroposterior direction at the angles between the dorsal and lateral sides of the blastopore.

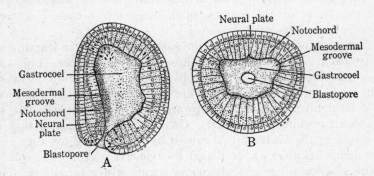

FIG. 53. Optical hemisections of amphioxus gastrula (14 hours after fertilization). *A*, interior view of left half. *B*, posterior end to show notochord and mesodermal grooves. ×166. (After Conklin.)

From each point of the crescent a band of mesodermal cells grows forward, while between them the notochord also grows forward to form a median band. Thus the roof of the gastrocoel is composed of three strips of chorda-mesoderm, mesoderm on each side, notochord in the middle. The cells of the mesodermal bands, being shorter than those of the notochord or endoderm, cause the bands to appear as grooves in transverse section (Fig. 53*B*). The later fate of the gastrula will be discussed on page 103.

GASTRULATION IN THE FROG

The gastrulation of the frog embryo has been interpreted in various ways by different investigators. The earlier accounts were based on the supposition that the embryo passed through a two-layered stage consisting of ectoderm and endoderm and that later the notochord and mesoderm split off (delaminated) from the endoderm. Vogt, after his work on gastrulation in the urodele amphibia (1925), in which he followed the movements of the organ-forming areas of the blastula by means of vital dyes, (Fig. 54), studied the gastrulation of an anuran (*Bombinator*). Later Pasteels (1937) confirmed these results using another anuran (*Discoglossus*). The organ-forming areas in the blastula of the frog (*Rana*) and their subsequent migrations have not yet been studied by the Vogt technique. In the account which follows it is assumed that the blastula has the same organ-forming

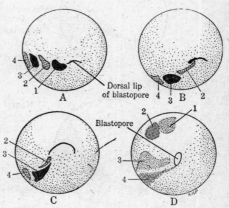

FIG. 54. Diagrams of the *Triton* egg showing movement of surface areas stained with Nile blue and neutral red during gastrulation. Areas on surface shown with sharp outline, those on interior without outline. (After Vogt.)

areas as other anura (*Bombinator* and *Discoglossus*) and that the movements of these areas are also essentially similar.

In reading the following account of gastrulation we should make frequent reference to the illustrations. Surface views of the embryo during gastrulation are shown in Fig. 45. Photographs of sagittal sections are illustrated in Fig. 57. Interpretation of the surface views according to the findings of Vogt and Pasteels is presented in Fig. 55, and a similar interpretation of the sections is given in Fig. 57.

The first stage in the gastrulation of the frog is the formation of a groove on what will later be the dorsal side of the embryo in the region formerly occupied by the gray crescent (Fig. 45). The location of the groove is $23°$ below the equator of the blastula. Along this groove, cells are pushed into the interior (involution), while at the same time the cells immediately above the groove are growing down over the surface of the embryo to cover them (epiboly). In this way a two-layered fold is produced at the dorsal lip of the blastopore (Fig 57).

As the two-layered fold grows down over the cells of the vegetal hemisphere, it extends laterally, thus forming the lateral lips of the blastopore (Fig. 45). And, since it is covering a spherical surface,

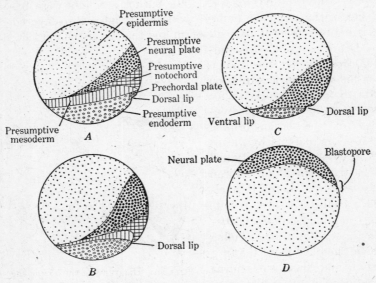

Fig. 55. Surface maps of stages in gastrulation of the frog. All from left side. *A*, dorsal lip stage (10). *B*, lateral lip stage, midgastrula (11). *C*, ventral lip stage, late gastrula (12). *D*, neurula, yolk plug stage (13).

the ends of the fold eventually meet to form the ventral lip (Fig. 45, 57). Epiboly and involution take place at all points on the lip of the blastopore, but chiefly at the dorsal lip, which moves approximately $65°$ around the egg. At this time the egg presents the appearance of a black sphere with a small white circular area, known as the yolk plug.

As a direct result of the fact that the small cells of the marginal zone grow over the larger blastomeres and roll in at the dorsal lip, it is obvious that they must also converge towards the median line at the dorsal lip, which may be thought of as a bottleneck. Once inside the bottleneck they tend to diverge from the median line. These movements are illustrated in Fig. 56. To these four types of movement, epiboly, involution, convergence, and divergence, must be added a fifth, elongation, or growth in length, which prevents a heaping up of material in the median line.

With these mass movements taking place during gastrulation, the history of the organ-forming areas may now be followed. Just before the appearance of the dorsal lip, the area formerly occupied by the gray crescent, marginal zone, is presumptive chorda-mesoderm, with the notochord occupying the median portion (Fig. 55A, 57A). Below the marginal zone is the white presumptive endoderm with its large yolk-laden cells. Just below the presumptive notochord is a small area of endoderm which will naturally undergo involution before the notochord and is known, from its final location, as the prechordal plate. Above the marginal zone is the ectoderm, of which the material later destined to form the neural plate forms a crescent immediately adjacent to the presumptive notochord.

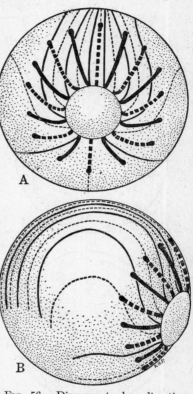

When involution commences at the dorsal lip of the blastopore, the first material turned in will be endodermal (Fig. 55B, 57B). This will form the anterior wall and sides of the gastrocoel. The roof in the midline will be formed by the prechordal

FIG. 56. Diagrams to show direction of cell movements during amphibian gastrulation. *A*, from posterior surface. *B*, from left side. Thick lines on exterior surface. Thin lines on interior. (After Vogt.)

plate. This will be followed by the notochord in the midline, with a wing-like extension of mesoderm on either side. As the chorda-mesodermal crescent undergoes involution, the presumptive neural plate will undergo convergence and elongation as it moves towards the dorsal lip (epiboly). In this way it will come to lie over the chorda-mesoderm (Fig. 55C, 57C). By this time the ventral lip of the blastopore has been formed, and the gastrocoel is still a slit-like cavity. The huge yolk-laden cells of presumptive endoderm, which appear externally as

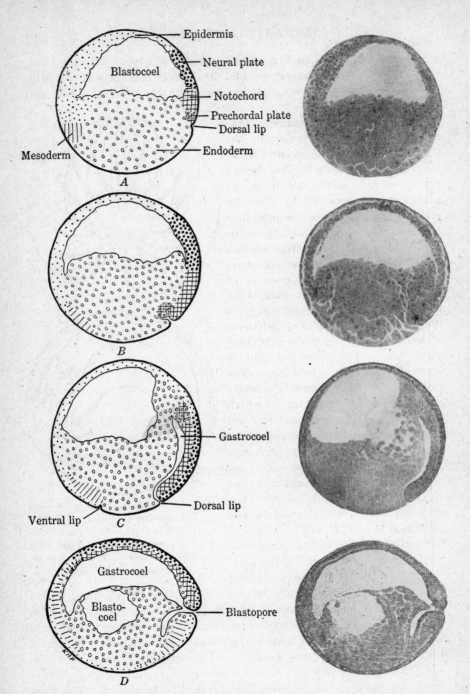

FIG. 57. Sagittal sections of frog embryos in gastrulation. *A*, dorsal lip. *B*, lateral lip. *C*, ventral lip. *D*, neurula. ×22. Photographs by George Svihla.

a large circular yolk plug, continue inward to form the floor of the gastrocoel. They are in direct continuity with the smaller endodermal cells which were the first to undergo involution.

The gastrocoel now expands at the expense of the blastocoel (Fig. 57D), which is either pressed out of existence or merged with the gastrocoel by the rupture of the thin partition separating them. The yolk-plug has withdrawn into the interior as the lips of the blastopore close together. This closing process commences at the dorsal side, and the two lateral sides of the blastopore press together to form a short slit (sometimes called the primitive streak). The blastopore closes last of all at the ventral extremity of the slit. It is claimed that in some species of frogs the ventral portion of the slit remains open and will later form the anus, but this is not the case with the *Rana pipiens* material studied by the author. In the closing stages of gastrulation the rearrangement of the heavy yolk-laden cells brings about a rotation of the gastrula, of approximately 80°, so that the blastopore is now at the posterior end of the embryo (*55D*).

During this period, the neural plate and notochord are greatly elongated. Mesoderm turned in at the ventral lip of the blastopore unites with that from dorsal and lateral lips, but there is still a circular area (mesodermal lacuna) in which ectoderm and endoderm are in contact. Cells from the endodermal lateral walls of the gastrocoel are growing upward, under the mesoderm, to form a new roof of endoderm, but there is still a strip roofed only by notochord. This is known as the endodermal lacuna, (dorsal lacuna, Dalcq and Gerard) which disappears by the continued upward growth of the endoderm during neurulation (page 105).

GASTRULATION IN THE CHICK

The gastrulation of the chick is accomplished in two stages. In the first of them, the endoderm separates from the mesectoderm. During the second, a primitive streak appears, and from this streak the chorda mesoderm cells move inward between the endoderm and ectoderm.

There is considerable difference of opinion as to the precise manner in which the first stage of the process is accomplished. Most textbooks, including earlier editions of this one, have described the process as it takes place in the pigeon's egg according to Patterson (1909). More recently a number of investigators have challenged this account, at least for the hen's egg, the most detailed description being that of Pasteels (1937). While the author prefers Pasteels' theory, he will also set forth Patterson's for comparison.

Patterson's account. The first indication of gastrulation is the thinning of the blastoderm at the posterior end and the complete separation of the cells from the yolk at that region (Fig. 58A). In other words, there is a crescentic area, almost a quarter of the circumference, of the blastoderm which lacks the zone of junction completely. Here the cells roll inward (involution) (Fig. 59) and multiply until they have spread completely under the upper layer to roof in the old blastocoel and convert it into the new gastrocoel, whose floor is made up of undivided yolk. The slit-like opening where the zone of junction disappeared is compared to the blastopore, and the rim along which involution took place is considered the dorsal lip.

There is very little overgrowth at the dorsal lip while involution is taking place, and consequently the edges of the blastoderm on either side swing around to enclose the lip region in the advancing germ wall. In this way the blastopore is compressed laterally and concrescence (Fig. 60) takes place.

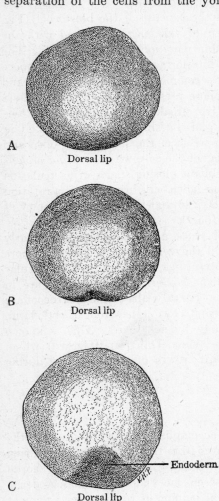

FIG. 58. Surface views to show three stages in the gastrulation of the hen's egg. (After Patterson.)

Pasteels' account. On the surface of the blastoderm, before gastrulation takes place, the area pellucida is surrounded by the area opaca. Within the area pellucida a vaguely delimited line marks off the embryonic area from the extra-embryonic area (Fig. 61A). Within the embryonic area, there is a region (without sharp boundaries) distinguished as the area of presumptive endoderm. During the first hours of incuba-

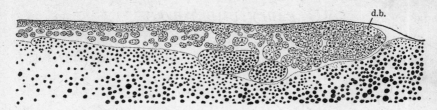

FIG. 59. Sagittal section through early gastrula of pigeon (36 hours after fertilization). Posterior half of section only. *d.b.*, dorsal lip of blastopore. (From Richards after Patterson.)

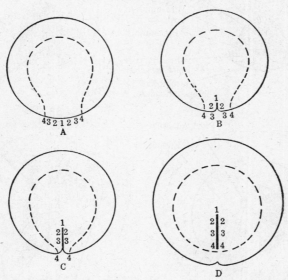

FIG. 60. Diagrams showing four stages in the process of concrescence. (After Lillie.)

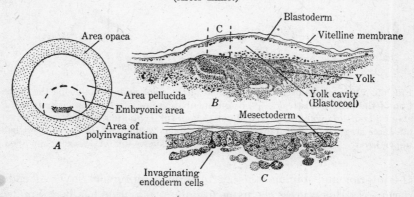

FIG. 61. Polyinvagination in the chick blastodisc. *A*, diagram to show area of polyinvagination. *B*, section of unincubated blastoderm. *C*, enlargement of area marked *C* in 61 *B*. (After Dalcq from a preparation of Pasteels.)

95

tion, small grooves appear in the endodermal area. Sections (Fig. 61*B*) show that these grooves mark the places where cells are migrating to

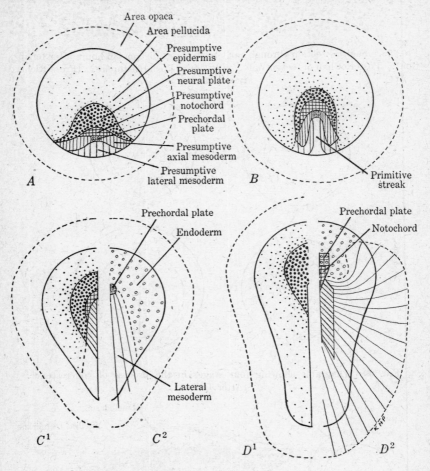

FIG. 62. Map of the organ-forming areas of the chick embryo following the formation of the primitive streak. *A*, before incubation and after polyinvagination. *B*, about 8 hours of incubation. *C*1, about 15 hours of incubation, left half, upper layer. *C*2, same stage, right half, lower layer. *D*1, about 24 hours of incubation, left half, upper layer. *D*2, same stage, right half, lower layer. (After Pasteels, modified.)

the interior and joining together to form a continuous layer of endoderm. To this process the name of polyinvagination has been applied.

Whether the endoderm is formed by involution (Patterson) or polyinvagination (Pasteels), the embryo is now composed of endoderm (lower layer) and ectomesoderm (upper layer). Pasteels, Hoadley, Willier, and others have worked on the organ-forming areas of the embryo at this stage and, while the accounts differ in minor details, the general organization of the embryo is fairly well agreed upon. For this account we shall use the description of Pasteels, according to whom the greater part of the embryonic area is now composed of the ectoderm (Fig. 62A). A crescentic region occupying the posterior part of the ectodermal area is the presumptive neural plate. Immediately posterior to this is another crescent with the presumptive notochord in the central portion. Immediately posterior to the presumptive notochord comes the prechordal plate, separating two wings of presumptive mesoderm which will give rise to the somites. Behind this crescent is the area of presumptive lateral mesoderm.

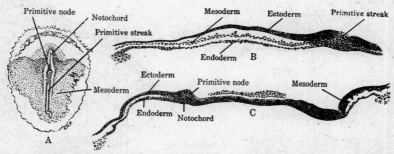

Fig. 63. Blastoderm of chick to show early stage in development of notochord. *A*, surface view at 20 hours (after Duval). *B*, transverse section, left half only. *C*, sagittal section. (*B, C*, after Lillie.)

The embryonic area elongates while the cells of which it is composed converge towards the midline, heaping up to form an axial primitive streak. In a more advanced embryo the primitive streak is differentiated into primitive groove in the middle, primitive folds on either sides, a primitive pit at the anterior end of the groove, and a primitive (Hensen's) node in front of the pit where the primitive folds unite (Fig. 63).

At the anterior end of this streak, the wings of the neural and mesodermal crescents have turned towards the midline (Fig. 63B). Now the material nearest the primitive streak migrates downward and turns outward between the upper and lower layers. At the anterior end (primitive node) the prechordal plate turns in first, followed by the notochord (formerly known as the head process (Fig. 63C). At the sides the lateral mesoderm turns in first, followed by the axial mesoderm. The mesoderm of the future tail bud turns in at the posterior end. During this process the embryo elongates, and the primitive streak seems to be drawn towards the posterior end, with the result that the wings of neural plate close together in front of it (Fig. 63*D*). The embryo at this stage may be compared with the neurula of the frog.

GASTRULATION IN MAN

The mammalian blastocyst at the time of implantation consists of an outer layer of trophoblast and an inner embryonic mass. No human embryo in this stage of development has yet been described. In the rhesus monkey, however, Streeter (1938) has shown that just prior to implantation the embryonic mass consists of three kinds of cells.

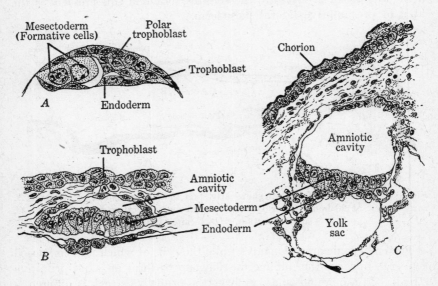

FIG. 64.   Early primate embryos during germ layer formation.   *A*, monkey (8 days), before implantation ×370 (after Streeter).   *B*, human (12 days), after implantation ×200 (after Hertig and Rock).   *C*, human (15) days ×130 (after Brewer).

A thin layer of cells (Fig. 64*A*) on the side of the mass away from its point of attachment to the trophoblast represents the endoderm. Certain large cells are interpreted as " formative cells " which will give rise to the rest of the embryo proper. Joining the trophoblast are smaller " polar " (nodal) cells, whose fate will be discussed in a later section (page 131).

The origin of the endoderm is still uncertain, some writers considering that it takes place by splitting (delamination), others by the wandering of certain cells out of the mass before combining to form the endodermal layer. In later stages the formative cells flatten out to form with the endoderm cells underlying them, an embryonic disc. Above the disc a space appears which is the precursor of the amniotic cavity, to be discussed in a later chapter (page 124).

The youngest human embryo yet described, Hertig-Rock (1941), is about eleven days old (Fig. 65). The embryonic disc consists of a thick layer, which may be considered embryonic mesectoderm,

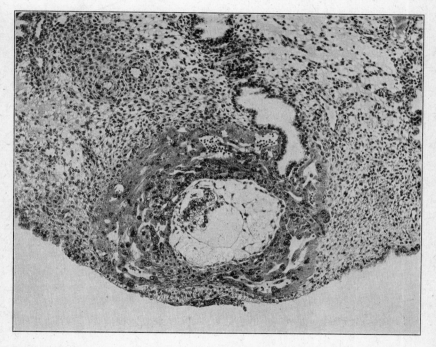

FIG. 65. Section through human embryo (Hertig-Rock, 7699) just after implantation. Estimated age, 11 days. ×100. (From *Contributions to Embryology*, Vol. 29, Carnegie Institution of Washington, by permission.)

and a thin layer of endoderm. An amniotic cavity is present, and the trophoblast consists of an outer syncytial plasmatrophoderm (syncytiotrophoderm, plasmatrophoblast), a cellular cytotrophoderm (cytotrophoblast), and delicate cells growing into the cavity of the blastocyst. These latter cells have been interpreted as extra-embryonic mesoderm. It is difficult to avoid the conclusion that the trophoblast is a layer of extra-embryonic mesectoderm, precociously separated in accordance with the process of implantation. In comparison with the early gastrula of the chick, the trophoblast may be compared to the area opaca, the embryonic disc to the area pellucida. The endoderm, possibly by the formation of a slit-like cavity which later enlarges, is transformed into a vesicle (Fig. 64C).

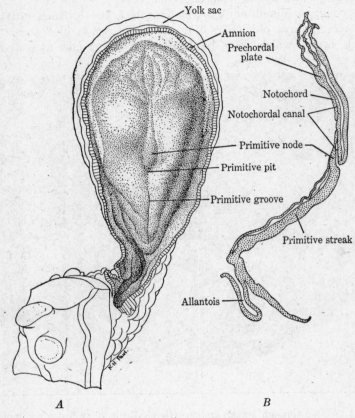

Fig. 66. Human embryo in primitive streak stage. *A*, surface view. *B*, sagittal section. ×50. (After Heuser.)

In later human embryos a primitive streak appears in the embryonic disc, much as it does in the chick (Fig. 66*A*). In this streak there is a well-marked primitive groove terminating in a primitive pit at the anterior end. Just in front of the pit is the primitive (Hensen's) node. In a longitudinal section (Fig. 66*B*) it can be seen that the primitive node marks the point from which the notochord, preceded by the prechordal plate, has grown forward. The notochord at this stage is hollow with a prominent notochordal canal which opens to the exterior by means of the primitive pit.   In the days of phylogenetic embryology there was much argument as to whether this pit represented a persistent blastopore or neurenteric canal.   In any case it soon disappears through the disintegration of the cells which form its floor.   The embryonic mesoderm grows out from the sides of the primitive streak as in the chick.   With the backward growth of the primitive node, the length of embryo is increased.

While, for obvious reasons, the human embryo has not been mapped with vital dyes, there is no reason to suppose that the areas are not similar to those described for the chick blastoderm.

NEURULATION

The neurula is a term originally applied to the amphibian embryo at the time when the neural plate first became visible.   More recently authors have come to use neurulation as a convenient expression to describe the period during which the neural plate is transformed into the neural tube.   This process takes place by the formation of neural folds at the margin of the neural plate.   As the folds rise and arch over toward the midline, a neural groove develops between them. Finally the folds meet, converting the groove into a tube.   The inner layers of the folds fuse to form the lining of the tube while the outer layers become the epidermal covering of the region.   The cells where inner and outer layers were originally continuous are cut off between the tube and its epidermal covering to form a band of tissue known as the neural crest (Fig. 159).

During the period of neurulation the gastrula is transformed into an early embryo with the cylindrical shape characteristic of the vertebrate body.

Growth in length.   There are in general two methods of growth by which the cylindrical shape is attained.   In the first, characteristic of small-yolked eggs with a spherical gastrula, the main factor is growth in length, along the anteroposterior (cephalocaudal) axis.   In the second type, which is characteristic of large-yolked eggs, the embryo is modeled from a flat disc into the form of a cylinder connected with a great yolk sac by some sort of pedestal or stalk.   Much of this modeling is done by the outgrowth of the head and the tail respectively, especially among the anamniote vertebrates, but there is also some actual undercutting, especially evident among the Amniota.   This under- cutting is accompanied by the formation of amniotic folds, as will be seen in the development of the chick.   A diagram of cross-sections through the body of a small-yolked embryo (Fig. 67*A*) and a large-yolked embryo (Fig. 67*B*) will make clear the difference between the cylindrical embryo and the plate-like embryo before it has been remolded.

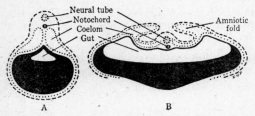

FIG. 67. Diagrammatic transverse sections showing effects of yolk on form of embryo. *A*, small-yolked embryo (frog). *B*, large-yolked embryo (chick). (After Assheton.)

Metamerism. With growth in length is associated a second factor in the development of the vertebrate body, that of metamerism. This is first indicated by the appearance of metameres such as the enterocoels in the amphioxus or somites in the true vertebrates. In later organogeny are found further evidences of metamerism in the nervous system, nephric system, vascular system, and others. However, the primary metamerism of the body is shown in the mesoderm. The somites are formed successively, commencing at the anterior end and therefore affording a basis of classifying the early embryos of any species by the number of these units present.

General plan of the body. The body of the vertebrate is basically a tube within a tube, i.e., a digestive tube within a body tube.

The digestive tube is endodermal in origin and originates from the gastrocoel. The small-yolked form has a tubular intestine from the

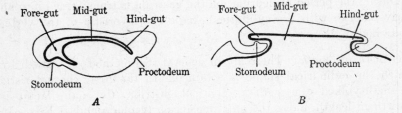

FIG. 68. Diagrammatic sagittal sections showing effects of yolk on form of embryo. *A*, small-yolked embryo (frog). *B*, large-yolked embryo (chick).

beginning. It is only necessary to form anterior and posterior openings, for the blastopore either closes or is roofed in by the neural folds. The new openings arise from ectodermal pits, the stomodeum at the anterior end, the proctodeum at the posterior end. (Fig. 68*A*). In general these openings are not completed until after the yolk has been wholly consumed. The gastrocoel of large-yolked embryos has only a roof and sides of endoderm, for the floor is composed of the yolk. Hence the rolling in or undercutting of the body commencing at the head end, and later at the tail end, forms a pocket at each end, the fore-gut and hind-gut respectively (Fig. 68B). The mid-gut is the remainder of the open gastrocoel connected with the developing yolk sac by means of the yolk stalk.

Between the two tubes lies the mesoderm. The ventral mesoderm of small-yolked embryos (lateral of large-yolked forms) splits into a somatic and splanchnic layer. The first of these is closely applied to the ectoderm to form the somatopleure; the second is associated with the endoderm to form the splanchnopleure. The space between is the coelom or body cavity.

The head. The vertebrate body is distinguished by a well-marked region at the anterior end, containing the mouth, visceral arches, special sense organs (nose, eye, and ear), and the highly developed brain. Herein the amphioxus differs from the vertebrates, for it has so little head that some zoologists make a special group (Acraniata) to contain it.

The anterior end of the body is the region where the neural folds first arise and where they first meet. It is the first part of the body to be freed of the yolk in the large-yolked embryos. This region contains the fore-gut, from which, among other structures, the pharynx is formed. Here accordingly are found the visceral (pharyngeal, " gill ") clefts or their representatives.

The tail. All vertebrate embryos, even those of species in which the adult is tailless (frog, man), possess a tail in early stages. This region is characterized by the absence of a digestive tube and coelom. The tail arises from a caudal bud appearing at the point where the posterior ends of the neural folds fuse together immediately above the point where the cloaca will open. Here the cells are small, their division rapid, and the various structures appear suddenly, so that the contributions of the several germ layers cannot well be distinguished.

The appendages. The paired appendages of vertebrates arise as buds, which later develop into fins or limbs.

NEURULATION IN THE AMPHIOXUS

During gastrulation the area of the chorda-neural crescent nearer the blastopore was turned inward to form the notochord plate.

The cells of the chorda-neural crescent remaining on the exterior of the embryo give rise to the neural plate on the dorsal surface. A longitudinal fold arises on either side of this plate (Fig. 69*B*) and grows towards the midline to fuse over the neural plate (Fig. 70*B*). At the posterior end of the embryo the folds unite with the ventral lip of the

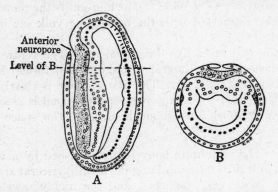

FIG. 69. Sections of amphioxus embryo (19 hours after fertilization). *A*, para-sagittal section. *B*, transverse section. ×166. (After Conklin.)

blastopore, which here consists solely of ectoderm. In this way the neural plate comes to form the floor of a tube which is open at the anterior end (anterior neuropore), and communicates with the gastro-coel at the posterior end by a short passage (neurenteric canal) (Fig.

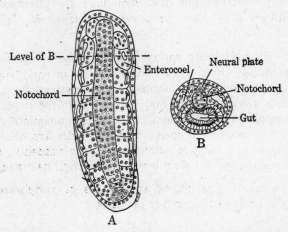

FIG. 70. Sections of amphioxus larva (24½ hours after fertilization). *A*, frontal section. *B*, transverse section. ×166. (After Conklin.)

69*A*). The folds referred to correspond only to the outer (epidermal) portions of the neural tube in the frog and other vertebrates, for the inner (neural) portions do not appear until a later stage (Fig. 70*B*).

A longitudinal groove in the notochord plate deepens (Fig. 69B) and the folds on either side come together to form a solid cord separate from the ectoderm above and the mesoderm on either side (Fig. 70*B*). The mesodermal grooves also become deeper. Transverse constrictions meantime appear in the lateral grooves, which divide them into a series of pouches (enterocoels). Finally these pouches are constricted off from the gastrocoel and become the paired somites (Fig. 70*A*).

The endoderm, which formerly occupied the floor and anterior end of the gastrocoel, extends upward to form new sides and a new roof. The gastrocoel, now for the first time completely lined with endoderm, is the primordium of the digestive tube.

With this section, our account of the early development of amphioxus will be concluded, as in later development it diverges widely from that of the vertebrates.

NEURULATION IN THE FROG

During this period the egg of *Rana pipiens* elongates until it is approximately 2.5 to 2.7 mm. in length. Some of the epidermal cells develop long cilia, by the aid of which the embryo rotates slowly inside

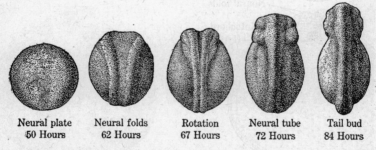

| Neural plate | Neural folds | Rotation | Neural tube | Tail bud |
| 50 Hours | 62 Hours | 67 Hours | 72 Hours | 84 Hours |

Fig. 71. Neurulation in the frog embryo. ×10. (From Shumway, *Anatomical Record* 78 : 143.)

its envelopes of jelly. The neural plate (Fig. 71) forms typical folds which are more widely separated at the anterior end. The folds meet in the midline and finally fuse to form a neural tube. In the head region, on either side and in front of the neural plate, is the sense plate, from which the primordia of the nasal pit, lens of the eye, and inner ear will develop. Posterior and lateral to the sense plate is the gill plate in connection with which the visceral grooves (furrows) appear. The first is between the sense plate and gill plate. The fifth is posterior to the gill plate. At a later stage the second, third, and fourth will appear, in the order named, on the gill plate itself.

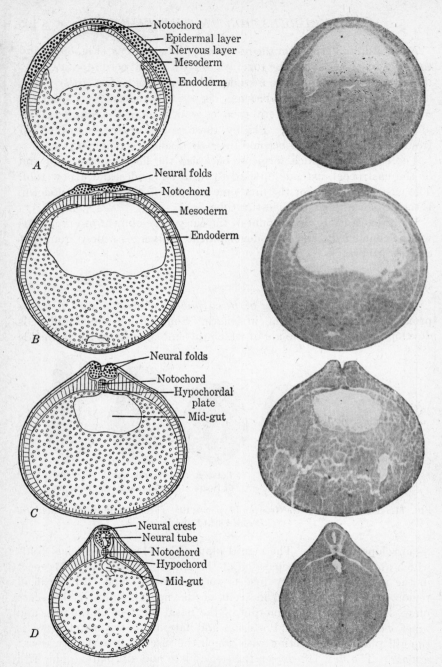

FIG. 72. Transverse sections of frog embryos during neurulation. *A*, neurula stage. *B*, neural fold stage. *C*, stage of rotation, late neural fold. *D*, neural tube stage. ×24. Photographs by George Svihla.

On the ventral side of the head, while the neural folds are forming, two pigmented bands (Lieberkind, 1937) of ectoderm thicken to give rise to the oral suckers, adhesive, cement-forming glands by means of which the embryo attaches itself to the egg jelly or other objects after hatching. Between these bands a longitudinal groove represents the stomodeum which will invaginate at a later stage to open into the fore-gut and form the mouth. The proctodeum, on the other hand, is represented by a pit which has persisted since the closing of the blasto-pore and invaginated while the neural folds were closing. In this way communication was established with the hind-gut to form the cloacal aperture or vent.

Sections through the stages just described show that the ectoderm has split into two layers, a thin outer epidermal layer and an inner thicker nervous layer (Fig 72*A*). The appearance of the neural plate is due to the thickening of the nervous layer of the ectoderm, most marked in the region from which the neural crests will form. A similar thickening of the nervous layer is seen in the sense plate and gill plate. This nervous layer of the ectoderm moves towards the midline from either side, heaping up to make the neural folds (Fig. 72*B*). It increases rapidly in thickness especially on the median side of each fold, thus elevating the folds (Fig. 72*C*), causing them to arch over, and eventually to fuse (Fig. 72*D*).

The roof and sides of the gastrocoel are first covered with chorda mesoderm, the position of the notochord marked by a median thicken-ing (Fig. 72*A*). The wings of endoderm are seen growing up to form the new roof (Fig. 72*B*). In this stage they are separated only by the lower portion of the notochordal band which is still attached to the mesoderm on either side, and now unites with the endoderm. This part of the notochordal band later (Fig. 72*C*) loses its connection with the remainder of the notochord, the mesoderm, and endoderm and will be-come the hypochord, or subnotochordal rod (Fig. 72*D*), which is found only in amphibian embryos during early stages. Its evolutionary significance and function are both unknown .

NEURULATION IN THE CHICK

This term may be applied to the period during which the neural folds are forming, i.e., up to the time the neural folds have met in the head region (24 hours) (Fig. 73).

The first indication of the formation of the neural plate is seen in a thickening of the ectoderm in the midline of the body overlying the notochord and in front of the primitive streak. Around the anterior

and lateral margins of this plate, the neural folds appear, much as in
the frog except that no division of the ectoderm into epidermal and
nervous layers is apparent.   At the end of the first day the neural folds

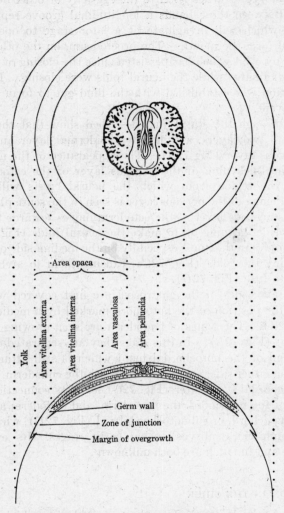

·Area opaca·

Area vitellina externa

Area vitellina interna

Area vasculosa

Area pellucida

Yolk

—Germ wall

—Zone of junction

—Margin of overgrowth

FIG. 73.   Diagrams to show embryonic and extra-embryonic areas of chick embryo
at 24 hours of incubation.   Above, surface view.   Below, transverse section.

have come together in the head region (Fig. 215).   The body of the
chick is cut off from the blastoderm by the outgrowth of a head fold
accompanied by an undercut, the subcephalic pocket, which appears

soon after the neural folds. The head fold extends backward in the form of an inverted U as the lateral folds arise. These are also accompanied by undercuts known as the lateral sulci. A tail fold does not arise until later.

The formation of a head fold involves both ectoderm and endoderm. The endodermal pocket so produced is the primordium of the fore-gut and its opening is called the anterior intestinal portal (Fig. 222).

The backward movement of the primitive node prolongs the notochord towards the posterior end as it is growing forward at its anterior end. Thus it comes to lie between the sheets of mesoderm. In these sheets transverse constrictions appear next to the notochord, thus cutting off somites, pair after pair, until the first six pairs have been formed at the end of the first 24 hours. Beyond the somite region the mesoderm delaminates into an upper layer of somatic mesoderm next the ectoderm and a lower layer of splanchnic mesoderm next the endoderm. This split does not extend all the way to the somites, leaving a short strip of intermediate mesoderm which is neither segmented nor split. The segmented region corresponds to the epimere of the frog, the intermediate zone to the mesomere, and the delaminated layer to the hypomere. It is to be noted that the mesodermal wings at the 24-hour stage have grown forward and united in front of the head fold, leaving an area devoid of mesoderm, a region known as the proamnion.

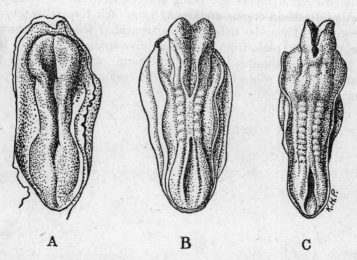

A   **B**   **C**

Fig. 74. Growth of the human embryo. *A*, neural folds (after Ingalls). *B*, neural tube commencing, seven somites (after Payne). *C*, ten somites, (after Corner).

NEURULATION IN MAN

The embryonic disc of the human embryo corresponds to the area pellucida of the chick. In it a head fold and neural folds form in a manner also essentially similar (Fig. 74A). There is a fore-gut and anterior intestinal pocket. The mesoderm develops axial, intermediate, and lateral regions, and, in the axial region, the first six pairs of somites have been formed by the end of the third week (Fig. 74B).

SUMMARY

During cleavage the fertilized egg is divided into a large number of daughter cells or blastomeres which arrange themselves about a cavity to form the blastula. The pattern of cleavage and the form of the blastula vary according to the amount and distribution of the yolk in the fertilized egg. The organ-forming regions of the fertilized egg are segregated into different groups of cells which compose the organ-forming regions of the blastula.

During gastrulation, the blastomeres are reorganized into different strata or germ layers about a new cavity, thus forming a gastrula. The method of gastrulation varies according to the type of blastula formed after cleavage. The layers segregated during gastrulation are the ectoderm, the endoderm, and the middle germ layer or chorda mesoderm, including the notochord and the mesoderm proper.

While the germ layers are being segregated from each other the primordia of certain organs are arising from their respective presumptive regions. Thus the notochord is separated from the mesoderm proper, the neural plate from the presumptive epidermis. In the mesoderm proper, the somites begin to take form, and the somatic layer separates from the splanchnic to form the coelom. This is the period of neurulation.

Chapter 6

EMBRYONIC FORM AND EXTRAEMBRYONIC STRUCTURES

While the germ layers are being segregated, the primordia of several great organ systems are localized. Before proceeding to an account of the way in which the organ systems develop from the different germ layers (organogeny), we must examine the way in which the vertebrate body assumes its form. This is found to be closely connected with certain structures (adnexa) which develop also from the germ layers and play an important part in embryonic (and fetal) life, but which are discarded before hatching (or birth). These extra-embryonic structures are the yolk sac, the amnion, chorion, and allantois, as well as a structure found only in the mammals, the placenta.

EMBRYONIC FORM

In the preceding chapter, under the discussion of neurulation, we have described the body form of the early embryo. In the following paragraphs will be found a short sketch of the external embryonic characters in later development. These include the primordia of the sense organs located in the head, nose, eye, and ear; the stomodeum and proctodeum; the visceral clefts and arches; the limb buds and the tail.

EMBRYONIC FORM, FROG

After the formation of the neural tube, frog embryos have been arranged in series according to their length. It has long been known that the embryos of different species of frogs vary so much in body length that it is hard to compare them on this basis. Accordingly, stages have been described for *Rana sylvatica* (Pollister and Moore, 1936) and for *Rana pipiens* (Shumway, 1940). The stages for *R. pipiens* (Figs. 45, 71, 75, 76) are:

1. Unfertilized egg.
2. Fertilized egg (gray crescent).
3. Two-cell stage.
4. Four-cell stage.
5. Eight-cell stage.

   6. Sixteen-cell stage.
   7. Thirty-two-cell stage.
   8. Mid-cleavage stage.
   9. Late cleavage stage.
  10. Dorsal lip (early gastrula) stage.
  11. Lateral lip (mid-gastrula) stage.
  12. Ventral lip (late gastrula) stage.
  13. Neural plate (neurula) stage.
  14. Neural fold stage.
  15. Stage of rotation (late neural folds).
  16. Neural tube stage.
  17. Tail-bud stage.
  18. Stage of muscular response (to mechanical stimulation).
  19. Stage of heart beat (and gill buds).
  20. Hatching stage (capillary circulation in first gill).
  21. Stage of mouth opening (cornea of eye transparent).
  22. Stage of tail fin circulation.
  23. Opercular fold stage.
  24. Operculum over right gills.
  25. Operculum complete.

On either side of the head the optic vesicles, the primordia of the eyes, push out from the brain and make well-marked bulges. The ectoderm immediately external to each optic cup will later give rise to the lens of the eye. Anterior to each eye is a depression in the ectoderm, the nasal (olfactory) pit. These pits are the primordia of the nose. Posterior to each eye a similar otic (auditory, acoustic) pit originates, the primordium of the inner ear. On the ventral side, folds of ectoderm rise to form the oral suckers. Between them there appears an ectodermal pit called the stomodeum or primordium of the mouth. On the ventral side of the body, just anterior to the base of the tail, is a similar pit, the proctodeum, or primordium of the cloacal opening.

On the sides of the head five dorsoventral grooves appear (in the order I, V, II, III, IV). These are the visceral (branchial, " gill ") grooves, some of which will later break through into corresponding out-pushings from the fore-gut, the visceral (pharyngeal, " gill ") pouches, to form the visceral (pharyngeal, " gill ") clefts. For the present we need simply note that they separate six transverse bars or ridges which are known as the visceral arches. Each visceral arch contains an aortic arch. Arch I (mandibular) contributes to the formation of the jaws. Arch II (hyoid) contributes to the gill cover (operculum) and to the support of the tongue. Arches III, IV, and V are often known as

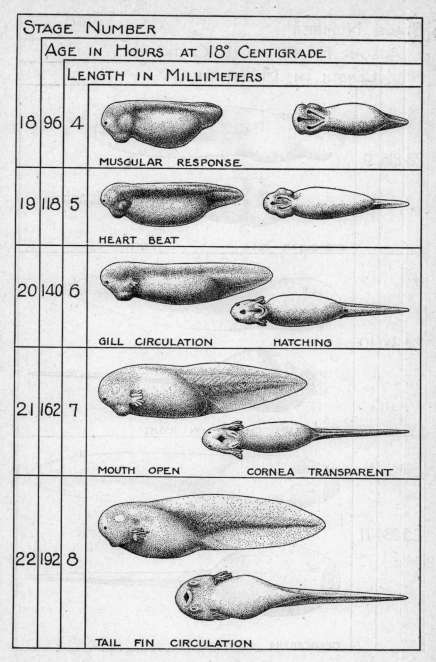

STAGE NUMBER			
	AGE IN HOURS AT 18° CENTIGRADE		
		LENGTH IN MILLIMETERS	

18	96	4	MUSCULAR RESPONSE
19	118	5	HEART BEAT
20	140	6	GILL CIRCULATION HATCHING
21	162	7	MOUTH OPEN CORNEA TRANSPARENT
22	192	8	TAIL FIN CIRCULATION

FIG. 75. Stages in development of frog after neurulation. ×7½. (From Shumway, *Anatomical Record* 78 : 145.)

113

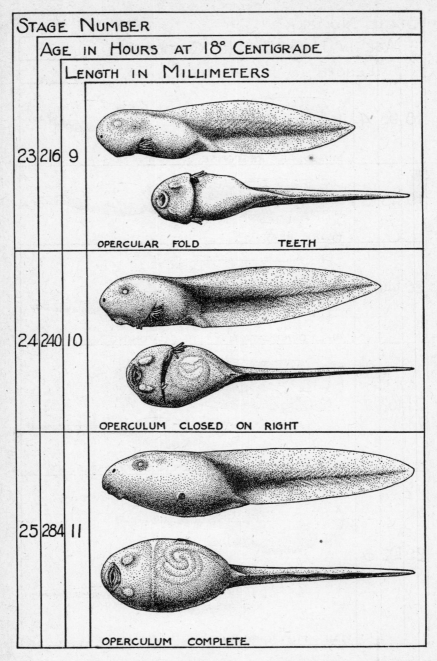

Stage Number		
Age in Hours at 18° Centigrade		
Length in Millimeters		

23 216 9

OPERCULAR FOLD   TEETH

24 240 10

OPERCULUM CLOSED ON RIGHT

25 284 11

OPERCULUM COMPLETE

Fig. 76. Stages in development of frog, continued from Fig. 74. ×7½. (From Shumway, *Anatomical Record*, 78 : 147.)

branchials 1, 2, and 3, respectively. On arches III, IV, and V develop
outgrowths which become the external gills (branchiae). That on V

PHARYNGEAL DERIVATIVES

Pouches (*From endoderm*)	Arches	Clefts	Aortic Arches	Grooves (*From ectoderm*)
	Visceral arch I (mandibular)		Aortic arch I	
Visceral pouch I (hyomandibular)		Visceral cleft I (spiracle of elasmobranchs)		Visceral groove I
	Visceral arch II (hyoid)		Aortic arch II	
Visceral pouch II		Visceral cleft II		Visceral groove II
	Visceral arch III (1st branchial)		Aortic arch III	
Visceral pouch III		Visceral cleft III		Visceral groove III
	Visceral arch IV (2nd branchial)		Aortic arch IV	
Visceral pouch IV		Visceral cleft IV		Visceral groove IV
	Visceral arch V (3rd branchial)		Aortic arch V	
Visceral pouch V		Visceral cleft V		Visceral groove V
	Visceral arch VI (4th branchial)		Aortic arch VI	
Visceral pouch VI (vestigial in frog)		Visceral cleft VI (lacking in frog)		Visceral groove VI (lacking in frog)

is rudimentary. Later an opercular fold grows from arch II to cover the external gills completely on the right, but with an opening on the left known as the opercular aperture. While this is taking place the grooves between arches II, III, IV, and V break through and join the corresponding visceral pouches to form the visceral clefts. Internal gills (demibranchs) develop in the clefts, and the external gills disappear. Meantime the mouth has opened and developed horny jaws.

The tail arises by the backward growth of the tissue in the neural folds (Bijtel) at the point where they united over the blastopore. The notochord and neural tube grow backward, carrying epidermis and muscle-forming material with them. Dorsal and ventral folds make their appearance in the tail to form the tail fin.

The paired limbs arise as limb buds. Although the posterior buds are the first to make their appearance, the anterior buds arise first but are concealed beneath the operculum until the time of metamorphosis. The one on the left side appears first, pushing through the opercular aperture.

EMBRYONIC FORM, CHICK

The developmental stages of the chick are usually expressed in number of hours of incubation at 103° F., but, since Lillie (1908) pointed out the value of the somite number as an index of development, this method has been employed by many investigators.

The head fold of the chick appears with the neural folds, so that the head is lifted above the blastoderm at 24 hours of incubation (6 somites). Finally there is a posterior tail fold accompanied by a subcaudal pocket appearing on the third day. Outgrowth at the folds, with some undercutting as well, causes the body of the embryo to stand up from the surrounding blastoderm to which it is attached by a short pedestal, the umbilical stalk. The head bends down sharply at the cephalic flexure, but, pressing against the yolk, it turns or twists toward the right, so that the left side of the head rests on the yolk (Fig. 77C, D). The ventral bend is known as flexure, the dextral twist is known as torsion. Flexure and torsion commence in the middle of the second day of incubation, and continue in a caudal direction until, at the end of the fourth day, the chick lies completely on its left side.

The primordia of the brain and sense organs arise much as they do in the frog. A stomodeum appears early in the third day of incubation, the proctodeum during the fourth day. Four visceral grooves (in the order I, II, III, IV) and five arches appear between the end of the second and beginning of the fourth day of incubation. Only the first three clefts actually open into the fore-gut, and they are soon closed again.

The tail arises from the backward growth of the tail fold but never attains any great length.

The limb buds appear during the third day of incubation.

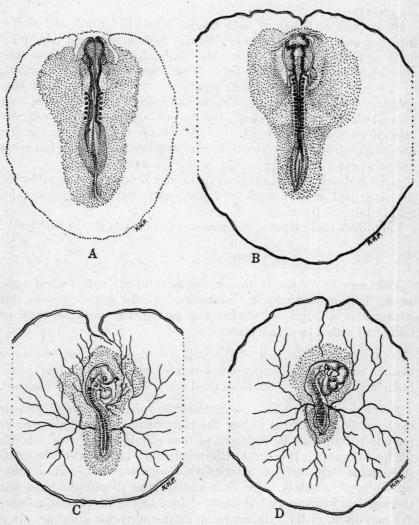

FIG. 77. Growth of the chick embryo. *A*, 25 hours of incubation. *B*, 38 hours of incubation. *C*, 48 hours of incubation. *D*, 68 hours of incubation. Compare Figs. 215, 221, 227, 233. *A, B*, approx. ×9; *C, D*, approx. ×4. (After Duval.)

BODY FORM IN MAN

Human embryologists distinguish three periods during intra-uterine development: the period of the ovum, from fertilization to germ-layer formation, two weeks; the period of the embryo, until the embryo has assumed a definitely human appearance, the end of the second month; and the period of the fetus. It is the second of these with which we are concerned.

By the end of the third week the head fold is formed, and at the fifth the tail fold is developed. Neural folds are formed and unite much as in the chick (Fig. 74). The primordia of eye, ear, and nose also originate in a similar manner. Five visceral grooves are formed, by the end of the fifth week, separating six visceral arches; but, although the visceral pouches appear and unite with the grooves, true visceral clefts are not formed. By the end of the seventh week, the visceral grooves have disappeared. A cephalic flexure appears in the fifth week. The neck (cervical) flexure develops in the week following and accelerates the disappearance of the visceral grooves.

A tail is developed from the tail fold which is quite prominent during the sixth and seventh week of development but is overgrown and resorbed during the eighth.

Limb buds make their appearance toward the end of the fifth week.

THE YOLK SAC

Yolk sacs are found in the development of all large-yolked eggs, among both anamniotes and amniotes. As the name implies, this structure is a larger or smaller bag protruding from the body or connected with it by a yolk stalk.

Origin and development. The yolk sac develops from the outer margin of the blastoderm, which advances under the vitelline membrane and around the yolk mass until the yolk is completely enclosed.

Function and fate. This sac contains the yolk, which, in meroblastic cleavage, is not divided among the blastomeres. But it plays a far more important part in development than simply acting as a reservoir for food reserves. It is lined with endoderm just like that of the intestine, and is furnished with arteries, veins, and capillaries, which make up the area vasculosa. The endodermal lining digests the yolk, and the vitelline veins carry the digested food to the developing embryo. We may think of the yolk sac as an extra-embryonic intestine. It is interesting to note that in some viviparous elasmobranchs, like the dogfish, the yolk sac continues to be of use, even after the yolk is consumed. Pressed against the wall of the uterus it absorbs the uterine " milk " which this organ secretes (much like a tertiary egg envelope) and conveys it to the embryo through the vitelline veins. A similar device is seen among the marsupials (page 129). The yolk sac is usually drawn up into the body when the umbilicus closes and is later resorbed.

THE DISPOSITION OF THE YOLK IN THE FROG

The frog has no yolk sac, for the yolk is divided among the large blastomeres which later make up the floor of the intestine. The mass of these cells, however, creates a bulge on the ventral surface of the embryo (Fig. 75) which resembles externally a small sac.

THE YOLK SAC OF THE CHICK

The yolk sac of the chick is formed by the advancing edge of the blastoderm. Looking down on the blastoderm of the chick at the end of the first day of incubation (Fig. 73), we distinguish a series of concentric rings. Proceeding from the periphery inward, we note first the area vitellina externa, consisting of the margin of overgrowth and the zone of junction (page 84). Then comes the area vitellina interna, in which we can distinguish the ectoderm and endoderm, the latter closely applied to the yolk. Finally we distinguish the area vasculosa into which the mesoderm has pushed, splitting, as it advances, into the somatic layer (next to the ectoderm) and the splanchnic layer (next the endoderm). Between the somatic and splanchnic layers lies the exocoel (extra-embryonic coelom), as the coelom is called when it extends beyond the boundaries of the embryo. The blood vessels of the area vasculosa develop in the splanchnic mesoderm. The exocoel separates the splanchnopleure (endoderm and splanchnic mesoderm) from the somatopleure (somatic mesoderm and ectoderm), so that it can be said that the yolk sac of the chick consists of splanchnopleure. By the end of the fourth day of incubation the yolk is completely covered except for a small area at the vegetal pole, known as the yolk sac umbilicus (Fig. 82C, D). When the chick hatches, the yolk sac, still attached to the intestine, is drawn into the coelom and gradually disappears.

THE YOLK SAC OF MAN

In man, as in other mammals, the yolk sac arises in connection with gastrulation. The endoderm growing out from the lower surface of the embryonic knob apparently reorganizes itself by splitting to form a very small yolk sac (Fig. 78*A*). The roof of this sac forms the roof of the digestive canal; the anterior end is set off (with the head fold)

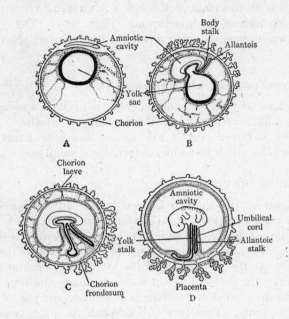

FIG. 78. Diagrams to show development of extra-embryonic structures in human embryo. Four stages illustrated by sagittal sections. (After Corning.)

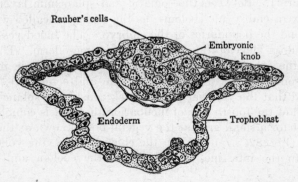

FIG. 79. Section of early bat embryo showing extension of endoderm beyond embryonic knob. (After Van Beneden.)

to make the fore-gut; the posterior end is set off (with the tail fold) to make the hind-gut (Fig. 78*B*, *C*). The remainder constitutes the small yolk sac. This sac is later squeezed between the amnion and chorion (Fig. 78*D*), and loses its connection with the intestine, through the degeneration of the yolk stalk.

In other mammals (Fig. 79) the endoderm grows completely around the interior of the trophoblast and forms a larger yolk sac. In the rat, where the embryonic knob hangs well down in the cavity of the blastocyst, the endoderm grows up around it to form an external covering, (Fig. 80), a condition known as entypy (endoderm external to ectoderm). In the guinea pig the distal wall is absent.

Among the marsupials the yolk sac sometimes presses against the chorion, as it does in the opossum (*Didelphys*), and its area vasculosa serves to convey nutriment and oxygen from the blood vessels of the uterine wall (Fig. 86).

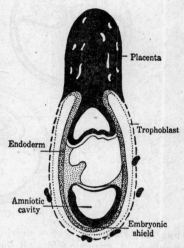

FIG. 80. Section of embryo of white rat, to show entypy. (After Grosser.)

AMNION AND CHORION

Most of the anamniote vertebrates lay their eggs in water to hatch and become larvae. In such a medium the eggs are less susceptible to violent changes in temperature, to desiccation, or to mechanical injury. The tertiary egg envelopes in which they are wrapped often protect them from being eaten. The amniotes, however, either lay their eggs under terrestrial conditions or retain them within the maternal body for a considerable period. These eggs are protected by two membranes, known as the amnion and chorion (serosa, false amnion). The amnion or inner membrane is formed of somatopleure, which is continuous with the somatopleure of the embryo. It contains an amniotic fluid in which the embryo floats, attached by an umbilical stalk to the yolk sac. The chorion or outer membrane is likewise formed of somatopleure and is continuous with the amnion at a point known as the amniotic (sero-amniotic) raphe. The cavity of the chorion is continuous with the coelom and is therefore called the exocoel. The two membranes usually arise from folds of somatopleure which unite on the dorsal side of the embryo (Fig. 81). The amnion and chorion are always associated in development with another extra-embryonic structure known as the allantois which will be described in a later section.

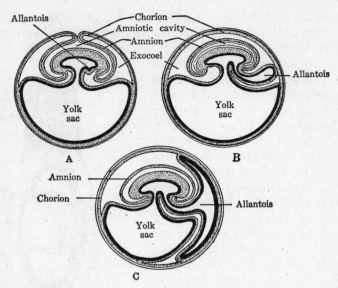

FIG. 81.   Diagrams to show development of extra-embryonic structures.   Sagittal sections.   *A*, amniotic folds.   *B*, folds united, allantois extending into exocoel.   *C*, chorio-allantois.   (After Kerr.)

AMNION AND CHORION OF THE CHICK

In the chick the amnion is a thin sac of somatopleure completely surrounding the embryo and continuous with the somatopleure of the embryo at the umbilical stalk.   It surrounds an amniotic cavity filled with amniotic fluid.   The chorion is a similar sac pressed up against the shell membrane and connected with the amnion at the amniotic raphe.

The process of amnion and chorion formation begins in the region anterior to the head fold of the embryo known as the proamnion (Fig. 215), which at first contains no mesoderm.   Here the ectoderm shows a thickening, which gradually extends around the head on either side. This thickening indicates the line of separation between the amnion-forming and chorion-forming somatopleure.   The coelom on either side of the head expands, forming the amniocardiac vesicles (Fig. 218). This pushes up the somatopleure in front of the head to form the head fold of the amnion, which slips over the head of the embryo, assisted by the downward bending of the head (cephalic flexure).   The lateral extension of this fold, in the form of an inverted U, causes the elevation and fusion of the lateral folds.   The tail fold of the amnion arises independently in the same manner as the head fold.   There is in this region, however, no area free from mesoderm comparable to the proamnion.

The cavity of the amnion is formed by the fusion of the amniotic folds. Soon after its completion, muscle fibers arise in the amniotic wall and initiate a rhythmic contraction which rocks the embryo in the

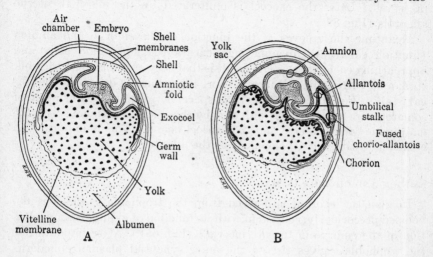

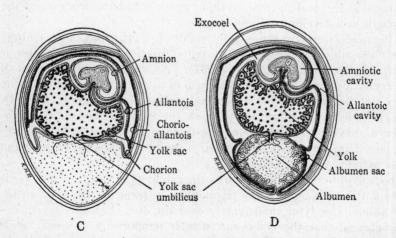

Fig. 82. Diagrams of extra-embryonic structures in chick. Four stages illustrated by transverse sections. (After Duval).

amniotic fluid and prevents adhesion to the amniotic wall. The cavity of the chorion (exocoel) is continuous with the coelom as it is the space between the somatic and splanchnic mesoderm. As the edge of the blastoderm grows down over the yolk, the exocoel forms a great cavity separating the embryo, amnion, and yolk sac from the shell membrane against which the chorion presses. This cavity is interrupted only by the amniotic raphe (Fig. 239), where continuity with the amnion is preserved. Later the exocoel is obliterated by the ingrowth of the allantois (Fig. 82).

Meantime the grooves at the junction of the embryo and amnion (limiting sulci) are invaginating beneath the embryonic body and approaching each other. The result is that they crowd against the yolk stalk and, surrounding it, form a short tube which is called the umbilical stalk. For a time there is a space between the outer wall of somatopleure and the inner wall of splanchnopleure continuous with the embryonic coelom above and the exocoel below. This is important in connection with the development of the allantois.

AMNION AND CHORION IN MAN

In man the chorion is derived from the trophoblast, which is developed precociously, consistent with its function of aiding the implantation of the embryo in the uterine wall (Fig. 65). After implantation the trophoblast gives rise to the outer syncytial plasmotrophoderm, which seems to be concerned with breaking down the surrounding maternal tissue, and the inner cellular cytotrophoderm, from which the chorionic villi develop at a later stage.

The amniotic cavity arises, presumably, from the split in the embryonic mass which we have already noted (page 99). This process is known as cavitation (Mossman, 1937). As we have seen, the floor of the cavity gives rise to the mesectoderm of the embryonic disc while the sides and roof make up the ectodermal portion of the amnion (Fig. 64). The mesodermal portion comes from the somatic mesoderm of the embryo growing out and around the ectodermal portion. In later development the amnion enlarges until it completely fills the exocoel and fuses with the chorion (Fig. 78).

In many other mammals, such as the rabbit (Fig. 51), the embryonic mass flattens out against the trophoblast to form the embryonic disc. The trophoblast lying immediately over the disc (Rauber's layer) degenerates so that the embryonic disc is temporarily exposed. Soon thereafter embryonic folds (Fig. 83) appear much as in the chick, the inner layer forming the amnion, while the outer layer, continuous with the trophoblast, joins it in forming the chorion.

Mossman has described methods of amnion formation intermediate between fold formation and cavitation, and has suggested that fold formation is characteristic of groups which have only a superficial attachment between chorion and uterine endothelium, while cavitation is found in those groups in which implantation is comparatively deep.

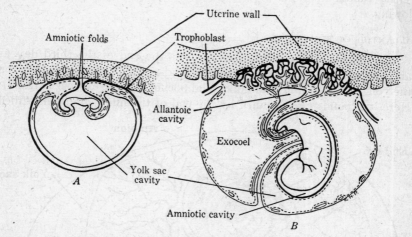

Fig. 83. Formation of amnion by folds in the rabbit. *A*, early. *B*, late. (After Mossman.)

THE ALLANTOIS

The development of an amnion and chorion is always accompanied by the appearance of another sac, the allantois. This extra-embryonic structure appears as an evagination from the hind-gut and is therefore lined with splanchnopleure. It grows out through the exocoel of the umbilical stalk into the exocoel of the chorion, which it usually fills. It is filled with an allantoic fluid, which receives the nitrogenous wastes of the embryo in the form of uric acid (Needham) and may be thought of in the first instance as an extra-embryonic urinary bladder. As it fills the chorion, its walls, being composed of splanchnic mesoderm in the outer layer, easily fuse with the mesodermal layer of the amnion, chorion, and yolk sac, whenever these structures come together. Furthermore, it has an area vasculosa served by the allantoic (umbilical) veins and arteries. This area vasculosa when applied to the chorion is the region where the blood is nearest to a source of atmospheric oxygen. Here an exchange of gases, carbon dioxide for oxygen, takes place, and the allantois may be considered as an extra-embryonic lung.

In the cleidoic egg of reptiles, birds, and egg-laying mammals, the allantois also takes part in the formation of an albumen sac wherein this material is digested. In the marsupials and placental mammals it contributes to the formation of a placenta (hemiplacenta in marsupials) whereby digested food is obtained from the maternal circulation. These functions of the placenta will be discussed in the sections following.

ALLANTOIS OF THE CHICK

The allantois (Fig. 84) arises towards the end of the third day as an evagination from the floor of the hind-gut. It grows out between the yolk and the wall of the subcaudal pocket into the exocoel (Fig. 82). Here it expands greatly until by the end of the ninth day it has filled

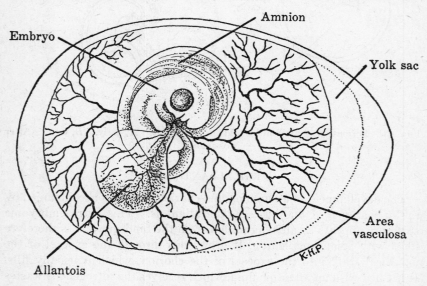

FIG. 84. The embryo chick and its extra-embryonic structures on the sixth day of incubation. × 1½. (After Duval.)

the entire exocoel. Its outer wall unites with the chorion (Fig. 82) to form a chorio-allantois; its inner wall unites with the amnion above and the yolk sac below.

Now the chorion, carrying with it an inner fold of allantois, grows down beyond the yolk-sac umbilicus (page 119), and around the mass of albumen, which has become more viscous through the loss of water and is displaced towards the lower side of the egg. The albumen is enclosed in a double-walled sac of chorion with the allantois between the two walls of the sac (Fig. 82). The layer next to the albumen is the ectoderm of the chorion, but the mesoderm of the allantois supplies the blood vessels. It is interesting to observe that it is the ectoderm of the albumen sac which absorbs the albumen, whereas in the yolk sac it is the endoderm which carries on this function.

By the twelfth day of incubation the albumen sac is closed except at the yolk-sac umbilicus, where it has an open connection with the yolk sac. On the sixteenth day the albumen is consumed. On the seventeenth the yolk-sac umbilicus closes by the constriction of a ring of mesoderm derived from the old edge of the blastoderm. The yolk sac with the remains of the albumen sac still attached is retracted into the body cavity of the chick on the nineteenth day of incubation, aided by contractions of the amnion and the inner wall of the allantois.

ALLANTOIS OF MAN

In most of the mammals there is a well-developed allantois, arising like that of the chick, growing into the exocoel, and uniting with the chorion to participate in the formation of the placenta, but the primate allantois is rudimentary. It arises as a minute tubular evagination which develops from the endodermal roof of the gastrocoel even before the formation of the tail fold. It grows out into the body stalk, a mass of mesoderm connecting the embryo with the chorion (Fig. 78) for a short distance, but never gets so far as the chorion. However, the allantoic (umbilical) blood vessels continue down the body stalk to the chorion, where they form a chorionic area vasculosa in the region of the developing placenta. Bremer (1916) suggested that mammals with a large allantois have large mesonephroi (fetal kidneys, page 162) and a thick placenta, while those with a small allantois have small mesonephroi and a thin placenta through which excretory products can be discharged to the maternal circulation.

THE ESTROUS CYCLE

Before discussing the placenta, the extra-embryonic structure peculiar to mammals, it will be well to review the mammalian estrous cycle, intimately concerned with ovulation and implantation.

It will be recalled that ovulation takes place in the human species on the average of once every 28 days. The egg is fertilized, if sperm are present, near the opening (ostium) of the oviducal tube. Three days (Hartman) are usually spent in the tube, while the egg, pushed by muscular contractions and possibly ciliary action, moves on to the uterus. During this time cleavage takes place, and the egg is probably in the morula stage on entering the uterus. In the uterus it spends about a week, free or loosely attached to the uterine wall. During this time it becomes a blastocyst and loses the zona pellucida. About the ninth or tenth day it is implanted in the uterine wall, which is now ready to receive it.

The preparation of the uterine wall for implantation is a periodical phenomenon among the mammals and is divided into four stages. It commences with estrus, the period of the sexual urge, which in most mammals coincides with the time of ovulation, and is the time in which the lining of the uterine wall is thick, soft, and spongy owing to changes in the capillary circulation. If the egg is fertilized after ovulation the uterine wall takes part in the process of placentation (page 133). If fertilization does not take place, the outermost layer of the uterine lining is shed, sometimes accompanied by the loss of blood, during a short stage known as the metestrum. There follows a shorter (diestrum) or longer (anestrum) period of rest, for in some mammals there are many periods of estrus in the year; in others it takes place annually. Before the next estrus there is a short period (proestrum), during which the wall of the uterus undergoes the changes preparatory to implantation.

The human cycle is known as the menstrual cycle, because it is almost monthly in its recurrence. It varies considerably in individuals and is easily affected by physical and mental factors. In a generalized cycle of 28 days, four phases are distinguished: proliferation (days 7–15 after menstruation), during which the inner layer of the uterus (endometrium) thickens; secretion (days 16–28), during which the glands of the uterus secrete a fluid rich in glycogen; menstruation (days 1–5), during which the proliferated layer is sloughed off, accompanied by hemorrhages; repair (days 5–6).

The period of proliferation is conditioned by a hormone, estrin, formed in the follicle of the maturing egg. The egg itself is discharged from the follicle about the fourteenth day of the menstrual cycle. The period of secretion, on the other hand, is conditioned by a different hormone, progestin, formed by a yellowish body, corpus luteum, which develops in the empty follicle after ovulation and persists through the period of pregnancy.

If the egg is not fertilized the corpus luteum degenerates and is replaced by a white body (corpus albicans). In the absence of progestin, a new menstrual cycle is initiated by estrin formed in the next follicle to mature.

It should be noted at this point that the ovarian hormones, progestin and estrin, are secreted only through the control of the pituitary gland. Among many other hormonal activities this gland secretes substances known as follicle-stimulating hormone (F.S.H.) and luteinizing hormone (L.H.), which stimulate the secretion of estrin and progestin respectively.

The current theory of the menstrual cycle may be stated roughly as follows. F.S.H. stimulates the Graafian follicle to form estrin, which in turn initiates the phase of proliferation in the uterine wall. At high concentration estrin inhibits the secretion of F.S.H., thus permitting the secretion of L.H., which results in ovulation, the formation of a corpus luteum and its secretion progestin. This hormone initiates the period of secretion in the uterine wall. At its high concentration, unless fertilization of the egg intervenes, progestin inhibits the formation of L.H., hemorrhages lower the concentration of both estrin and progestin in the blood, and the cycle is recommenced.

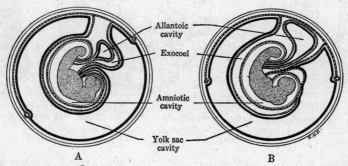

Allantoic cavity

Exocoel

Amniotic cavity

Yolk sac cavity

A   B

FIG. 85. The extra-embryonic structures of marsupials. Diagrammatic. *A, Didelphys. B, Perameles.* (After Jenkinson.)

THE PLACENTA

After this excursion into the physiology of the uterus we return to the placenta. This structure has been defined (Mossman, 1937) as an apposition or fusion of the fetal membranes to the uterine mucosa for physiological interchange. The most external extra-embryonic membrane of mammals is the chorion, which in itself does not develop a vascular area, and must receive its blood vessels from some other source, either the yolk sac or the allantois. Accordingly, two main types of placentation are distinguished, yolk-sac placentation and allantoic placentation. Among the marsupials, which do not develop a true placenta, a uterine milk secreted by the uterine glands is absorbed through the chorion and carried to the body of the embryo through the vascular system of the yolk-sac (Fig. 85) allantois, or both. The human placenta is often described as chorionic because the allantois is vestigial and never grows out to meet the chorion, but the blood vessels of the allantois grow out from it and down the umbilical cord to vascularize the chorion. Mossman therefore suggests that it should be known as chorio-allantoic.

The vascularized area of the chorion is distinguished by the presence of villi, outgrowths of the chorion, which are provided with capillaries and either fit into depressions of the uterine wall or penetrate more or

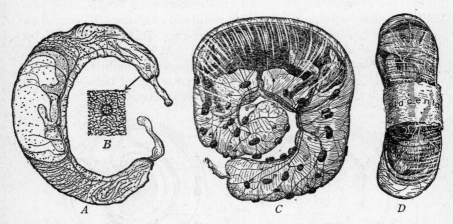

FIG. 86. Types of placentation in mammals. *A*, diffuse, pig. *B*, detail of *A*. *C*, cotyledonary, sheep. *D*, zonary, dog. (From Arey.)

less deeply into the maternal tissue. The first type is known as indeciduate, exemplified by the pig (Figs. 86, 87); the second is known as deciduate.

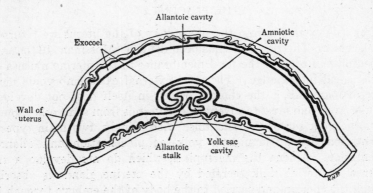

FIG. 87. Diagram of extra-embryonic structures in the pig. (After Smith.)

Types of placentation are also distinguished by the shape of the placenta. That of man is discoidal, for example, while in the pig the villi are scattered over the surface of the chorion (diffuse placenta). Much more important, however, is the finer structure of the placenta, which depends upon the amount of destruction wrought by the villi and consequently upon the number of tissues through which material must pass on its way between the fetal and maternal blood streams. The accompanying table, based on Mossman, and Fig. 88 show that the human placenta is of the hemochorial type, in which the separating layer consists only of the fetal trophoblast connective tissue and endothelial lining of the capillary.

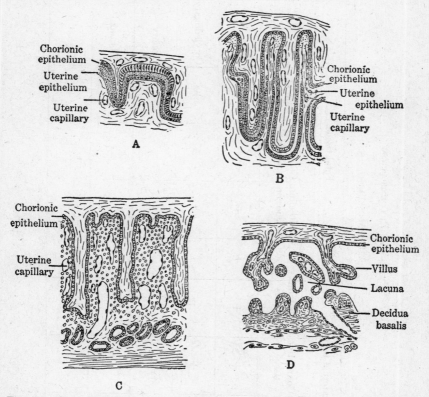

FIG. 88.   Sections through placentae of *A*, pig; *B*, cow; *C*, cat; and *D*, human. (Semidiagrammatic after Grosser.)

Development of the human placenta.   The human embryo is implanted in the blastocyst stage.   It burrows deeply into the uterine mucosa, and the polar cells (page 98) grow out to form the plasmotrophoderm.   This syncytium breaks down the surrounding maternal tissue to form a food supply (embryotroph) for the embryo.   Soon thereafter projections from the chorion grow out to become villi.   These are bathed in maternal blood which is brought into the intervillous space

Types of Placentation

(After Mossman)

Placental type	Maternal tissue			Uterine lumen	Fetal tissue			Villous distribution	Loss of deciduae	Example
	Endothelium of capillary	Connective tissue	Epithelium of uterus		Epithelium of chorion	Connective tissue	Endothelium of capillary			
Epitheliochorial	+	+	+	+	+	+	+	Diffuse	Indeciduate	Pig
Syndesmochorial	+	+	−	+	+	+	+	Cotyledonary	Indeciduate	Cow
Endotheliochorial	+	−	−	−	+	+	+	Zonary	Deciduate	Cat
Hemochorial	−	−	−	−	+	+	+	Discoidal	Deciduate	Man
Hemoendothelial	−	−	−	−	−	−	+	Discoidal	Deciduate	Rat

and carried thence by the eroded uterine capillaries. Only those villi which are in contact with the decidua basalis (Fig. 90) persist; the others degenerate, thus differentiating the chorion into the chorion frondosum, with villi, and the chorion laeve, devoid of the same.

The placenta is non-allantoic. It will be recalled that the embryonic knob retains its connection with the trophoblast as the body stalk. Into the body stalk grows the small evagination from the hind-gut which represents the endodermal lining of the allantois. It never

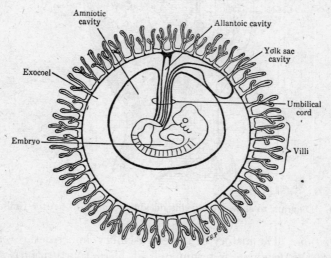

FIG. 89. Diagram of extra-embryonic structures in man. (After Kölliker.)

comes in contact with the trophoblast and soon degenerates. The limiting sulci of the amnion approach each other and become the walls of the umbilical cord. This encloses (Fig. 89) the body stalk, yolk stalk, allantoic stalk, as well as the umbilical arteries and umbilical veins which grow out from the body of the embryo towards the trophoblast. These umbilical blood vessels represent the allantoic vessels of all other amniotes.

The deciduae. It will be remembered that the blastocyst burrows into the uterine wall, eroding epithelium, connective tissue, and blood vessels. As the embryo increases in size, this erosion continues and the embryo sinks into the compact layer of the mucosa and comes in contact with the spongy layer. The mucosa grows around the burrowing embryo, shutting it off from the cavity of the uterus. There may now be distinguished (Fig. 90) three regions in the mucosa: (1) the decidua basalis, to which the blastocyst is attached; (2) the decidua capsularis, which cuts off the blastocyst from the uterine cavity; and (3) the decidua vera, including the remainder of the uterine lining.

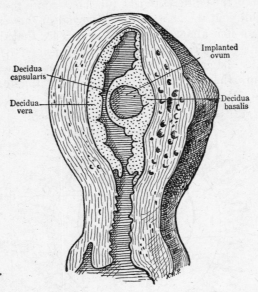

Fig. 90. Diagram to show the uterine deciduae (human). (After Kollmann.)

Parturition. The history of the extra-embryonic structures, as well as that of the deciduae, is terminated by birth (parturition). Owing to the absence of an allantoic sac, the amnion enlarges to fill the exocoel. Later, growth of the fetus results in pressing the chorion laeve and decidua capsularis against the decidua vera and obliterating the uterine cavity (Fig. 91). At birth the placenta, carrying with it the decidua basalis, and the attached membrane, which represents the fused amnion, chorion laeve, decidua capsularis, and decidua vera, are cast off as the caul or "after-birth."

SUMMARY

The method by which the external form of the vertebrate embryo is assumed is closely connected on the one hand with the shape of the gastrula and on the other with the presence or absence of certain extra-embryonic structures, the yolk sac, amnion, chorion, and allantois.

With growth in length we associate the occurrence of metamerism, or the serial repetition of parts, and the formation of a head and a tail. The paired limbs arise as buds.

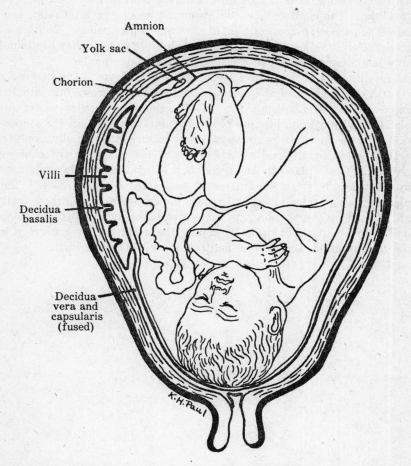

Amnion

Yolk sac

Chorion

Villi

Decidua basalis

Decidua vera and capsularis (fused)

K. H. Paul

FIG. 91.   Diagram of fetus (near term) to show relationships of extra-embryonic structures and deciduae.   (After Ahlfeld.)

The yolk sac is found only in embryos developing from extremely telolecithal eggs.   It is lined with endoderm and functions as an extra-embryonic intestine.   The splanchnic layer of the mesoderm adjacent to it develops an area vasculosa, which conveys the digested yolk to the body of the embryo.

The amnion and the chorion arise typically from folds of somatopleure, which fuse above the embryo, thus giving rise to an inner membrane, the amnion, and an outer one, the chorion.   The amnion, lined with ectoderm internally, contains amniotic fluid in which the embryo develops. The chorion, lined with somatic mesoderm internally, contains the exocoel, a continuation of the embryonic coelom. Neither of these membranes has any vascular system of its own. They are found only in the development of reptiles, birds, and mammals.

The allantois always develops in amniote embryos. It arises as a ventral evagination of the hind-gut and typically grows out into the exocoel which it completely fills. It functions as an extra-embryonic bladder and lung, and because of its vascular area may act (in connection with the chorion) as an organ of nutrition, e.g., as an albumen sac.

In mammals the blood vessels of the allantois invade the chorion, giving rise to the placenta, an organ where substances may be exchanged by diffusion between the maternal and fetal blood streams. The placenta is connected to the embryo by the umbilical stalk, whose walls are formed by the amnion. In some mammals, such as the carnivores and primates, parts of the uterine wall, the deciduae, are concerned in the formation of the placenta, and cast off with them at birth.

CHAPTER 7

DIGESTIVE SYSTEM

The vertebrate digestive system is a tube of which the inner lining is derived from endoderm. Although the main part of the tube can be traced back to the original gastrocoel (archenteron), its openings — mouth, anus, gill clefts, etc. — arise from ectodermal pouches or grooves, and the digestive tube itself is ensheathed in splanchnic mesoderm. All three germ layers, therefore, contribute to the digestive system of the adult.

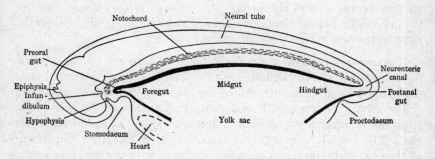

FIG. 92. Diagram of a generalized vertebrate embryo, to show endodermal derivatives.

At an early stage the digestive cavity manifests three divisions based on the position of the yolk mass (Fig. 68). They are the fore-gut, anterior to the yolk mass; the mid-gut, dorsal to the yolk mass; and the hind-gut posterior to it. The fore-gut (Fig. 92) soon obtains an opening to the exterior through the invagination of an ectodermal pit, the stomodeum, which is surrounded on either side by the first visceral arch. For a time an oral plate of ectoderm and endoderm separates fore-gut and stomodeum, but this later ruptures to form the mouth. Similarly the hind-gut, temporarily separated by a cloacal plate from the proctodeum, acquires an opening at the base of the tail known as the vent. In mammals this is later divided to form the anus and urogenital orifice.

The later history of the digestive tube is one of specialization. The different regions of the tube enlarge, elongate, give rise to new struc-

137

tures, frequently by evaginations, and assume their special functions. Among these new structures are a number of endocrine glands, to be discussed in this chapter, and the lungs, which will be considered in Chapter 8. It will be recalled that the allantois originated as an evagination of the hind-gut. This portion of the hind-gut is the cloaca, which contributes also to the urogenital system (Chapter 10).

The stomodeum. The rupture of the oral plate, which separates the stomodeum from the fore-gut, results in the formation of the oral cavity, or mouth. From the stomodeum, another invagination, the hypophysis (hypophyseal pouch, Rathke's pocket), grows upward in front of the fore-gut, and eventually fuses with an evagination from the floor of the neural tube, the infundibulum, to form the pituitary gland, an organ of internal secretion. The pituitary gland, it should be noted, is often known as the hypophysis because of its final position on the ventral side of the brain. In some vertebrates, e.g., the frog, the primordium of the hypophysis has no cavity and should be described as an outgrowth rather than an invagination.

The fore-gut. As the stomodeum joins the fore-gut a little posterior to the anterior end of the latter cavity, there is a blind pocket of endoderm, anterior to the mouth, called the preoral gut (Seessel's pocket).

The cavity of the mouth is a compound structure, derived in part from the ectodermal stomodeum and in part from the endodermal fore-gut. The boundary line between these is soon lost after the rupture of the oral plate, owing to unequal local growth of the different regions of the mouth. The boundaries of the mouth are the upper jaws, formed from the maxillary ridges, and the lower jaws, derived from the mandibular ridges. On these ridges the teeth arise in the same way as the placoid scales of the elasmobranchs (page 200). Two elements are concerned: an ectodermal enamel organ, shaped like an inverted cup; and a mesodermal dental papilla, which fills the cavity of the enamel organ. The enamel organ gives rise to the outer enamel layer of the tooth, while the papilla forms the dentine (Fig. 93). The dentine is in the general form of a hollow cone, the cavity of which is filled with connective tissue, and contains the nerve and blood vessel. The glands of the mouth (salivary glands, etc.) develop late. They are usually considered ectodermal in origin, but direct evidence is lacking as they arise in the region where the boundary between ectoderm and endoderm is difficult to establish.

After the mouth comes the pharynx, relatively inconspicuous in the adult, but very important in development because of the structures derived from it. The nasal passages of the air-breathing vertebrates open into the mouth (amphibia) or pharynx (higher reptiles, birds, and mammals) by means of the posterior nares (choanae). The origin of the nose will be considered in Chapter 16. It will be sufficient to note here that a portion of these passages arises from part of the original cavity of the mouth, cut off by the palate.

On the boundary line between mouth and pharynx is the tongue, which in the amniote vertebrates has a double origin, an ectodermal primordium arising from the floor of the mouth at the point where the first visceral arches meet, and an endodermal primordium posterior to the first, and arising from the point where the second visceral (hyoid) arches join. It is generally held that the taste buds are ectodermal in origin, but apparently endodermal in the frog (see page 142). Between the two primordia of the tongue is the thyroid gland. This organ arises

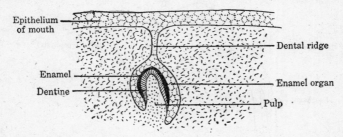

FIG. 93. Diagram to show origin of vertebrate tooth (lower jaw).

as a ventral evagination from the floor of the pharynx. As it grows out from the pharynx it becomes attached to the pericardial chamber (page 158), and when this chamber grows caudad the thyroid is dragged with it. In this way the thyroid is detached from its thyroglossal duct and becomes an endocrine (internally secreting) gland.

On the sides of the pharynx six pairs of lateral pouches (the number is greater in cyclostomes and less in the frog) appear. In the lower vertebrates these take part in the formation of the gill slits (Chapter 8), but they also give rise to certain structures common to all vertebrates, the epithelial bodies, which are the primordia of certain ductless glands, especially the parathyroids and thymus. Furthermore, the first visceral pouches become associated with the inner ear (Chapter 16) and give rise to the middle ear.

The fore-gut, anterior to the stomach, becomes divided into a ventral trachea (Chapter 8) and the dorsal esophagus, a canal leading to the stomach (Fig. 95). The cavity of the stomach is dilated, its endodermal lining develops numerous minute digestive glands, and its mesodermal covering develops a layer of smooth muscles.

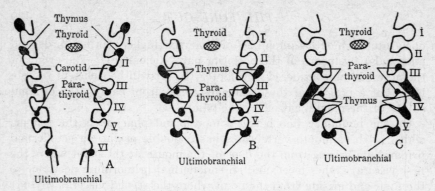

FIG. 94. Diagrams showing origin of epithelial bodies in *A*, frog; *B*, chick; and *C*, man.

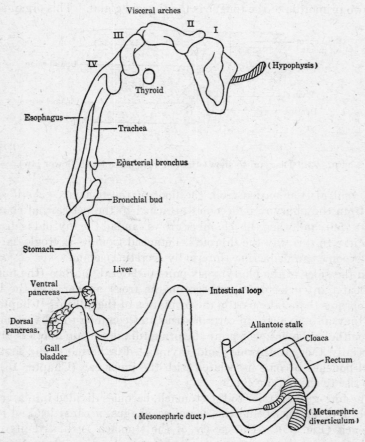

FIG. 95. Endodermal derivatives in 10-mm. pig. (From a wax reconstruction by G. W. Hunter and L. T. Brown.)

Posterior to the stomach, the fore-gut is converted into the anterior portion of the intestine. Here two very large digestive glands and their ducts arise. They are the liver and pancreas. The liver arises from the ventral side of the duodenum as an evagination which grows forward, expanding into an hepatic vesicle at the distal end and retaining its connection with the duodenum by a narrow hollow stalk, the common bile duct (Fig. 96). The anterior surface of the hepatic vesicle becomes subdivided into many hepatic cords containing tubules, the bile canaliculi. In this process of growth and subdivision the liver grows about the vitelline veins (Chapter 11) which are broken into a system of hepatic capillaries (Fig. 130). The hepatic vesicle becomes the gall bladder, to which the bile, formed in the glandular portion of the liver, is carried by means of the hepatic ducts. It releases these secretions into the duodenum *via* the common bile duct (ductus choledochus).

The pancreas arises usually from two diverticula of the duodenum at the level of the hepatic diverticulum (Fig. 95), but the number of primordia is variable. One appears on the dorsal side of the duodenum just posterior to the stomach; the other arises on the ventral side, posterior to the hepatic diverticulum. The primordia increase in size, and break up into masses of secretory tubules. At the distal end of each the primordia unite and their proximal ends become the pancreatic ducts, one or more of which may be suppressed in later organogeny. The pancreas, as well as elaborating a digestive pancreatic juice discharged through the pancreatic duct, forms a hormone (insulin), which is carried away by the blood stream. It functions therefore as an endocrine gland in addition to its digestive function.

The mid-gut. All the regions of the digestive tract mentioned so far are derived from the fore-gut. The intestine is derived in part from the fore-gut, in part from the mid-gut, and in part from the hind-gut. It is impossible to indicate exactly which regions arise from these divisions of the gut, as both the fore-gut and the hind-gut expand at the expense of the mid-gut during the consumption of the yolk. The intestine is richly glandular throughout its length and is variously subdivided in the different vertebrates. Two main divisions may be noted, the small intestine (ileum) and the large intestine (colon). The floor of the mid-gut is either very thick, as in the amphibia, or widely open as in large-yolked embryos. With the consumption of the yolk in many vertebrates the yolk sac is drawn up into the body. It sometimes becomes a part of the intestinal floor.

The hind-gut. The boundary of the hind-gut is also a changing one. In general, this region gives rises to the cloaca, which receives the ureters (Chapter 10), gives off the allantois and bladder, and discharges its contents to the exterior by a common vent, arising from the proctodeum. In mammals the cloaca is divided into a dorso-posterior rectum and a ventro-anterior urogenital sinus.

The proctodeum. This is an ectodermal pit, separated for a time from the cloaca by a cloacal plate. When the latter is ruptured the cloaca acquires its orifice, the vent. In mammals, of course, the cloacal plate ruptures at two points, giving rise to the anus and urogenital orifice respectively. For a time there is a blind pocket of endoderm posterior to the cloaca, which is known as the postanal gut.

THE FROG

Stomodeum. In the frog the stomodeal pit is at first a groove lying between the primordia of the oral suckers (Figs. 75, 76, 199, 205). The groove deepens at its anterior end to open in stage 21 to become the mouth (Fig. 210). It remains round during larval life and is enclosed by the mandibular ridges. Outside these, folds of ectoderm project as the larval lips, on which horny larval teeth develop. These larval structures are lost at metamorphosis, when the definitive jaws and teeth are formed in the usual way. The primordium of the hypophysis arises as a solid outgrowth from the stomodeum (Figs. 198, 199), and later acquires a cavity and joins the infundibulum.

Fore-gut. When the mouth opens, a plug of cells forms in the esophagus so that, while water can enter the mouth and pass out through the gill clefts, no food can continue into the stomach and the young larva continues to subsist on its yolk. The plug disappears in stage 23. The origin of the tongue is, as usual, from an anterior ectodermal swelling and a posterior endodermal one (gland field). An experiment (Holtfreter) indicates that the taste buds are of endodermal origin. Six visceral pouches can be found. The first never loses its closing plate, which persists to give rise to the ear drum, while the pouch itself becomes the middle ear. The sixth pouch is vestigial. The others, II, III, IV, and V, arise in that order (Fig. 208) and by the rupture of their closing plates become gill slits (Chapter 8).

The thyroid arises, just before hatching, as a solid diverticulum of the pharynx; it soon detaches itself and divides into two bodies which later become vesicular. The thymus glands are formed from epithelial bodies (Fig. 94*A*) on the dorsal side of the second visceral pouches.

Epithelial bodies arise from the ventral side of the second visceral pouches to become the carotid glands. Those of the third and fourth pouches, it is claimed, persist and have been called parathyroids (pseudothyroid). The vestigial sixth pouches become the ultimo-branchial (suprapericardial) bodies (Fig. 94).

The esophagus is short, and the stomach a simple dilation, first noticeable in stage 24. The liver arises as a backward ventral divertic-

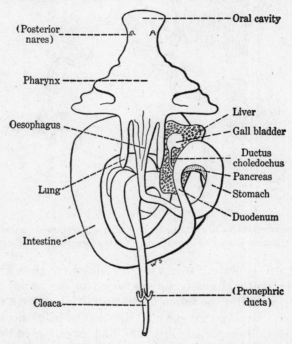

Fig. 96. Endodermal derivatives of 11-mm. *Rana pipiens* embryo. From a wax plate reconstruction representing a cast of the digestive tract prepared by F. P. Eshleman and V. E. Hanes. Dorsal view.

ulum of the fore-gut, easily recognized at the time the neural folds are forming. It is not, however, until after the esophageal plug disappears that the spongy complex of bile canaliculi and hepatic capillaries becomes evident. Three pancreatic primordia appear in stage 23 and fuse; the dorsal duct disappears, while the two ventral ducts fuse to become the adult pancreatic duct (Fig. 96).

Mid-gut. The intestine of the tadpole, which is long and coiled (about nine times the body length), becomes resorbed during metamorphosis until it is about one-third of its larval length (Fig. 97).

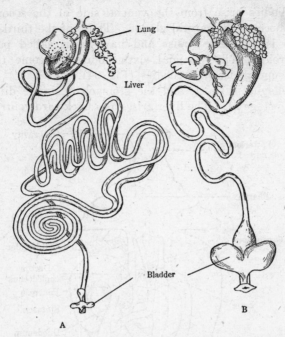

FIG. 97. Digestive system in *A*, tadpole, and *B*, frog, to show actual shortening of the intestine after metamorphosis. (After Leuckart wall-chart.)

Hind-gut. The cloacal region of the intestine gives rise to the rectum. The postanal gut is not connected to the neural tube by a neurenteric canal after the fusion of the neural folds above the blastopore. There is, however, a pigmented streak at the site where a neurenteric canal might be expected (Fig. 198), and, in earlier editions of this book, the general practice of considering this a neurenteric canal was followed in the belief that the cavity had been obliterated in the process of preparing the specimen for observation. The urinary bladder of the frog arises from the ventral side of the cloaca during metamorphosis.

THE CHICK

Stomodeum. The mouth opens on the third day of incubation (Fig. 234). The teeth are represented only by the tooth ridges, which are the first stage in the appearance of the enamel organs. These appear on the sixth day of incubation and disappear shortly after the cornification of the jaws. This results in the formation of the beak and the egg tooth, the latter a horny projection on the upper jaw which is used in breaking through the shell at the time of hatching, and soon after disappears. The hypophyseal primordium arises as an evagination on the second day (Fig. 229), loses its connection with the stomodeum on the third, and unites with the infundibulum on the eighth.

Fore-gut. The primordia of the tongue appear on the fourth day. Five visceral pouches appear (Fig. 98), of which the first three open to the exterior during the third day of incubation (Fig. 233). The first cleft closes during the fourth day, and the dorsal part of the pouch be-

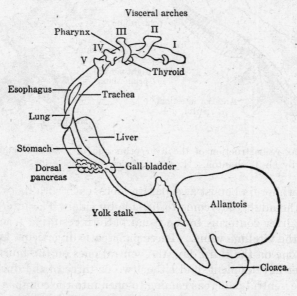

FIG. 98. Endodermal derivatives in a 72-hour chick.

comes the tubotympanic cavity. With the extension of the cervical flexure, the remaining pouches are crowded together and disappear. The thyroid appears on the second day, separates from the pharynx (Fig. 236) on the fourth, and on the seventh divides into two bodies which migrate backward to the junction of the common carotid and subclavian arteries. The thymus arises from the dorsal epithelial bodies of the third and fourth visceral pouches (Fig. 94B) while the parathyroid rudiments arise from the ventral epithelial bodies of the same pouches. The fifth pouch gives rise to the ultimobranchial bodies.

The esophagus is relatively long; and a dilation, the crop, forms at its posterior end. The gastric region is divided into an anterior proventriculus, which contains the gastric glands, and a muscular gizzard at the posterior end. The liver primordium arises at the edge of the anterior intestinal portal on the second day and, therefore, presents the aspect of an anterior ventral and two posterior lateral diverticula for a short time (Fig. 99). Later in the same day the two lateral primordia are brought together on the ventral side of the fore-gut as the anterior intestinal portal moves back. The anterior (dorsal) and posterior

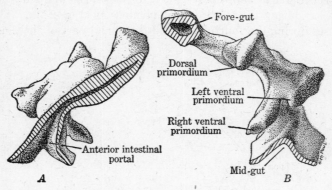

FIG. 99. Wax reconstruction of the liver primordia in a 48-hour chick embryo, prepared by G. T. Stanton. *A*, anterior view. *B*, posterior view. ×100.

(ventral) primordia persist as separate lobes, each with its own hepatic duct. In the adult they come to lie side by side. The internal structure of the liver conforms to the usual pattern resulting from its relations with the vitelline veins. Three pancreatic diverticula are formed, the dorsal one on the third day, the ventral ones on the fourth. They fuse in later development, and either two or three of the ducts persist, those of the ventral pancreas coming to open into the common bile duct.

Mid-gut. The anterior portion of the mid-gut becomes the small intestine, the large intestine arising from the posterior region.

It must be remembered that when the chick hatches the yolk has not been entirely consumed and that the yolk sac is drawn into the body of the chick, still attached to the mid-gut. When the yolk has been entirely consumed, the shrunken yolk sac pinches off and degenerates.

Hind-gut. About the middle of the second day, just posterior to the primitive streak, ectoderm and endoderm join to form a small area which is not invaded by mesoderm. As the tail fold forms, this is carried around to the ventral side of the embryo, where it is known as the cloacal (anal) plate. The rupture of this plate early in the fourth day puts the hind-gut in direct communication with the developing amniotic cavity. Anterior to the cloacal plate a broad evagination gives rise to the allantois during the third day. No urinary bladder is formed but the cloaca is ultimately divided into three regions: an anterior portion, the coprodeum, into which the rectum enters; an intermediate part, the urodeum, into which the urogenital ducts enter; and the terminal proctodeum.

MAN

Stomodeum. The mouth opens during the second week of development, and the lips separate from the gums in the fifth. Two sets of teeth are formed, the first (deciduous) dentition consisting of ten teeth in each jaw, the second (permanent) dentition being composed of sixteen teeth per jaw. The deciduous teeth do not erupt through the gums until after birth. The last are not shed until the individual is eleven years old. The major salivary glands arise during the second month of development and are believed to arise from the ectodermal portion of the mouth. The hypophysis arises as a pouch (Fig. 244), becomes attached to the infundibulum, and loses its connection with the mouth during the second month. The division of the primitive mouth into nasal and oral chambers will be described in Chapter 16.

Fore-gut. The tongue arises from an ectodermal primordium which becomes the body of the tongue and consists at first of a swelling on the ventral side of each mandibular arch and a median swelling (tuberculum impar) between them. To this an endodermal primordium formed by swellings on the base of each hyomandibular arch is added to form the root of the tongue. Between these two primordia the thyroid gland arises as a ventral evagination from the pharynx. After it is detached from the pharynx, the site of its origin is marked by a small pit (foramen cecum). The primordia of the tongue unite during the sixth week.

Five pairs of visceral pouches (Fig. 100) are formed by the end of the first month. None of these normally opens to the exterior. The first pair forms the middle ear on each side, i.e., the auditory (Eustachian) tube and tympanic cavity. It is no longer believed that the groove (fossa) in which the palatine tonsil develops is the persistent second pouch. Ventral epithelial bodies from the third pair of pouches (Fig. 94C) join to become the thymus gland, which becomes attached to the pericardium and is dragged with it into the thorax. Those from the fourth pair degenerate or join the thymus gland. Dorsal epithelial bodies from the third and fourth pair of pouches become the parathyroid glands, which are dragged with the thymus to the level of the thyroids, in which they embed themselves. The vestigial fifth pouches give rise to the ultimobranchial bodies, which also become attached to the thyroid, either to become incorporated in this gland or degenerate.

The esophagus, at first relatively short, lengthens as the backward movement of the heart and lungs displaces the stomach. The latter organ (Fig. 248) arises as a dilation of the fore-gut posterior to the esophagus. Continued growth, mainly on the dorsal surface, produces the greater curvature, and a displacement of the whole organ so that the cephalic end is moved to the left and the caudal end to the right. This is followed by a rotation of the stomach on its long axis through 90° to the left. The liver arises during the third week as a ventral groove in the duodenum. The groove soon becomes a sac, which grows forward and ventrally into a mass of mesoderm which will become the septum transversum (page 158). The anterior wall becomes the glandular portion when it grows around the vitelline veins, while the more posterior part will become the gall bladder (Fig. 249). The connection between liver and duodenum persists as the common bile duct.

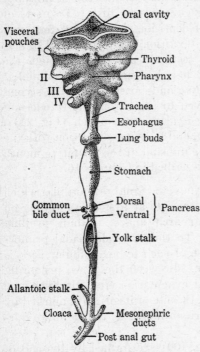

Fig. 100. Endodermal derivatives in a 5-mm. human embryo. Ventral view. × 25. (After Prentiss.)

The pancreas appears slightly later, with either two or three primordia according to whether or not one of the ventral primordia is suppressed. The ventral pancreatic duct persists and opens into the common bile duct. The ducts branch extensively, giving rise to hollow acini which secrete the pancreatic juice and solid islands which never have any cavities communicating with the ducts but discharge the hormone insulin into the blood vessels supplying the gland.

Mid-gut. The intestine consists of portions contributed by all three divisions of the gut, and is most conveniently divided into a cranial portion anterior to the yolk stalk and a posterior caudal portion. The yolk stalk is detached from the intestine during the fifth or sixth week, and the rapid growth of the intestine throws it into a loop (Fig. 250) which rotates (counterclockwise from the ventral side) and descends into the umbilical cord (seventh week). In the caudal portion the point of division between small and large intestines is marked by the formation of a blind pouch, the cecum. The distal end of the cecum does not grow as rapidly as the proximal region and so remains a finger-like projection known as the vermiform appendix. The small intestine, growing more rapidly than the large, is thrown into a set of six primary coils, each of which develops secondary coils.

Hind-gut. The cloaca becomes divided, by a frontal partition, into a dorsal rectum and a ventral urogenital sinus (page 178). The cloacal membrane is correspondingly divided into a rectal and a urogenital plate, and the final openings are the anus and the urogenital orifice.

CHAPTER 8

RESPIRATORY ORGANS

The early embryo, before the development of the blood vascular system, takes in oxygen and gives off carbon dioxide at its surface. After the development of blood vessels, respiratory exchange may take place in any thin epithelium in which the blood corpuscles are brought into contact with the oxygen-carrying medium.

In vertebrates whose development takes place in natural waters, such as fish and amphibia, ectodermal outgrowths on the visceral arches receive blood vessels from the aortic arches and become external gills (branchiae). As the blood stream passes through the aortic arches immediately after leaving the heart, the blood is oxygenated before distribution to the body generally. It appears to be in connection with the development of these external gills that the gill clefts are formed with the result that water admitted at the mouth and passing through the clefts creates a current in the vicinity of the external gills. In vertebrates with cleidoic development, birds and reptiles, the first circulation is that of the yolk sac. This, however, is remote from atmospheric oxygen, and the chick first acquires a special organ of respiration when the allantois brings its blood vessels to the chorion. Mammals, with their intra-uterine mode of development, soon develop the placenta, which is the organ of fetal respiration.

The adult, too, may have one of many different respiratory organs, whose epithelia may be either ectodermal or endodermal in origin. Thus, we find that, among the amphibia, respiration may take place in the skin as a whole (lungless salamanders); in specialized outgrowths on the visceral arches, external gills (*Necturus*); or in the so-called hairs of the African frog, *Astylosternus*. In this group are to be found also examples of endodermal respiratory organs, the internal gills and lungs. Internal gills are otherwise found only among the fish, while the lungs are the characteristic respiratory organs of the amniotes.

External gills. Among the amphibia, external gills (Figs. 75, 193, 206) may arise on the three visceral arches posterior to the hyoid arch (arches III, IV, and V). A small gill bud consisting of an ectodermal layer and mesodermal core elongates rapidly and soon acquires a capillary loop from the adjacent aortic arch. The gill branches several

times, a capillary loop growing into each branch. The complexity of
the branchial outgrowth differs markedly in different species, and can
be reduced or augmented experimentally by reducing or increasing
the temperature at which development is carried on. Except among
Gymnophiona and Caudata, a fold from the hyoid arch, known as the
opercular fold, grows back to cover the external gills, thus enclosing
them in an opercular chamber, which may open by a pore on each side
or by one only. After the formation of the operculum the external gills
atrophy and are resorbed while a completely new set of internal gills
develop to replace them.

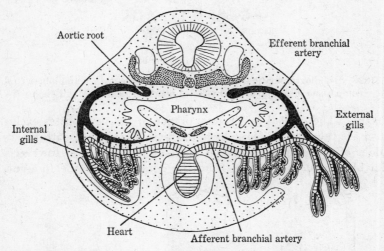

FIG. 101. Diagram to show relations of external and internal gills in frog embryo
(After Maurer.)

Internal gills. Internal gills (Figs. 101, 212) are formed on the
ventral surfaces of the visceral arches and grow out into the visceral
clefts as filaments or thin sheets (demibranchs). They are formed by
all fish and by the amphibia (excepting the Gymnophiona and the
Caudata). It will be recalled that the first visceral cleft does not have
a permanent opening to the exterior except in elasmobranchs and a
few ganoids. Demibranchs may arise in all other clefts. The third,
fourth, fifth, and sixth visceral arches may develop a demibranch on
both anterior and posterior surfaces, the two demibranchs of each
arch constituting a gill. The first cleft, or spiracle, sometimes forms a
gill-like structure (pseudobranch). The origin of the internal gills is
disputed, some investigators claiming that they arise from the endodermal portion of the cleft, others that they are formed from ectoderm.

In early embryonic life the filaments of the internal gills of some fish
are elongated and have been called external gills.   Gills are not formed
by the embryos of reptiles, birds, and mammals, but filaments corresponding to those mentioned above have been described in early embryos of reptiles and birds.

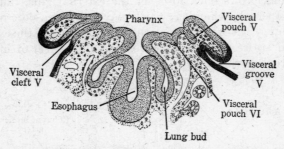

Fig. 102.   Semidiagrammatic frontal section through pharynx of amphibian to show
comparison of lung buds and visceral pouches.   (After Makuschok.)

Lungs.   The typical respiratory organs of the vertebrates exclusive
of fish are the lungs.   These have often been compared with the swim
bladder of fish and the so-called lungs of the Dipnoi.   However, the
swim bladder usually arises from the dorsal side of the fore-gut, in

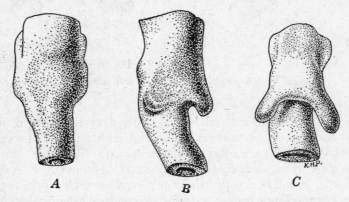

Fig. 103.   Three stages in the development of lung buds and trachea in the turtle,
Emys.   (After Hochstetter.)

either the esophageal or gastric region, while the lungs arise from the
sides or floor of the pharynx.   In the amphibia the lungs arise as a pair
of evaginations from the sides of the pharynx, posterior to the last pair
of visceral pouches, which they resemble greatly (Fig. 102).   The portion of the pharynx from which these pouches arise is cut off from the

esophagus above by a pair of lateral longitudinal grooves which meet in the midline progressively from the rear forward. In this way the ventral portion of the pharynx is converted into the trachea, opening into the pharynx by the glottis and, at its posterior end, dividing into the lung buds. In the higher vertebrates, reptiles, birds, and mammals, the bilateral origin of the lungs is not so apparent, as the first structure to appear is the laryngotracheal groove (Fig. 103). As the trachea is cut off from the esophagus above, the lung buds arise from the bifurcation of the trachea at its posterior end. These lung buds elongate to become the primary bronchi, which form many branches (secondary, tertiary, etc.), terminating in small alveoli.

THE FROG

External gills. Gill buds (Fig. 75) appear on the third and fourth visceral arches in stage 19. By stage 20, the bud on the third arch has formed its first branch and blood is circulating in the capillary loop. In this stage a vestigial gill bud forms on the fifth visceral arch. The gills on the other arches attain their greatest complexity in stage 22. The opercular fold (Fig. 76) is evident in the succeeding stage (23), completely covers the external gills on the right side (24), and completes the opercular chamber in stage 25. There is an opercular opening persisting on the left side, through which the water taken in at the mouth escapes after passing through the visceral clefts.

Internal gills. As the external gills are covered by the opercular fold, a new set of internal gills is forming on the ventral surfaces of the visceral arches. These arise as rows of filaments, each row representing a demibranch. There are two rows (anterior and posterior) on arches III, IV, and V, but only a single row on the anterior side of arch VI. From the floor of the pharynx, a flap of tissue (velar plate) grows over the visceral clefts on either side to cover them loosely and prevent the escape of food (Fig. 212). A series of small projections from the walls of the clefts serve as a strainer to supplement this protection. During metamorphosis the gill clefts and opercular chamber are filled with rapidly growing cells, and this area is reworked to become part of the body wall.

Lungs. The lungs of the frog arise as a pair of lateral evaginations from the pharynx in stage 22, and the trachea is distinct from the esophagus in the following stage. During the period of metamorphosis the lung buds expand greatly and are divided by septa to form the alveoli.

. THE CHICK

Neither external nor internal gills are formed in the development of the chick, unless such filaments as have been described by Boyden may be considered an embryonic vestige.

The lungs. In the chick the laryngotracheal groove is the first part of the respiratory apparatus to appear, which it does early in the third day of incubation. By the end of that day, the lung buds have appeared (Fig. 237). These push ahead of them the splanchnic mesoderm which forms their outer covering. The portion of the coelom into which they grow will be cut off from the rest to form the pleural cavity (Chapter 9). The original lung buds branch extensively during the first week of incubation, and during the second some of these branches grow out among the viscera and even into the hollow bones, where they become the accessory air sacs of the adult.

MAN

The lungs arise toward the end of the fourth week from a laryngo-tracheal groove. This separates itself from the overlying esophagus by lateral grooves, after which the freed posterior end grows rapidly and divides to form the primary bronchi (Figs. 100, 247). The one on the right side divides again before its fellow on the left. The bronchial buds continue their branching until seventeen generations of bronchi are formed. After birth, branching is renewed and, in all, twenty-four generations are present. The dividing bronchi have pushed into the mesodermal mass, in which esophagus and trachea are suspended, which will later be the mediastinum, the dividing wall between the pleural cavities. The origin of these cavities will be discussed in Chapter 9. As the bronchi push out into the pleural cavities, the mesodermal cap which is pushed ahead of them will become the visceral pleural lining.

The anterior portion of the laryngotracheal groove gives rise to larynx and trachea. The opening into the larynx, the glottis, is at first a longitudinal slit. But, by the formation of the epiglottis from a swelling at the base of the third and fourth visceral arches and from the two arytenoid swellings at the bases of the fifth arch, the opening is widened at the anterior end to assume the T-shape characteristic of the adult glottis. The laryngeal cartilages arise from the fourth and fifth visceral arches, and the vocal cords from folds on either side of the larynx.

Chapter 9

COELOM AND MESENTERIES

The body cavity or coelom of vertebrates arises by the splitting of the lateral mesoderm into a somatic (parietal) layer next to the ectoderm and a splanchnic (visceral) layer next to the endoderm. Cavities may appear in all three divisions of the mesoderm; if in the myotomes, they are known as myocoels; if in the nephrotomes, they are called nephrocoels; the cavity of the lateral mesoderm is the coelom or splanchnocoel (Fig. 104). In some forms the three cavities are confluent. The connection, however, is a temporary one, and the myocoels soon disappear. In other forms they make a transitory appearance and are entirely disconnected from the other cavities, while in many vertebrates myocoels are never formed. The nephrocoels will be considered with the urogenital organs. The coelom in amphioxus has a metameric origin from the ventral portions of the enterocoels, which unite in this

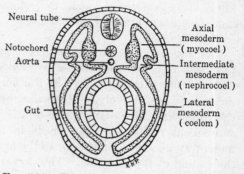

Neural tube

Notochord

Aorta

Gut

Axial mesoderm (myocoel)

Intermediate mesoderm (nephrocoel)

Lateral mesoderm (coelom)

Fig. 104. Diagrammatic transverse section of a generalized vertebrate to show the regions of the mesoderm and coelom.

region after the disappearance of the intervening anterior and posterior partitions. In vertebrates the coelomic cavity arises from the splitting of the lateral mesoderm into a dorsal somatic and a ventral splanchnic layer. In the amniotes this split continues out into the extra-embryonic mesoderm, thus giving rise to the exocoel, or cavity of the chorion. The coelom does not extend anterior to the visceral arches. Transitory cavities have been found in the arches and, indeed, in the head itself, and these have been interpreted as the remains of a cephalic coelom. It will appear later that these are more probably the rudiments of cephalic myotomes. The coelom does not extend into the tail.

In these regions the organs, instead of lying in a coelomic space, are loosely packed with a tissue known as mesenchyme. It was formerly

155

assumed that the mesenchyme originated wholly from mesoderm, but it has been shown that in the amphibia, at least, mesenchyme may originate in part from the neural crest (page 217).

Somatopleure and splanchnopleure.　The somatopleure has already been defined as the outer layer of the lateral mesoderm together with the ectoderm with which it becomes associated.　Between these two there is an invasion of mesenchymatous cells from the dermatomes and myotomes which give rise to the corium of the skin (see Chapter 14) and to its dermal musculature (see page 209).　The somatic mesoderm lining the outer wall of the coelom becomes the outer peritoneal lining. The splanchnopleure is the inner layer of the lateral mesoderm plus the endoderm with which it is associated.　Between these two occurs a migration of mesenchyme cells which give rise to the splanchnic musculature and blood vessels, while the splanchnic mesoderm itself forms the inner peritoneal lining of the coelom.

The mesenteries.　In all the vertebrates, the coelom is divided for a time into right and left halves by sagittal partitions above and below the alimentary canal, known as the dorsal mesentery and the ventral mesentery, respectively.　These are formed by the inward growth of the splanchnic mesoderm above and below the digestive tube and the subsequent fusion of these sheets in the median line.　The ventral mesentery disappears posterior to the liver, probably in connection with the coiling of the intestine.　The dorsal mesentery (Fig. 105) persists as the support of the alimentary canal, and frequently becomes subdivided into regions which are named from the supported organ, such as the mesogastrium which supports the stomach, the mesoduodenum, etc.　In the formation of the ventral mesentery, two organs, the heart and the liver, owing to their ventral position, are caught in between the two advancing sheets of splanchnic mesoderm.　In these regions, therefore, the ventral mesentery is divided into an upper and a lower half. The ventral mesentery dorsal to the heart becomes the dorsal mesocardium; that part which is ventral to the heart is the ventral mesocardium (Fig. 106A).　Both eventually disappear as the heart increases in size and complexity.　In the region of the liver, the dorsal half of the mesentery becomes the dorsal mesohepar (mesohepaticum), while the ventral portion is the ventral mesohepar (Fig. 106B).　The primordia of the pancreas lie originally in the dorsal and ventral mesenteries, respectively, but with the rotation of the stomach all are included in the dorsal mesentery.　The peritoneal supports of the urogenital organs will be considered in the following chapter.　The spleen (see page 190) arises in the mesogastrium, close to the wall of the alimentary canal, and is probably mesodermal in origin.

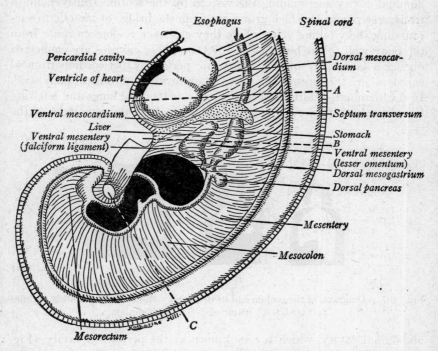

FIG. 105.   Diagram of mesenteries in early human embryo from left side.   *A, B,* and *C* indicate planes of sections shown in Fig. 106.   (From Arey after Prentiss.)

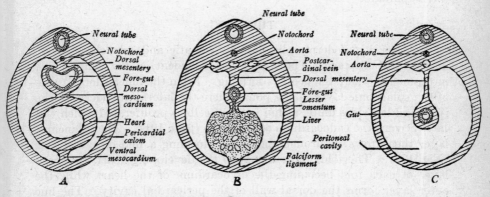

FIG. 106.   Diagrams of mesenteries in early human embryo as seen in transverse sections.   Compare Fig. 105.   (From Arey after Prentiss.)

Later divisions of the coelom.   The coelom becomes divided into an anterior pericardial cavity surrounding the heart and a posterior abdominal cavity surrounding the viscera by the septum transversum, a transverse partition which grows out from the bridge of mesoderm surrounding the vitelline veins where they cross the coelom *en route* from the body wall to the heart (Fig. 107*A*).   These cavities are connected during a large part of the embryonic period by pericardioperitoneal canals where the septum has failed to unite with the ventral body wall. In the mammals, additional septa develop behind the lungs and separate the pleural cavities, which contain the lungs, from the remainder of the

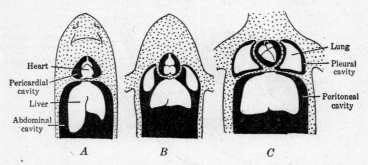

Fig. 107.   Diagrams of the coelom and its divisions.   *A*, fish.   *B*, amphibia, reptiles and birds.   *C*, mammals.   (After Kingsley.)

abdominal cavity, which is now known as the peritoneal cavity (Fig. 107*C*).   The pleural cavities are separated from each other in the median line by the mediastinum.   The partition separating the lungs from the viscera receives musculature from the myotomes and becomes the diaphragm.

THE FROG

The lateral mesoderm splits into its somatic and splanchnic layers in the tail-bud stage.   The split is most evident on the ventral side in the region where the heart is forming.   From the inner (dorsal) side of the splanchnic layer at the point where the lateral mesoderm of the right and left sides unite, a thin layer of cells is proliferated which will later become the endocardium of the heart (page 191).   The splanchnic layer then grows up around these cells, forming a fold on either side (Fig. 134).   The folds unite dorsal to the developing heart, the inner layer of each fold becoming the myocardium of the heart while the outer layer forms the dorsal wall of the pericardial cavity.   The line along which the two folds meet becomes the temporary dorsal mesocardium. The line where the somatic and splanchnic mesoderm of right and left sides first met is the origin of the ventral mesocardium, which then can be said to have arisen before the dorsal mesocardium. It is also the first to disappear.

In the region posterior to the heart the lateral mesoderm on either side splits (Fig. 207) before uniting at the ventral side of the body. This gives rise to the abdominal cavity. The separation of the abdominal cavity from the pericardial cavity is accomplished by the growth of folds (sometimes called lateral mesocardia) from the outer peritoneal layer which continue inward to the common cardinal veins (page 189). These are in contact with the anterior surface of the mesodermal covering of the liver, from which a layer is split off to unite with the peritoneal folds and so form the septum transversum. This is not completed until during metamorphosis. The ventral mesentery disappears as fast as it is formed so that the coelom becomes continuous on the ventral side as soon as the two split sheets of lateral mesoderm unite. The dorsal mesentery persists in its entirety.

THE CHICK

In the chick embryo the lateral mesoderm splits very early (Fig. 217). Consequently, as the subcephalic pocket and lateral sulci cut off the anterior region of the chick at the end of the first day of incubation, there will be a U-shaped cavity on the ventral side which is the primordium of the pericardial cavity. In cross-section this appears as two dilated portions of the coelom, which are known as the amniocardiac vesicles (Fig. 218). On the inner or splanchnic wall of each, the heart develops (page 193), while the outer or somatic wall gives rise to the amniotic folds. As the splanchnic layers are brought together, the developing heart is caught between them and so temporarily suspended by a dorsal and a ventral mesocardium. The ventral mesocardium disappears immediately, the dorsal one soon afterwards. The septum transversum is formed from the ventral mesentery, between heart and liver, two lateral folds of somatic mesoderm extending to the vitelline veins (lateral mesocardia) and two lateral closing folds extending from the ventral mesentery to the lateral mesocardia.

Posterior to the septum transversum, the pancreas grows into the dorsal mesentery (Fig. 238), and the liver into the ventral mesentery. The ventral mesentery persists only as the gastrohepatic omentum between liver and stomach, and as the falciform ligament between the liver and the ventral body wall. Posterior to the duodenum the dorsal mesentery persists in its entirety, while the ventral mesentery disappears.

MAN

From the first, the U-shaped pericardial cavity is distinguishable from the abdominal cavity, inasmuch as it never communicates directly with the extraembryonic coelom as does the abdominal cavity. As in the chick, its posterior boundary is coterminous with that of the foregut, but it is in communication with the abdominal cavity by means of the parietal recesses, passages which correspond to the peritoneopericardial canals of the anamniotes. The recesses are divided frontally by the vitelline veins into dorsal and ventral parietal recesses. With the formation of the septum transversum (Fig. 105), the ventral recesses are incorporated into the pericardial cavity. The dorsal recesses become the pleural cavities; and the pleuroperitoneal septum, which divides them from the peritoneal cavity, is formed by the upward growth of the diaphragm. The musculature of this organ arises from the fourth cervical myotome during the backward growth of the diaphragm. The rotation of the stomach results in a rearrangement of the mesenteries, for an account of which the reader is referred to any of the larger textbooks on human embryology.

CHAPTER 10

UROGENITAL SYSTEM

The vertebrate urogenital system is a complex of organs whose primary function is either excretory (nephric) or reproductive (genital). In most vertebrates they are intimately associated in using common ducts and openings for the discharge of their respective products from the body. The nature of this association is clearly revealed by the study of their development. Both sets of organs arise in the intermediate mesoderm or mesomere. Their ducts open into the endodermal cloaca and are discharged through a vent which serves also for the rectum, or by means of a urogenital orifice, which in either case is lined with ectoderm.

Excretory organs. The excretory system of vertebrates is essentially a paired series of nephric tubules, developed in the intermediate mesoderm, which collect nitrogenous wastes from the blood and discharge them to the exterior by two longitudinal ducts emptying into the cloaca. The intermediate mesoderm in the anterior part of the body is divided into nephrotomes corresponding to the somites. There are three different types of kidneys among the vertebrates (Fig. 108).

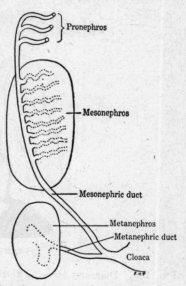

Fig. 108. Diagram to show relationships of vertebrate excretory systems.

The first is the pronephros, which arises in the anterior nephrotomes and is the functional kidney in the larval stages of the fish and the amphibians. The second is the mesonephros, which arises from nephrotomes posterior to the pronephros and from the undivided intermediate mesoderm (nephrogenic cord) behind them. It is the functional kidney of adult anamniotes and embryonic or fetal amniotes. The third is the metanephros, which is the functional kidney of adult amniotes.

161

The pronephros. This organ is formed during development by all vertebrates, but is best developed in free-swimming aquatic larvae like the tadpole (Fig. 120). It develops typically from the nephrocoels of the more anterior nephrotomes. The nephrocoels elongate to form tubules, whose distal ends turn caudad and unite with each other to form the pronephric duct, which grows backward toward the cloaca. The ventral ends of nephrocoels open into the coelom, and these openings, the nephrostomes, become lined with long cilia. Typically each

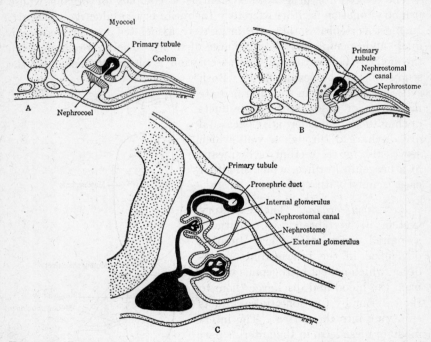

FIG. 109. Diagrams showing three stages in the development of the pronephric tubule. (After Felix.)

nephric tubule has associated with it a capillary net from the dorsal aorta (Fig. 109). The capillary net is called a glomerulus, and with its nephric tubule forms the excretory unit known as a nephron. The pronephros exists as a functional unit only during larval life, and it is generally believed that it has no excretory function in higher vertebrates. In all vertebrates it degenerates during the development of the mesonephros.

The mesonephros. The mesonephros, like the pronephros, is developed by all vertebrates. It becomes the adult kidney of the anamniotes, but is functional during the embryonic (and fetal) period only of the amniotes. Portions of the mesonephros become associated with the genital organs of the adult (page 169).

In the lower vertebrates the mesonephros also develops as a series of segmental nephrocoels, but in the nephrotomes posterior to those containing the pronephric tubules. In the nephrogenic cord, and in higher vertebrates generally, nephrocoels do not appear, and the mesonephric tubule originates from a solid clump of cells which later acquires a cavity (Fig. 110). Only in the more anterior and earlier developed tubules of lower vertebrates are nephrostomes formed, and these do not persist. The mesonephric tubules grow toward the pronephric ducts, with which they unite. After the degeneration of the pronephric tubules the duct is known as the mesonephric (Wolffian) duct.

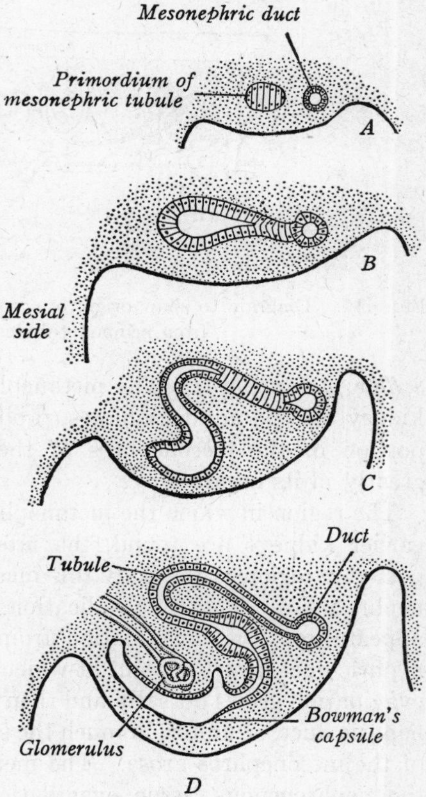

A glomerulus connected with the dorsal aorta and the cardinal veins arises in connection with each tubule, as in the pronephros. An important difference between the pronephros and the mesonephros lies in the fact that the number of nephric tubules in each nephrotome is greater in the mesonephros (Fig. 111). These arise by the constriction of the posterior median part of

Fig. 110. Diagrams showing four stages in development of mesonephric tubule. (From Arey after Felix.)

each mesonephric tubule into a small vesicle which gives rise to a secondary tubule; each of these tubules acquires a glomerulus (and in lower vertebrates a nephrostome) at the proximal end. The connection of these secondary tubules with the Wolffian duct, however, is attained by an evagination from the duct itself which grows out as the collecting duct to meet the developing secondary tubule. From these secondary tubules, tertiary ones bud off and develop in like manner, acquiring connections with the collecting duct through an evagination of this canal. As many as eight tubules may be formed in a single segment by this process of budding. This complexity is greatest at the posterior end of the mesonephros. In the amniotes, the mesonephros (except for that portion associated with the genital organs) disappears after the metanephros has been formed.

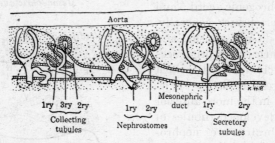

Fig. 111.   Diagram to show origin of secondary and tertiary mesonephric tubules from primary tubules.   (After Brauer.)

The metanephros.   The metanephros, which is found as a separate kidney only in adult amniotes, probably is equivalent to the posterior portion of the mesonephros of the anamniotes, which it resembles greatly in its organogeny.

The region in which the metanephros arises is, like that in which the earlier kidneys are found, the intermediate mesoderm. But in the posterior region of the body this mass is never segmented into separate nephrotomes. The first indication of metanephros formation is the appearance of an evagination from the dorsal surface of the mesonephric duct near the point at which the latter enters the cloaca. This evagination grows dorsally and then turns forward to become the metanephric duct, or ureter, in much the same manner as the collecting ducts of the mesonephros arose. The metanephric duct then sends out into the nephrogenous tissue evaginations which increase in length and branch repeatedly to form the collecting tubules of the metanephros. Around the distal end of each tubule, a small mass of the nephrogenous tissue condenses and acquires a lumen like the nephrocoels of the pronephros and mesonephros (Fig. 112; *1, 2*). From these vesicles the secretory nephric tubules arise by a process of elongation and later fuse with the collecting tubules just described (Fig. 112; *3, 4*). In each of the tubules a capsule develops for the reception of a glomerulus, which is a capillary network from an arteriole of the renal artery (Fig. 112; *4, 5*). Development proceeds from the posterior end toward the anterior, instead of in the opposite direction as in the earlier types of kidneys. The metanephric duct at first empties into the mesonephric duct, from which it arose. In later development it acquires a direct connection of its own to the urinary bladder.

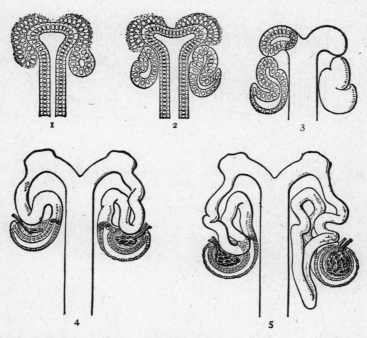

FIG. 112. Diagrams to show origin and development of metanephric tubules. Collecting tubule in center, secretory tubules to right and left; the one on the right relatively more advanced. (From Arey after Huber.)

The urinary bladder. This structure takes its origin as a sac-like evagination from the floor of the cloaca and therefore is lined with endoderm. The mesonephric ducts of the amphibia discharge their contents into the cloaca directly above the opening of the bladder but have no direct connection with it. In birds and most reptiles which have no urinary bladder, the portion of the mesonephric duct posterior to the point where it joins the metanephric duct is drawn into the wall of the cloaca so that each of these ducts opens into the cloaca separately. The region of the cloaca into which the ducts empty is known as the urodeum. It is from the floor of this region of the cloaca that the allantois had taken its origin at an earlier time. In mammals the distal part of the cloacal evagination gives rise to the allantois while the proximal part becomes the urinary bladder. Connecting the two is a

constricted passage (Figs. 113, 114) known as the urachus. During
the growth of the bladder the posterior part of the mesonephric duct is

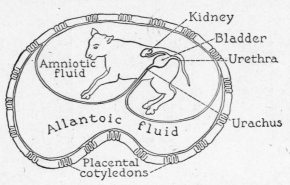

FIG. 113.   Diagram to show relations of urinary bladder, urachus and allantois in
fetal calf.   (From Windle.)

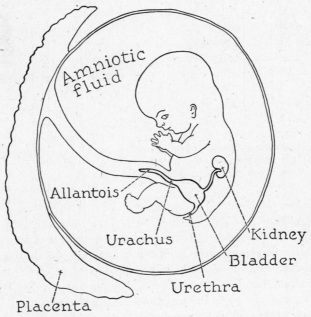

FIG. 114.   Diagram to show relations of urinary bladder to urachus and allantois in
human fetus.   (From Windle.)

incorporated into it so that both mesonephric and metanephric ducts
empty separately.   As the bladder enlarges the metanephric ducts retain their connection with it while the mesonephric ducts shift backward

so that they enter the cloaca posterior to the mouth of the bladder. Meantime a frontal wedge of mesoderm grows back to divide the cloaca into an upper tube, the rectum, and a lower one, the urogenital sinus. The history of this structure will be considered after that of the reproductive organs.

Reproductive organs. The reproductive or genital organs may be grouped into two classes: (1) the primary genital organs, or gonads, in which the germ cells develop; and (2) the accessory genital organs, whose original function is the discharge of the germ cells from the body.

The gonads consist of the germ cells and the subordinate tissues, blood vessels, nerves, connective tissue, etc., which make up a large part of these glands. In an earlier chapter it has been shown that the primordial germ cells may first appear in the endoderm of the gut wall and thence migrate by way of the splanchnic mesoderm, dorsal mesentery, and peritoneum to their definitive position in a thickening of the peritoneum on the mesial side of the nephrotomes. This thickening is called the genital ridge (Fig. 115*B*). A considerable body of evidence is accumulating to indicate that germ cells may also arise from the cells of the genital ridge itself.

The genital ridge is now invaded by mesenchymal cells, and projects into the coelomic cavity. The anterior and posterior ends of the ridge degenerate, and the middle portion enlarges and is separated by a longitudinal groove from the mesonephros so that it hangs in the coelom suspended by a fold of the peritoneum, known as the mesorchium in the male or the mesovarium in the female. The germ cells have by this time become transformed into gonia (Chapter 3), and the germ glands are known as gonads.

Within the gonads, the gonia come to lie in nests, close to the germinal epithelium. Tubular outgrowths from the nephric tubules of the mesonephros approach these nests. The later history of the gonads differs in the two sexes.

Testis. In the male, the nests of spermatogonia become tubules which connect with the tubules growing in from the mesonephros (Fig. 115*A*). The testicular parts of these canals are known as the seminiferous tubules, the nephric portions as the efferent ductules. The walls of the seminiferous tubules are composed of spermatogonia and sustentacular cells which act as nurse cells to the developing sperm. Between the tubules lie partitions of mesenchyme which make up the stroma of the testis and contain the interstitial cells, which are supposed to be concerned in the formation of the male hormone. It is because of the presence of these cells that the testis is̹ sometimes spoken of as the "interstitial gland." It is now well established that the testis secretes a "male" hormone. Eventually,

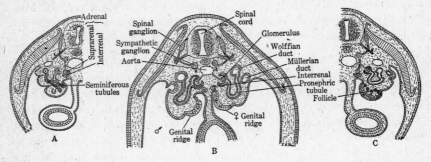

FIG. 115. Diagrams to show early development of the gonads in transverse sections. *A*, testis. *B*, genital ridge. *C*, ovary. (After Corning.)

the tubules become separated from the surrounding germinal epithelium by the development of a mesenchymatous layer called the tunica albuginea.

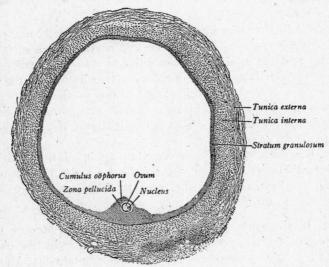

FIG. 116. Section of human vesicular (Graafian) follicle. (From Arey after Prentiss.)

Ovary. In the female, the nests of oögonia become separate follicles (Fig. 115*C*) which never attain connection with the mesonephric tubules. These tubules consequently degenerate. A follicle consists of a single oögonium surrounded by follicle cells, which may be compared to the sustentacular cells of the male. In the mammalian ovary the primary follicle is greatly enlarged to form a vesicular (Graafian) follicle (Fig. 116), which protrudes from the surface of the ovary. The follicle cells multiply and secrete a follicular fluid which presses the outer wall (stratum granulosum) away from the egg and a layer of follicle cells immediately surrounding it. These form a projection (cumulus oöphorus) into the cavity of the follicle. When ovulation takes place the wall of the follicle is ruptured, and the egg, still surrounded by its investment of follicle cells, now known as the corona radiata (page 34), is washed out with follicular fluid. After ovulation and fertilization the follicle cells enlarge, multiply, and secrete a yellow substance, the whole forming a corpus luteum (page 128). The existence of female hormones (page 128) formed in the ovary is now definitely proved. The tunica albuginea of the ovary develops much later than that of the testis but is also of mesenchymal origin.

The genital ducts. The sperms formed in the seminiferous tubules of the testis are discharged into the mesonephric tubules and thence

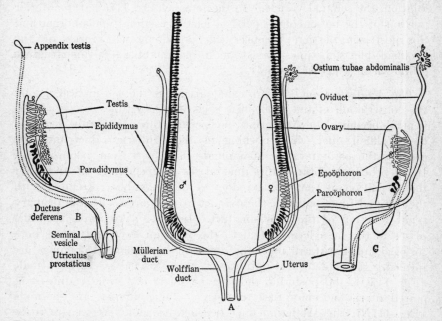

Fig. 117. Diagrams showing origin and early development of genital ducts. *A*, early stage showing mesonephros, gonads (male on left, female on right), and ducts. *B*, later stage in male, showing in broken lines the structures which degenerate. *C*, later stage in female. (After Felix.)

make their way into the mesonephric duct, which accordingly becomes the male genital duct. The ova, on the other hand, are discharged directly into the cavity of the coelom, whence they are received into a new tube, the oviduct, by means of an opening, the ostium tubae abdominale. The mesonephric duct is often called the Wolffian duct; the oviduct is frequently called the Müllerian duct. Both ducts appear in every embryo (Fig. 117*A*), but the later histories of the two differ according to the sex. The genital ducts of the teleost fish arise in a different manner, which is beyond the scope of this book.

The Wolffian duct. In the male (Fig. 117*B*), the efferent ductules toward the posterior end of the series becomes occluded, leaving only a few at the anterior end functional. These lose their renal corpuscles and shorten greatly. In the amniotes, where the metanephros acts as the functional kidney, this anterior group becomes the epididymis, while the more posterior, non-functional vestige becomes the paradidymis. The mesonephric duct persists as the deferent duct. At the point where the deferent duct enters the cloaca, there develops a dilation, the seminal vesicle. In the female (Fig. 117*C*), the anterior portion of the mesonephros persists as the vestigial epoöphoron, and the posterior portion becomes the paroöphoron. Traces of the Wolffian duct sometimes persist (as in mammals, where this structure is known as Gartner's canal).

The Müllerian duct. This canal arises in the elasmobranchs by the constriction of the pronephric duct into two tubes, of which the ventral becomes the Müllerian duct, while the dorsal tube becomes the Wolffian duct. The opening of the Müllerian duct into the coelom, the ostium tubae abdominale, is a persistent nephrostome. In all other vertebrates, this duct arises independently of and after the formation of the Wolffian duct, a fact possibly correlated with the delayed functioning of the oviduct as compared with the primary renal function of the Wolffian duct. In these vertebrates the duct arises in the mesoderm lateral to the Wolffian duct and grows both forward and backward until the abdominal and cloacal openings are formed. It is not formed until late in embryogenesis. In the female (Fig. 117*C*), the posterior ends of the ducts are usually dilated as paired uteri, and may fuse to form a single uterus. In the male (Fig. 117*B*), the Müllerian duct degenerates, but vestiges are to be found even in the adult, such as the appendix testis and prostatic utricle of man, which represent the anterior and posterior ends of the female duct, respectively.

The external genitalia. The genital organs so far considered are common to all vertebrates and are sometimes spoken of as the internal genitalia. External genitals are found only in those animals in which fertilization is internal. These organs serve the function of transmitting or receiving the sperm at the time of copulation. Internal fertilization is a phenomenon which has been observed in all classes of the vertebrates, but it is characteristic of all amniotes.

Although the external genitalia differ in the sexes, they are embryologically homologous. Two types are recognized, duplex and simplex. In the duplex type, characteristic of the sauropsids, sac-like extensions arise on each side of the cloaca, which in the male become the hemipenes or intromittent organ, while in the female they remain vestigial. In the simplex type, characteristic of mammals, a single median ectodermal prominence arises anterior to the cloacal aperture, to become the phallus (Fig. 118). In the male, the phallus enlarges and encloses the greater part of the uro-

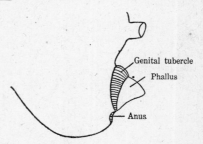

Fig. 118. Diagram to show the origin of the mammalian external genitalia. (After Felix.)

genital sinus. In this way it becomes the penis, while the enclosed sinus becomes the penile urethra. In the female mammal, the phallus becomes the vestigial clitoris, while the sides of the urogenital sinus remain open as the labia minora, which guard the opening of the urogenital vestibule. At the base of the phallus is a swelling, the genital tubercle, from which labioscrotal folds arise on either side of the urogenital opening. In the male they fuse to form the scrotum, an external sac into which the testes descend; in the female they remain separate as the labia majora.

Adrenal complex. Closely associated with the kidney, whether mesonephros or metanephros, is the adrenal gland. This is in reality a complex of two endocrine glands which are distinct in the fish and arise from separate primordia in all vertebrates (Fig. 119). The first component is the interrenal (cortical) tissue, which originates in the intermediate mesoderm mesial to the region in which the mesonephros and genital ridge appear. The second component is the suprarenal (medullary, phaeochrome) tissue, which arises from wandering ectoderm cells. These originated in the neural crest, were associated with the cells forming the sympathetic ganglia (Chapter

15), and finally came to take a position near the developing inter-renal cells. Both suprarenal and interrenal cells become arranged in cords on the ventral surface of the developing mesonephros and in close association with its blood vessels. In vertebrates which develop a metanephros the suprarenal and interrenal components become a separate adrenal gland. Each, however, produces its own hormone, epinephrin from the suprarenal component, cortin from the inter-renal.

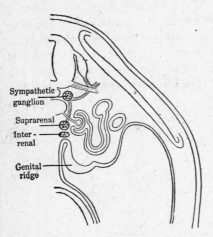

Sympathetic ganglion

Suprarenal

Inter-renal

Genital ridge

FIG. 119. Diagrams to show the origin of the suprarenal and interrenal components of the adrenal gland. (After Corning.)

THE FROG

Pronephros. The intermediate mesoderm of the developing frog is atypical. In stage 16 the intermediate mesoderm has lost its attachment to the lateral mesoderm, and, retaining its attachment to the axial mesoderm, is growing out between the lateral mesoderm and the ectoderm. In the anterior region it is divided into nephrotomes corresponding to the somites to which they are still attached. The longitudinal bulge on either side of the embryo so produced is known as the pronephric shelf. In later development the nephrotomes unite to form a nephrogenic cord and lose their connection with the somites. Later they acquire a new connection with the lateral mesoderm, which makes the nephrogenic cord appear to arise from the somatic layer of the lateral mesoderm (stage 17). Cavities appear in the nephrogenic cord about the time the lateral mesoderm is split into a somatic and splanchnic layer. These cavities unite to form a pronephric duct while pronephric tubules (Figs. 207, 208) develop in the region corresponding to somites II, III, and IV. These acquire nephrostomes in stage 20. The pronephric tubules elongate greatly and are contorted into coiled structures that push into the cardinal veins. From the dorsal aorta a vascular outgrowth, the glomerulus, (Fig. 212) on either side extends to the developing pronephros. The developing lungs projecting into the coelom later form shelves which cut off the portions of the coelom into which the nephrostomes open as the pronephric chambers. At stage 25 the pronephros on either side of the body is a large and conspicuous body (Fig. 120). A projection from the roof of the cloaca arises to meet the advancing pronephric ducts and seems to have moved forward by stage 25 so that the pronephric ducts are actually recurved before entering the cloaca.

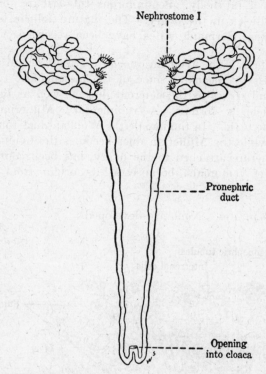

FIG. 120. Excretory system of 11-mm. *Rana pipiens* embryo. From a wax plate reconstruction. Ventral view. Prepared by Marian F. James and Phyllis T. Mrazek. ×40.

Mesonephros. Mesonephric tubules appear in the nephrotomes (somites VII–XII). These have nephrostomes in early larval life; but at the time the pronephroi degenerate the portion of each mesonephric tubule next to the nephrostome (peritoneal canal) breaks away from the remainder of the tubule and fuses with the posterior cardinal vein. The mesonephros is the functional kidney of the adult, and the Wolffian duct, therefore, functions as the ureter.

Urinary bladder. This arises as a ventral evagination from the floor of the cloaca during metamorphosis. The mesonephric ducts never acquire a direct connection to the bladder but open directly above it.

The gonads. The genital ridges arise soon after hatching. Sex can be distinguished at the time when the embryo is about 30 mm. in body length. The anterior portion of each genital ridge degenerates and becomes a fat body. Seminiferous tubules are formed in the testis and follicles in the ovary. The mature follicle is not of the Graaffian type. Hermaphrodites have been recorded.

The gonoducts. The Wolffian duct in the male acquires connection with the testis by means of some of the mesonephric tubules (vasa efferentia) and serves as the deferent duct as well as the ureter. A seminal vesicle is formed. A rudimentary Müllerian duct also appears in the male. In the female the Wolffian duct functions solely as a ureter while the Müllerian duct becomes the oviduct. Bidder's organ, a structure attached to the ovary, has been compared to the epoöphoron of mammals, because of its origin from mesonephric tubules.

External genitalia. None are developed.

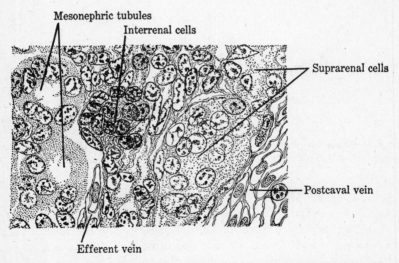

Mesonephric tubules
Interrenal cells
Suprarenal cells
Postcaval vein
Efferent vein

Fig. 121. Section through mesonephros of 55-mm. frog tadpole (*Rana pipiens*) to show interrenal and suprarenal cells. Prepared by Mary H. Phillips. ×660.

Adrenals. These arise from suprarenal and interrenal cells, which accumulate around the blood vessels on the ventral side of the mesonephros (Fig. 121). The brown color of the suprarenal cells distinguishes this area as a yellow-brown streak on the mesonephros.

THE CHICK

Pronephros. About twelve pronephric tubules arise (somites V–XVI), beginning on the second day of incubation. Nephrostomes are formed, but glomeruli do not appear until the third and fourth days of incubation, at which time the pronephros is degenerating. The pronephric duct arises at the ninth somite.

The development of the pronephros in the chick is very irregular; the number of pronephric tubules varies in different individuals or on the two sides of the same embryo; the tubules are often represented by solid cords; the number and size of the nephrostomes vary; and the whole appearance is that of a vestigial organ without a urinary function.

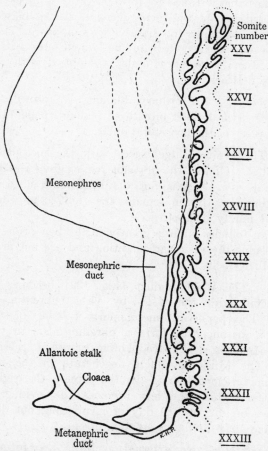

FIG. 122. Reconstruction of metanephric primordium in 6-day chick embryo. (After Lillie from Schreiner.)

Mesonephros. Mesonephric tubules (Figs. 122, 232) arise from the intermediate mesoderm between somites XII and XXX, the more anterior of which develop nephrostomes. The main part of the mesonephros, however, arises between somites XX and XXX, where the continued growth of the tubules causes the projection of this region into the coelom as the Wolffian body. It begins to degenerate on the eleventh day.

Metanephros. An evagination from the mesonephric duct comparable to the collecting tubules of the mesonephros grows out into the nephrogenic region of the intermediate mesoderm during the fourth day of incubation. This diverticulum gives rise to the ureter which branches many times to form a great number of collecting tubules. Meantime in the nephrogenous tissue between somites XXV–XXXIII a number of tiny vesicles appear. These elongate and finally become the secretory tubules which unite with the collecting tubules. Each secretory tubule is supplied with a glomerulus and capillary network.

Urinary bladder. No urinary bladder is formed. The cloaca persists and is later divided into three regions (page 147), of which the urodeum receives the urogenital ducts.

Gonads. The genital ridge arises with the mesonephros as the urogenital ridge. Of this the anterior region gives rise to the gonad on the mesial side. Sex is not distinguishable until the seventh day of incubation. In the female, the right ovary develops only partially and finally disappears.

The ovarian follicles enlarge greatly in the hen prior to ovulation, but never assume the vesicular condition and are not properly called Graaffian follicles.

Gonoducts. The Wolffian duct (Fig. 122) becomes the deferent duct, connected with the testis by vasa efferentia forming the epididymis. The persisting mesonephric tubules of the posterior region of the mesonephros form a paradidymis. In the female a vestigial epoöphoron and paroöphoron represent these bodies respectively. The Müllerian ducts degenerate in the male without ever acquiring a cloacal exit. In the female the right Müllerian duct disappears while the left becomes the oviduct. The shell gland appears on the twelfth day of incubation, but does not open into the cloaca until the hen is six months old.

External genitalia. No external genitalia are formed, although hemipenes are found in some other birds.

Adrenal glands. This gland arises from distinct suprarenal and interrenal components, which later become intermingled in a structure known as the suprarenal capsule embedded in the anterior portion of the kidney near the postcaval vein and gonad.

MAN

Pronephros. Between the third and fourth weeks of development pronephric tubules arise in somites VII–XIII, develop nephrostomes and glomeruli, but degenerate rapidly.

Mesonephros. The first mesonephric tubules rise in the region posterior to the degenerating pronephros, that is in somite XIV. At the height of their development (Figs. 123, 248–250) they extend from somite IX to somite XXVI. The intermediate mesoderm is unsegmented posterior to somite X, and the tubules arise from solid balls of nephrogenic tissue which later acquire cavities and elongate to join the old pronephric duct. There is no constant number of tubules per somite region, but at the end of the first month there are about thirty tubules in each mesonephros. The collection portion of each tubule arises from the original vesicle and not from the pronephric duct, as seems to be the case in the chick. In the second month of development the more anterior tubules disappear while new ones are being formed

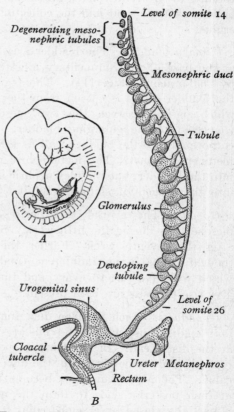

Fig. 123. Mesonephros in human embryos. *A*, 8-mm. embryo, after Shikinami, ×45. *B*, 10-mm. embryo, after Felix, ×35. (From Arey.)

at the posterior end. In this way, although about eighty pairs of tubules were formed in all, only about thirty are present at any one time. A glomerulus indents the distal end of each tubule to form a capsule (of Bowman). The mesonephros degenerates except for the structures taken over by the reproductive organs early in the third month, when the metanephros is capable of functioning.

Metanephros. The definitive kidney arises from a diverticulum of the mesonephric' duct (Figs. 242, 251), which gives rise to ureter, pelvis, calyces, and collecting tubules, and from the nephrogenous tissue into which this diverticulum pushes. The secretory tubules arise from condensations in this zone and later become hollow, elongate, and join the collecting tubules. Each has its glomerulus.

Urinary bladder. The bladder arises from the floor of the cloaca at the base of the rudimentary allantois with which it is connected by the urachus (Fig. 114). The region of the cloaca from which the bladder grows is cut off from the rectum by a urorectal septum which passes between the two mesonephric ducts, leaving them connected to the enlarging bladder. The mesonephric duct is incorporated into the bladder wall as far back as its junction with the metanephric duct. The metanephric ducts maintain their openings into the bladder, but the mesonephric ducts are carried back to enter into the urogenital sinus behind it.

Gonads. The genital ridge arises on the mesial side of the mesonephros during the fifth week. Sex is not, distinguishable until after the seventh week. Earlier the developing gonad might be thought of as in an indifferent condition, for the cortical region which will give rise to ovary and the medullary region which will give rise to testis are both present.

Gonoducts. Each Wolffian duct functions as a deferent duct, and both epididymus and paradidymis are formed, as is a seminal vesicle at the distal end. In the female, epoöphoron and paroöphoron are formed, while some portion of the duct itself may persist as Gartner's canal. The Müllerian ducts become the uterine tubes, which unite at their posterior ends to form the uterus and vagina. The latter is partially closed by a semicircular fold, the hymen, where it enters the urogenital sinus. In the male, vestiges of the anterior end of each Müllerian duct persist as the appendix testis, while the posterior end is represented by the rudimentary prostatic utricle. The dilation of the bladder results in the inclusion of the ureters (metanephric ducts) in its walls (Fig. 124). The genital ducts (Wolffian or Müllerian ducts) empty into the urogenital sinus posterior to the bladder, in a region which constricts to form the urethra. About this develop a number of outgrowths which acquire cavities and form the prostate gland in the male and the paraurethral glands in the female.

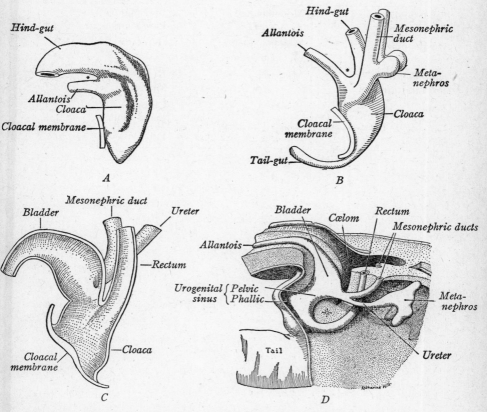

FIG. 124. Models showing relation of urogenital ducts to cloaca in human embryos. *A*, 3.5 mm. *B*, 4 mm. (Both after Pohlman, ×50.) *C*, 8 mm. ×50. *D*, 11 mm. ×25, after Keibel. (From Arey.)

External genitalia. These are of the mammalian type (page 171).

Adrenals. This gland, often called the suprarenal, arises from interrenal and suprarenal components, of which the first forms the cortex and the second the medullary portion. Both are included in a single capsule, which in the second month is almost as large as the metanephros and even at birth is a third the size of that organ.

Homologies of the Reproductive Organs

Male	Indifferent	Female
Testis	Gonad	Ovary
Epididymis Paradidymis	Mesonephros	Epoöphoron Paroöphoron
Ductus deferens	Mesonephric (Wolffian) duct	Gartner's canal
Appendix testis Prostatic utricle	Müllerian duct	Uterus and Tube Vagina
Penis	Phallus	Clitoris Labia minora
Scrotum	Labioscrotal swellings	Labia majora

CHAPTER 11

BLOOD-VASCULAR SYSTEM

The vascular system is mesenchymatous in origin. It consists of separate cells, the blood corpuscles, floating in a fluid matrix, the blood plasma, in a closed system of interconnected tubes, the blood vessels. Some vessels become lined externally with muscle fibers, and in one locality this muscular development gives rise to a pulsating heart, by means of which the blood is kept in circulation.

Origin of the blood-vascular system. The first indications of the vascular system are found in the splanchnopleure as blood islands (Fig. 125). In the telolecithal vertebrates this is always in the

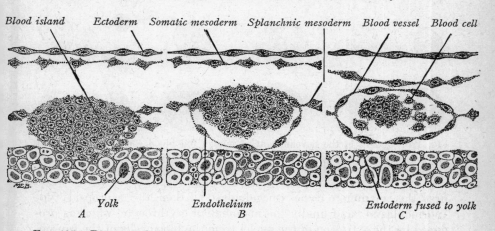

Fig. 125. Diagrams showing three stages in the development of a capillary from a blood island based on transverse sections of the area vasculosa in a seven-somite chick. (From Arey.)

extra-embryonic splanchnopleure. These blood islands originate as local aggregates of mesenchyme. Later, the inner cells separate as corpuscles, while the outer ones form the endothelial lining of a vesicle. These vesicles anastomose with each other to form the extra-embryonic vitelline circulation.

The blood corpuscles. The first corpuscles formed are the inner cells of the blood islands. Later corpuscles are budded off from

181

the walls of the capillaries into their cavities. Mesenchymal cells in regions where the capillary network is forming may develop into blood corpuscles and enter the blood stream. These first corpuscles are the hemoblasts (Fig. 126).

The erythrocytes, or red corpuscles, are distinguished by the presence of hemoglobin, which gives them their color. In the anamniotes these corpuscles have large vesicular nuclei with granular chromatin and a distinct cell membrane. In the sauropsida, the red corpuscles have small compact nuclei. The mammalian erythrocyte is distinguished by the absence of the nucleus in the adult. In the development of mammals there is a succession of red blood corpuscles:

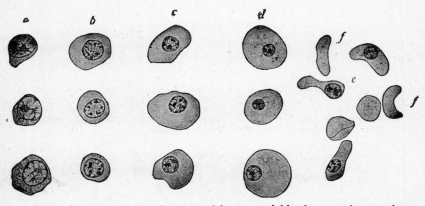

Fig. 126. Stages in the development of human red blood corpuscles. *a*, hemoblasts. *b*, megaloblasts (anamniote type). *c*, *d*, normoblasts (sauropsid type). *e*, normoblasts in process of becoming *f*, erythrocytes. (From Arey after Prentiss).

first the anamniote type (megaloblasts); then the sauropsid type (normoblasts); and finally the mammalian erythrocyte, which is produced by the extrusion of the nuclei from the blood cells of the sauropsid type (Fig. 126).

The leucocytes, or white blood corpuscles, are of many different types. Here it will be sufficient to distinguish the granulocytes, with distinctive types of cytoplasmic granules (according to which they are classified), and lymphocytes, which lack these granules. Although the matter cannot be considered definitely settled, most embryologists consider that all types of corpuscles arise from hemoblasts and that the large lymphocytes are nearest the ancestral type.

Hemoblasts become differentiated into the different types of blood corpuscles in the following blood-forming centers: (1) the yolk sac; (2) the embryonic capillaries; (3) the liver, the spleen, thymus,

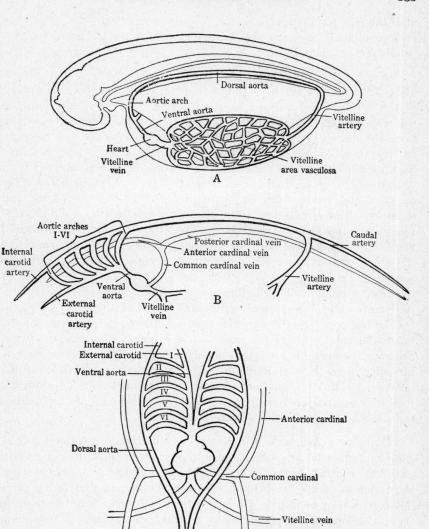

FIG. 127. Diagrams to show fundamental plan of embryonic circulation. *A*, early stage in side view. *B*, later stage in side view. *C*, same from above, aortic roots pulled apart.

and the lymph glands; (4) the bone marrow. In the adult the lymph glands give rise to lymphocytes, and the bone marrow to all types of corpuscles.

Origin of the blood vessels. The first embryonic blood vessels (Fig. 127) are the vitelline (omphalomesenteric) veins which appear at the ventrolateral margins of the fore-gut. These vessels unite in the region of the anterior intestinal portal with the heart, from which arise the paired ventral aortae. These bend up around the pharynx in the mandibular arch as the first aortic arches, and continue backward as the dorsal aortae. The primitive dorsal aortae, later known as the aortic roots, fuse at a very early stage to become the dorsal aorta, from which branches are sent to each myotome and to the vitelline circulation. . The posterior ends of the vitelline veins fuse in small-yolked forms, such as the frog, to form a subintestinal vein, which continues back to the tail. In large-yolked forms like the chick, the vitelline veins are widely separated and brought into connection only by the sinus terminalis, which makes a circuit of the area vasculosa. The vitelline veins are the ventral venous channels. A dorsal set of vessels soon originates independently. The first of these to appear are the anterior cardinal (precardinal) veins of the head. A similar pair, the posterior cardinal (postcardinal) veins, arise in connection with the nephric region. These, however, do not discharge their contents directly into the heart but into the anterior cardinals. The portions of the original anterior cardinals proximal to this juncture with the posterior cardinals are now called the common cardinal veins (Cuvierian ducts).

The heart. Although the heart is primitively a paired organ, the two primordia are soon fused into a single median tube connected with the ventral aortae in front and the vitelline veins (and later the common cardinals) behind. Around the endocardial lining there develops a coat of muscle fibers which later become striated to form the myocardium. Outside this is a lining of splanchnic mesoderm which forms the epicardium, continuous with the lining of a part of the coelom surrounding the heart, which will later be cut off by the septum transversum to form the pericardium. In this the heart is suspended for a short time by a dorsal and a ventral mesentery known respectively as the dorsal and ventral mesocardia.

The later history of the heart is one of growth and subdivision into special chambers. Because the local growth of the heart is limited by the anterior and posterior walls of the pericardium and by the mesocardia in which it is suspended, any extension in length must be accompanied by coiling. Experiments have shown that the coiling of the heart is due to intrinsic causes and not conditioned by the space at its disposal. The primary flexure of the heart is toward the right, thus changing the shape of the organ from a straight tube to a C-shaped one. Further growth results in the twisting of the heart into the shape of an S. Still later, the original posterior loop of the S is pushed forward and dorsad so that it comes to lie above the morphologically anterior end (Fig. 128).

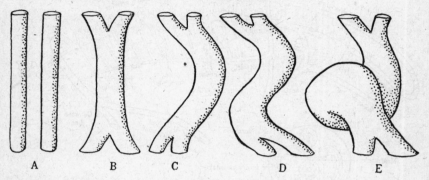

A   B   C   D   E

FIG. 128. Diagrams to show early stages in development of vertebrate heart *A*, paired heart tubes. *B*, same fused. *C*, primary flexure. *D*, later "S" stage. *E*, after anterodorsal displacement of atrium.

The original chambers of the heart are produced by local dilations, of which the most posterior is the sinus venosus; next to this is the atrium; in front of this, the ventricle; and finally, the bulbus arteriosus. The sinus is the chamber into which the primitive veins enter; the atrium is a thin-walled distensible chamber; the ventricle is a thick-walled, muscular, pulsating pump; and the bulbus is the chamber from which the blood enters the primitive arteries.

These chambers undergo different changes in the various types of vertebrates. Of these, the most important is a progressive differentiation, completed in the mammals and birds, of the atrium and ventricle into separate right and left halves, of which the right side receives venous blood from all parts of the body and transmits it to the lungs for respiratory exchange. From the lungs the blood is returned to the left side of the heart and thence conveyed to all parts of the body.

The arteries (Fig. 129). The ventral aortae fuse into a single median tube sending branches into each of the visceral arches. These branches, which unite with the dorsal aortae, are usually six in number and are known as the aortic arches. Anterior to these the ventral aortae continue forward as the external carotid arteries. Similar forward extensions of the dorsal aortae are known as the internal carotid arteries. In the region of the aortic arches the dorsal aortae remain separate as the aortic roots (radices aortae). Behind them, as has been mentioned, the paired vessels fuse as the median dorsal aorta.

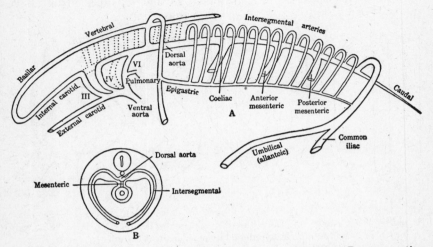

FIG. 129. Diagrams to show principal arteries; *A*, in side view, *B*, cross-section through mesenteric.

The aortic arches. In larvae breathing by means of external gills, a loop from each aortic arch grows out into the gill developing on the visceral arch with which it is associated. These loops are short-circuited when the external gills disappear.

In forms with internal gills, each aortic arch breaks up into capillaries in the demibranch and becomes divided into a ventral afferent branchial artery and a dorsal efferent branchial artery.

In vertebrates with a pulmonary respiration, aortic arches I and II, in the mandibular and hyoid arches, respectively, disappear. Arch III, in the first branchial arch, persists as the connection between the internal and external carotid arteries, while the dorsal aorta between arches III and IV disappears. Arch IV becomes the systemic arch connecting the dorsal and ventral aortae (Fig. 130*B*). In birds (Fig. 130*C*), the arch on the left side disappears; in mammals (Fig. 130*D*), that on the right degenerates. Arch V is greatly reduced and frequently disappears or has at most a vestigial and transitory existence. From arch VI the pulmonary arteries grow back to the lungs. The portion of the sixth arch distal to the pulmonary arteries is reduced in caliber and is known as the ductus arteriosus. It becomes occluded and degenerates in all the amniotes except some few reptiles.

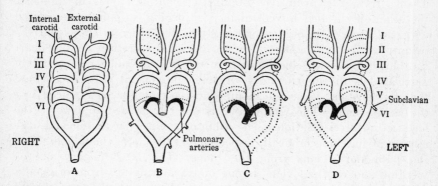

FIG. 130. Diagrams of aortic arches. *A*, hypothetical primitive type. *B*, in frog. *C*, in chick. *D*, in man. (After Kingsley.)

Intersegmental arteries. From the dorsal aortae are given off small branches between the myotomes (Fig. 129*B*). Some of these intersegmental arteries persist as the intervertebral arteries. The more anterior ones become united on either side by a dorsal longitudinal vertebral artery. These vertebrals subsequently fuse to form an anterior basilar artery which divides behind the pituitary, the two halves uniting with the internal carotid on either side. In the region where the anterior limb buds are developing, intersegmental arteries grow out, to give rise to the subclavian arteries. Similarly, in the region of the pelvic limb buds, intersegmental arteries give rise to the iliac arteries. In the amniota, the allantoic arteries grow out from the iliac arteries into the walls of the allantois. These become so important that for some time it appears as if the iliac arteries were derived from the allantoic instead of the reverse. These allantoic arteries, which degenerate at the time of birth, are known as the umbilical arteries in mammals, as they transverse the umbilical cord and supply the placenta.

Other important intersegmental arteries become the renal arteries of the kidneys and the genital arteries of the gonads.

Mesenteric arteries. From the dorsal aorta, a number of ventral branches, originally paired, but soon fused to become median vessels, pass down the dorsal mesentery. They unite with the capillaries of the yolk sac, which they supply with blood. Later, some of them develop branches over the alimentary canal which persist after the loss of the yolk sac as the coeliac and mesenteric arteries.

The veins. There are two primitive venous systems: the one arising from the primitive vitelline circulation (and, in amniota, the allantoic), which is ventral in position and originally associated with the embryonic organs of digestion; the other arising from the primitive cardinal veins, which are dorsal and return to the heart the blood which was distributed by the arteries and are intimately associated with the excretory organs. In general it may be said that the cardinal veins are modified to become (or be replaced by) the caval veins. The vitelline veins are reorganized to become the hepatic-portal circulation. The allantoic veins (or umbilicals) disappear at hatching or birth, respectively. To these should be added the pulmonary veins from the lungs. The later history of the vitelline and cardinal veins is one of transformation from originally paired vessels to more nearly axial ones. Eventually the systems become so related to the arteries that there is an accompanying vein for every artery.

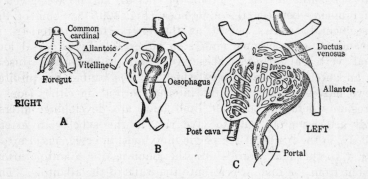

Fig. 131. Diagrams to show three stages in the development of the hepatic-portal venous system in man. (After Hochstetter.)

Hepatic-portal circulation. The vitelline (omphalo-mesenteric) veins are surrounded by the developing liver (Fig. 131), and within this organ the original channels are broken up into an intricate capillary network. The anterior portions of the veins extending from the liver to the heart become the hepatic veins. Posterior to the liver they are thereafter known as the portal veins. The manner in which the originally paired system becomes an axial one differs in the different groups of vertebrates and will be discussed in later paragraphs.

Caval circulation. The primitive cardinal veins are paired, and carry the blood from the head past the pronephric region into the sinus venosus of the heart. After the appearance of the posterior cardinals which join them at the anterior surface of the pronephros, the system has the form of a letter H (Fig. 132*A*). The upper limbs of the H are now known as the anterior cardinals. The cross-bar is represented by the common cardinals (Cuvierian ducts), and the lower limbs are the posterior cardinals. The anterior cardinals persist as the internal jugular veins of the adult. The common

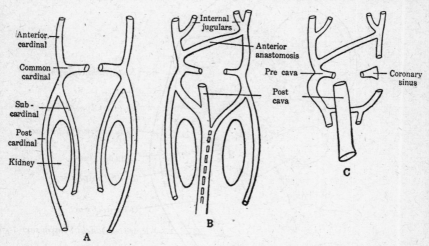

FIG. 132. Generalized diagram to show relationships of cardinal and caval veins.

cardinals unite, or one may degenerate, so that a single vessel, known as the precaval vein (anterior vena cava), from the anterior portion of the embryo enters the heart at the sinus venosus. The posterior cardinals lose their connection with the common cardinals and enter the heart through a new vessel, known as the postcaval vein (posterior vena cava), originating from the hepatics and subcardinals. The details, which differ in the different classes, will be described in later paragraphs. Meantime, it may be recalled that the cardinal veins of the embryo are associated with the excretory organs, from which they return blood to the heart. In some cases the posterior portions of these veins convey blood from the posterior region of the body to the mesonephros, in which case we may speak of a renal-portal circulation.

The pulmonary veins. These enter the left atrium and are new vessels which grow backward from the heart to the developing lungs.

The lymphatic system. This system serves to return to the veins the blood plasma which has escaped from the capillaries (Fig. 133). It contains white blood corpuscles of the ameboid type (lymphocytes), which have the power of making their way through the capillary walls. The lymphatics apparently originate as intercellular spaces in mesenchyme, which later become confluent and acquire a limiting endothelium. Like the blood vessels, the lymphatic

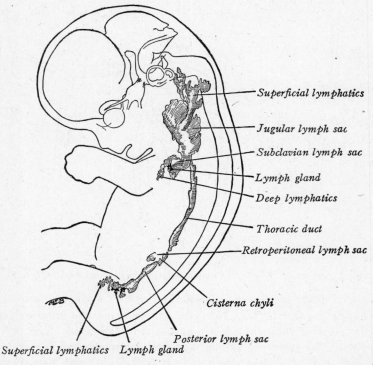

FIG. 133. Reconstruction of primitive lymphatic vessels in human fetus of two months. (From Arey after Sabin.)

capillaries anastomose and form larger vessels which drain into the veins. The walls of these central vessels are often muscular, and localized areas known as lymph hearts are found. So, too, there are localized distensible regions called lymph sacs. Some of these become lymph glands. The spleen, already alluded to in the section on mesenteries (page 157), is a hemolymph gland in which both lymphocytes and erythrocytes are proliferated during embryonic life.

THE FROG

Heart. The heart of the frog (Fig. 134) originates in stage **17** as a loose clump of cells proliferated from the dorsal side of the splanchnic layer of mesoderm at the point where the right and left sheets of lateral mesoderm come together. These cells organize themselves in the following stage into two small vesicles, which fuse shortly thereafter to form the endocardial lining of the heart. Meantime the splanchic layer itself has grown up around the heart as a fold on either side, the inner layer of the fold forming the epimyocardial

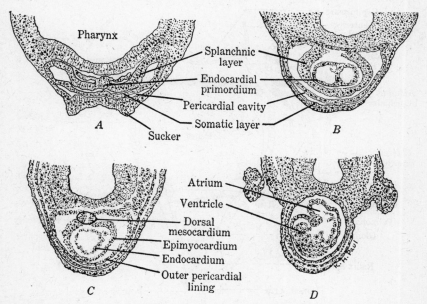

FIG. 134. Transverse sections to show origin of the heart in frog embryos (*Rana pipiens*). *A*, stage 17, *B*, stage 18, *C*, stage 19, *D*, stage 21. ×35.

wall of the heart, the outer giving rise to the outer lining of the pericardial chamber (page 158). Muscle cells appear in the myocardium, and the heart (Fig. 204) commences to beat in stage 19. The heart is at first a simple tube, but soon four regions are distinguishable. Commencing at the posterior end, we find first the sinus venosus, into which the meatus, formed by the fusion of the vitelline veins, enters. Then comes the thin-walled atrium (Fig. 210), continued by the muscular ventricle, which in turn opens into the bulbus arteriosus. This divides to give rise to the ventral aortae. The septum dividing the atrium into left and right atria, which receive blood from the lungs and the rest of the body respectively, is not formed until after hatching (stage 21).

Arteries. The origin of the aortic arches is difficult to distinguish in sectioned material, and these are first clearly indicated in stage 20 at the time when the circulation of the blood can be seen in the first gill bud (on the third visceral arch). Studies made with the aid of injected specimens indicate that the aortic arches arise as spaces in

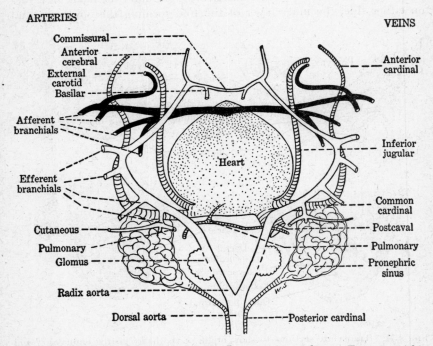

Fig. 135. Plan of circulation in 11-mm. *Rana pipiens* embryo. From a graphic reconstruction. Dorsal view.

the visceral arches. These spaces form ventral twigs (afferent branchial arteries) of the ventral aortae and dorsal twigs (efferent branchial arteries) of the dorsal aortae, respectively. In the gill buds these twigs unite to form capillary loops. Some writers have described an hyomandibular artery anterior to the afferent and efferent arteries of the third arch which courses through the second arch and supplies the first, but its homologies are still uncertain. Aortic loops arise in the third, fourth, fifth, and sixth visceral arches. After the appearance of the internal gills (Fig. 101), the ventral limb of each loop becomes the afferent branchial artery of its gill, while the dorsal limb becomes the efferent branchial. With the loss of branchial respiration, arch III becomes the proximal portion of the carotid arteries, arch IV the systemic arch which persists on both sides, and arch V disappears, while from arch VI arise vessels which carry blood to both the lungs (pulmonary arteries, Fig. 135) and skin (cutaneous arteries).

Veins. The vitelline veins anterior to the liver fuse to become the hepatic vein; posterior to the liver, the right vitelline vein disappears, the left becomes the hepatic-portal vein. The anterior cardinal veins become the internal jugular veins; the common cardinals become the precaval veins. The posterior cardinal veins fuse between the mesonephroi, and a new vein grows back from the hepatic vein to the right posterior cardinal, to form the postcaval vein. The posterior cardinals, anterior to their junction with the postcaval, degenerate. Posterior to this junction they persist as the renal-portal veins carrying blood from the iliac veins to the kidneys.

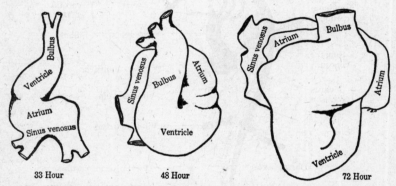

33 Hour   48 Hour   72 Hour

FIG. 136. Stages in the development of the heart of the chick, as shown in wax reconstructions from the ventral side.

THE CHICK

Heart. The chick's heart (Fig. 136) develops very much like the frog's, except that the paired primordia of the endocardium (Fig. 218) originate at a time while they are still separated by the open fore-gut (24 hours of incubation). Loose masses of cells migrate from the splanchnic layer of mesoderm on the side next the endoderm as in the frog (26–27 hours), form separate vesicles which are brought together on the ventral side of the fore-gut as the anterior intestinal portal moves back (27–28 hours), and finally fuse at 29 hours. The epimyocardium is also formed as in the frog. The heart tube formed in this manner bends to the right at 33 hours (Fig. 221), begins to beat at 44 hours, and has formed a right-handed coil at the end of the second day (Fig. 233).

The right and left halves of the heart are completely separated by three septa: the septum aorticopulmonale, which divides the bulbus into a chamber on the right leading to the pulmonary arteries and one to the left leading to the dorsal aorta; the interventricular septum, which divides the ventricle; and the interatrial septum, which divides the atrium into two atria. This separation is completed at the end of the first week of incubation. The sinus venosus is incorporated in the right **atrium**.

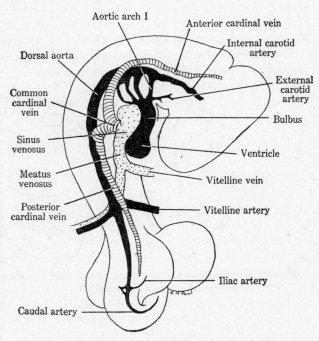

Aortic arch I
Anterior cardinal vein
Internal carotid artery
Dorsal aorta
External carotid artery
Common cardinal vein
Bulbus
Sinus venosus
Ventricle
Meatus venosus
Vitelline vein
Posterior cardinal vein
Vitelline artery
Iliac artery
Caudal artery

FIG. 137. Main blood vessels in the 72-hour chick.

Arteries. Six aortic arches are formed (Fig. 236): I and II disappear on the third and fourth days of incubation; III forms the proximal portion of the internal carotid artery; IV disappears on the left side but persists as the systemic arch on the right; V disappears; the pulmonary arteries arise from VI, but the distal portion of the right arch remains as the ductus arteriosus until the chick hatches (Fig. 130*C*).

The arteries of the head, internal and external carotids, arise as prolongations of the aortic roots and ventral aortae, respectively. The arteries of the body arise from intersegmental branches of the dorsal aorta. Up to the time of hatching the largest of these are the paired vitelline arteries, which return blood to the area vasculosa (Fig. 137).

Veins. The vitelline veins unite behind the sinus venosus to form the meatus venosus, which later becomes the hepatic vein. The portion of the meatus venosus surrounded by the liver breaks up into a capillary network within that organ. For a time the vitellines posterior to the liver serve as hepatic-portal veins. On the fifth day of incubation a small vessel arises in the dorsal mesentery and joins the vitellines, now united by several anastomoses. This vessel, the mesenteric vein, becomes the portal vein of the young chick, and the vitelline veins atrophy after hatching. The allantoic veins grow backward from the common cardinals to join the capillaries of the allantois; the right allantoic degenerates on the fourth day, and the left acquires a new connection with the meatus venosus, by way of the left hepatic vein. The allantoic vein degenerates at hatching. Two precaval veins are formed from the proximal portions of the anterior cardinals and common cardinals. The posterior cardinals at first return the blood from the mesonephroi to the heart. At the end of the third day of incubation a pair of veins, on the ventral sides of the mesonephroi appear to supplement them. These are the subcardinal veins. The postcaval vein arises from (1) a branch of the meatus venosus which grows back to meet the right subcardinal vein, (2) the fused subcardinals which carry blood from the mesonephros, and (3) the renal veins which develop in connection with the metanephros. The anterior sections of the posterior cardinals disappear, while the posterior sections, the renal-portal veins, carry blood to the mesonephros. After its degeneration, they join the common iliac veins, which pass directly to the postcaval vein.

MAN

Heart. The first primordium of the heart is a thickening of the splanchnic layer of mesoderm in front of the head fold. As the head fold and subsephalic pocket enlarge, this plate is carried underneath the fore-gut and lies on the dorsal side of the developing coelomic split (Fig. 138). Two converging tubes are formed from the cardiogenic thickening, and these later fuse, commencing at the anterior end. No ventral mesentery is formed. The heart loops to the right and forms a half coil so that the atrial limb lies dorsal to the ventricular limb. The subsequent partitioning of the heart into right and left halves is complicated, for two atrial septa are formed. The ventricle is separated by an interventricular septum, and the bulbus is divided

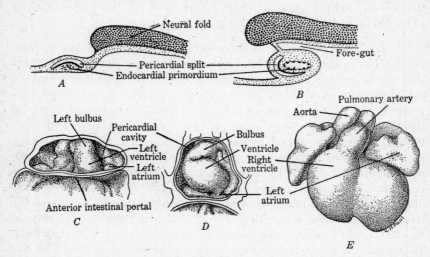

FIG. 138. Origin and development of the heart in human embryos. *A*, diagram of sagittal section before somite formation. *B*, same at 7-somite stage. (Both after Arey.) *C*, ventral view at 6-somite stage. *D*, same at 11-somite stage. (Both after Davis.) *E*, ventral view at 12-mm. stage (after Wirtinger).

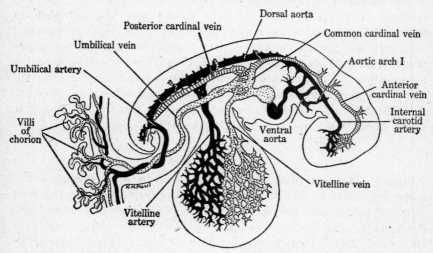

FIG. 139. Circulation in human embryo at end of the first month. (Diagram after Patten and Davis, modified.)

by two septa which unite to form a septum aorticopulmonale. The sinus venosus is incorporated in the right atrium, although the middle portion can be distinguished as the coronary sinus.

Arteries. The aortic arches are formed and have the same history as those of the chick, with the exception that it is the left fourth

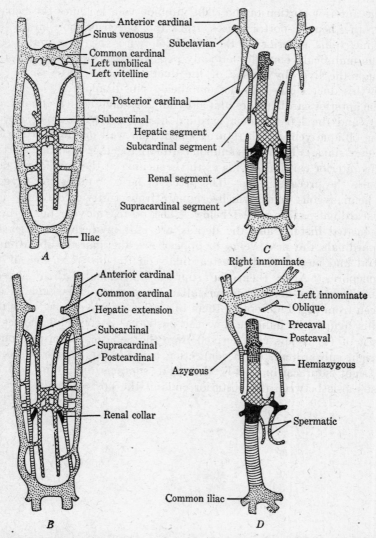

FIG. 140. Origin of caval veins in human development. *A*, 6 weeks. *B*, 7 weeks. *C*, 8 weeks. *D*, adult. (After McClure and Butler.)

aortic arch which becomes the systemic arch (Fig. 130D). The arteries of the body arise from dorsal, lateral, and ventral intersegmental branches of the dorsal aorta.

Veins. The umbilical veins are the first to appear, and after them the vitelline veins (Fig. 139). Both are enveloped by the enlarging liver.

The anterior portion of the right vitelline vein becomes the hepatic vein; the hepatic-portal arises from the posterior portion of the vitelline veins anterior to their junction with the mesenteric vein. Of the umbilical veins, the left only persists, with a direct connection through the liver by means of the ductus venosus (Fig. 252). At birth this duct closes and the umbilical vein disappears.

The anterior cardinals are united by an anastomosis (left innominate vein), and the left common cardinal disappears with the exception of the oblique vein which returns blood from wall of the heart to the coronary sinus. The right common cardinal, together with that portion of the anterior cardinal as far as the branching of the left innominate, becomes the precaval vein. The precaval later acquires the azygous and hemiazygous veins, which originate from posterior cardinals and supracardinals as described below. The postcaval vein has a more complicated history and the details are still in dispute. After the postcardinals the next veins to appear are the paired subcardinals, ventral and mesial to the postcardinals on the lower surface of the mesonephros. After them the supracardinals make their appearance. These are dorsal and mesial to the postcardinals, and, as can be seen from Fig. 140, replace them to a considerable degree. A study of this figure will indicate how the postcava of the adult comes to consist of (1) a new vein derived from the hepatic, (2) a portion of the right subcardinal, (3) a connection between the right subcardinal and right supracardinal, (4) the right supracardinal, and (5) an anastomosis between the posterior ends of the postcardinals.

CHAPTER 12

SKELETON

The skeleton of vertebrates consists of a system of supporting and protecting elements developed from mesenchyme. These elements pass through several conditions in later development. The primordia of the skeletal elements are preformed in connective tissue. These become transformed into cartilage, a process known as chondrification, through the activities of specialized cells, the chondrioblasts. Cartilage in turn is transformed into bone, through the action of osteoblasts, the process being known as ossification. Bones that pass through these three stages are known as cartilage bones. In the formation of some bones, the cartilaginous stage is omitted; they are known as membrane bones. Both cartilage and bone are typically surrounded by a membrane of mesenchyme, which is called the perichondrium or periosteum, as the case may be. The separate elements of the skeleton are connected with each other by ligaments, by cartilage, or in a bony union.

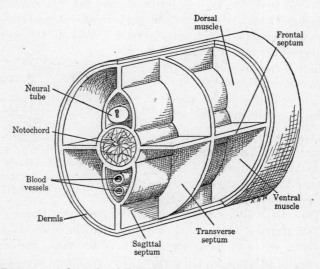

FIG. 141. Diagram to show the skeleton-forming regions as seen in the tail region of a vertebrate. (After Kingsley.)

199

Skeletogenous regions. The principal regions where skeleton may be formed in the vertebrate body (Fig. 141) are (1) the dermis of the skin, (2) the median sagittal planes between the myotomes on the right and left sides of the body, (3) the right and left frontal planes between the dorsal and ventral muscle masses, (4) the transverse planes between the myotomes, (5) around the notochord, neural tube, and axial blood vessels, (6) in the visceral arches, and (7) in the paired appendages. Skeletal elements formed in (1) are called the dermal skeleton; those formed in (2) to (5), the axial skeleton; those formed in (6), the visceral skeleton; and those formed in (7), the appendicular skeleton. The skull contains elements from all but the appendicular skeleton.

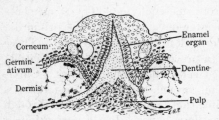

FIG. 142. Section of developing placoid scale (*Squalus acanthias*) to show origin of primitive dermal bone. Compare Fig. 93. (After Kingsley.)

The dermal skeleton. Among living vertebrates the most primitive example of derm bones is the placoid scales (Fig. 142) of the cartilage fish, which are formed in exactly the same way as teeth (Chapter 8). In the dermal skeleton two types of bones are distinguished. The investing bones (dermal plates) serve to envelop regions of the head and trunk. The substituting bones become so closely allied with the cartilaginous bones as to become fused with them or even to replace them in ontogeny. Many of the cranial bones are of this type. They may be distinguished by the fact that they do not pass through a cartilaginous stage in development.

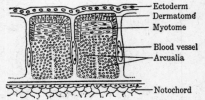

FIG. 143. Section through sclerotome of lizard (*Scleporus*) to show arcualia. (After Kingsley.)

The axial skeleton. The primitive axial skeleton is the notochord, whose origin has been discussed in Chapter 5. Around this a connective tissue sheath is formed by mesenchymal cells. The mesenchyme from each sclerotome now forms four little blocks, the arcualia (Fig. 143), two dorsal to the notochord and two ventral, from which the arches and centra of the vertebrae are formed, as well as the primordia of the ribs. The posterior arcualia of each somite unite with the anterior arcualia of the succeeding somite to form the definitive vertebra, which thus comes to lie at the point of separation between two myotomes. Eight elements are thus concerned with a single vertebra: right and left dorsal arcualia from the anterior half sclerotome, and from the posterior half sclerotome; and the corresponding ventral elements.

The vertebrae. In the prevertebral masses so formed appear centers of chondrification, one on each side of the spinal cord and one or more below the cord. These form, respectively, the neural arch and the centrum of the vertebrae, (Fig. 144). In the tail region, two centers of chondrification arise below the centrum, enclosing

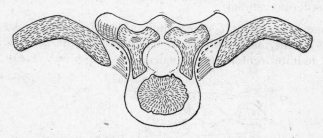

FIG. 144. Section to show ossification centers in human vertebra and ribs. (After Kollman.)

the caudal prolongation of the dorsal aorta, and form a hemal arch. With the chondrification of the vertebrae the notochord disappears in all but the most primitive vertebrates, persisting only between the vertebrae as nuclei pulposi of the intervertebral discs. Finally the vertebrae become ossified, and the spines, zygapophyses, and other differentiations are developed.

The ribs. Except in the caudal region, lateral processes arise from the vertebral primordia and grow out into the myosepta. They later become cartilaginous, and finally true bone. These are the ribs, of which there are two types, dorsal and ventral, distinguished according to the part of the vertebra from which they originate.

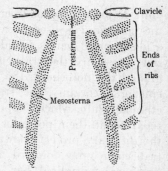

FIG. 145. Diagram to show origin of mammalian sternum. (After Kingsley.)

The sternum. The sternum, or breast bone, arises in the amphibians from the coalescence of two longitudinal bars of cartilage, which later articulate with the coracoids of the pectoral girdle, but do not come in contact with the ribs. In the amniota, the sternum arises from the fusion of the ventral ends of the anterior rib rudiments. In this way there arise two longitudinal bars, from which the unpaired sternum is formed by fusion along the mesial line (Fig. 145).

The skull. The skull is a complex of skeletal elements, arising from the chondrocranium, or primitive cranium of cartilage bones, which is derived in part from the protective covering of the brain and sense organs (neurocranium), and in part from the supporting elements of the visceral arches (splanchnocranium). This is supplemented by numerous investing and substituting bones from the original dermal skeleton (dermocranium).

Neurocranium. The neurocranium arises from the head mesenchyme. In this mass, which completely invests the brain and sense organs, definite centers of chondrification appear. These masses

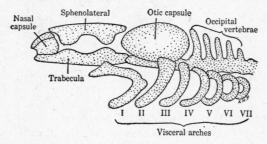

Fig. 146. Diagram showing components of chondrocranium (*Squalus acanthias*). (After Kingsley.)

unite to form the chondrocranium of the cartilage fish (Fig. 146). If the notochord is used as a point of orientation, on either side of it a parachordal bar is found. In front of each of these is a separate rod; these are the trabeculae. Between the two parachordals and around the notochord, the basilar plate arises as the support of the epichordal brain. The trabeculae also fuse in front to form the ethmoid plate, which supports the prechordal brain, but they remain separate at their posterior ends to form an opening through which the pituitary projects downward. In front of the ethmoid plate the trabeculae grow forward as the cornua. Dorsal to each trabecula, another longitudinal bar, the sphenolateral, arises. Between these two bars the cranial nerves make their way to the exterior.

Around each of the major sense organs a cartilaginous capsule develops. The olfactory capsules unite with the cornua, ethmoid, and sphenolaterals. The optic capsule rarely develops fully, usually persisting in the connective-tissue stage as the sclera of the eyeball.

The otic capsule, however, becomes completely chondrified and unites with the parachordals and the sphenolaterals. Between the two otic capsules and sphenolaterals arises a dorsal plate which forms a roof for the brain. In the amniotes, one or more neck vertebrae are consolidated with the occipital region.

The splanchnocranium. The digestive canal in the head region consists of the mouth, oral cavity, and pharynx, the walls of the pharynx being penetrated by the visceral clefts. There is no coelom here and the lateral mesoderm is not divided. Supplemented by mesenchyme from the neural crest it is divided into cartilaginous bars supporting the wall of this part of the body. These visceral arches are the mandibular, hyoid, and four (or more) branchial arches. The mandibular arch divides into dorsal and ventral portions, of which the dorsal portion becomes the pterygoquadrate cartilage (upper jaw of cartilage fish) while the ventral portion becomes the meckelian cartilage (lower jaw). The hyoid arch divides into a dorsal hyomandibular cartilage and a ventral hyoid cartilage which is usually divided into several centers of chondrification. The hyomandibular acts as a suspensory element for the jaws in the fish. It is homologized with a bone of the middle ear, the columella, in amphibians, and the stapes of mammals (see page 241). The hyoid becomes the support of the tongue. The branchial arches are usually divided into four parts and act as gill supports in the anamniota. They disappear or become pharyngeal and laryngeal cartilages in amniota.

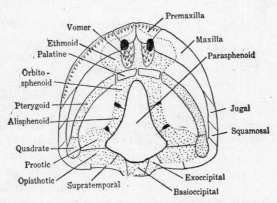

FIG. 147. Diagram showing components of vertebrate skull, generalized. Ventral view. Chondrocranium stippled, dermal elements in outline. (After Kingsley.)

Ossification of the chondrocranium. The limits of this book will not permit of an enumeration of all the bones formed from the chondrocranium (Figs. 147, 148, 149). They may be grouped, however, as follows: (1) the occipitals, formed from the occipital vertebrae; (2) the sphenoids, arising from the parachordals, basilar plate, tra-

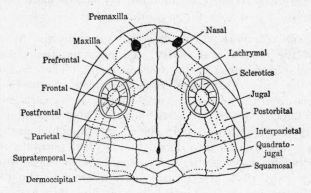

FIG. 148. Dorsal view of skull diagrammed in Fig. 147.

beculae, and sphenolaterals; (3) the ethmoids, from the ethmoid plate and nasal capsule; (4) the otics, from the otic capsule. The ptery-goquadrate bar gives rise to the pterygoid bones and the quadrate (which in mammals becomes the incus of the middle ear). The meckelian cartilage gives rise to the articular bone at its proximal end. This becomes the malleus, an-other ear bone, of the mammals. The remainder of the meckelian persists as cartilage. In the hyoids and the branchials, bones are formed which retain the names of their cartilaginous predecessors.

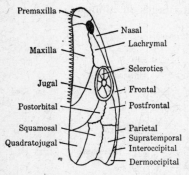

FIG. 149. Lateral view of skull diagrammed in Figs. 147, 148.

The dermocranium (Figs. 147, 148, 149). The derm bones which invest and, to some extent, supplant the ele-ments of the chondrocranium are too numerous to be more than mentioned here. The dorsal derm bones are, from front to rear, the nasals, frontals, and parietals, together with a number of smaller bones which appear in variable quantity in the different classes. The principal lateral elements, from front to rear, are the premaxillae, maxillae, jugals, quadratojugals, and squamosals. The floor of the chondrocranium is invested by the parasphenoids, palatines, and vomer. The lower

CHAPTER 13

MUSCLES

The musculature of the vertebrate is derived from mesenchyme (Fig. 151), of which the greater part originates from the myotomes and gives rise to striated muscle cells, controlled by the central nervous system, the skeletal musculature. A portion, however, originates from splanchnic mesoderm and gives rise to non-striated (smooth) muscle cells found in the skin, surrounding the alimentary canal,

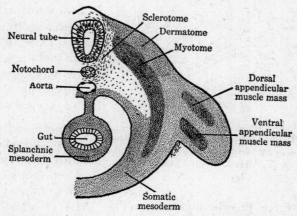

FIG. 151. Diagram of transverse section through vertebrate embryo in region of limb bud, to show origin of appendicular muscles. (After Corning.)

blood vessels, and the urogenital organs. They are controlled by the sympathetic nervous system (page 229) and make up the visceral musculature. Several exceptions to these general statements should be noted. The muscle cells of the heart are striated; the muscles derived from the visceral arches are both striated and controlled by the central nervous system, although derived from head mesenchyme. It will be noted later that the muscles of the iris of the eye (page 239) and of the sweat glands (page 215) are apparently ectodermal in origin.

Dermal musculature. Attached to the skin are striped muscles which are derived from skeletal musculature (see below) but have lost their attachment to the skeleton. The dermal musculature is best

developed in the amniotes. The muscles of expression in man are
dermal muscles supplied by the seventh cranial nerve (see Chapter 15).

Axial musculature. In this section are included all the muscles
arising from the myotomes and attached to parts of the axial skeleton,
which they move. They are originally metameric, but their later
history is obscured by subsequent migration, fusion, splitting, budding,
and degeneration. The intercostals, between the ribs, however,
preserve their original metamerism, which in the others may be traced
to some extent by the inner-
vation, since the connection
between a spinal nerve and
the muscle mass it supplies
is established early in organogeny and remains con-
stant. Thus it can be
shown that the musculature
of the diaphragm, supplied
by the phrenic nerve, arises
from a cervical myotome.

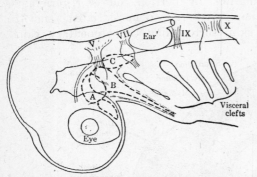

FIG. 152. Head of embryo dogfish (*Squalus
acanthias*), showing preotic somites (*A, B, C*) and
cranial nerves (V, VII, IX, X). (After Kingsley.)

Cranial muscles. Like the
cranium, the muscles as-
sociated with it are derived
from different sources. The
muscles of the eyeball arise
from the three preotic myotomes (Fig. 152), of which the first
forms all the muscles of the eyeball except the superior oblique,
derived from the second myotome, and the lateral rectus, derived
from the third head myotome. These are innervated by the third,
fourth, and sixth cranial nerves, respectively. The tongue muscu-

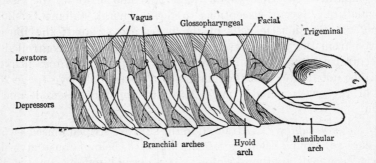

FIG. 153. Diagram to show hypothetical relationship of branchiomeric muscles to
visceral arches and cranial nerves. (After Wilder.)

lature is derived from the myotomes associated with the occipital vertebrae and supplied by the twelfth cranial nerve. The muscles of mastication, the facial muscle, and the laryngeal muscles, together with those of the ear bones, arise from the visceral arches (Fig. 153), and are supplied by cranial nerves V, VII, IX, X, and XI (see Chapter 15). These muscles can probably be traced back to head mesenchyme rather than splanchnic mesoderm as formerly assumed.

Appendicular muscles. It was formerly held that the appendicular muscles arose from processes proceeding from the myotomes in the neighborhood of the limb bud. This has been denied in the case of birds and mammals, and studies made in the author's laboratory

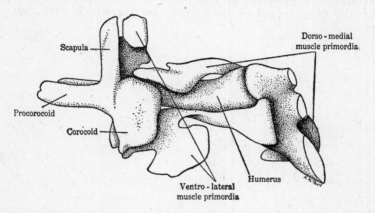

FIG. 154. Reconstruction of the pectoral muscle masses in a 17-mm. *Necturus*, prepared by H. F. DeBruine.

(Chen, 1935) on the development of the pectoral limb of *Necturus* indicate that even in the amphibia the appendicular muscles develop *in situ* from somatic mesoderm.

The limb bud develops as an undifferentiated mass of mesenchyme surrounded by ectoderm. In this blastemal mass, muscles and bones are laid down, the differentation proceeding from the proximal toward the distal end. The pectoral muscles differentiate before those of the pelvic appendage. The appendicular muscles are found in antagonistic groups: protractors, which move the limb forward; and retractors, which have the opposite effect; levators, which raise the limb; and depressors, which contract in the opposite direction. Like the axial muscles, these have become highly modified and specialized among the tetrapods (Fig. 154).

Visceral muscles. Under this head are included the muscles lining the alimentary tract, lungs, vascular organs, and urogenital system. All arise in the splanchnic mesoderm which surrounds the endothelial lining of the organs concerned.

Heart. The muscle of the heart arises as a network of smooth muscle fibers which later become striated. The fibers early become connected by protoplasmic processes to form a syncytium. It is interesting in this connection that the smooth muscle cells of the bladder of the dog have been transformed into what are apparently striated muscles when this organ is made to pulsate rhythmically by continued irrigation.

NOTE. The study of comparative myogeny has not arrived at the stage where it would be profitable to summarize our information about the development of the muscles in frog, chick, and man.

Chapter 14

INTEGUMENT

The integument consists of two parts, the ectodermal epidermis and the mesodermal dermis (corium). The epidermis soon delaminates into two layers, the deeper germinativum, from which new strata are proliferated towards the exterior, and an outer periderm or embryonic skin (Fig. 155). Beneath the periderm, cells derived

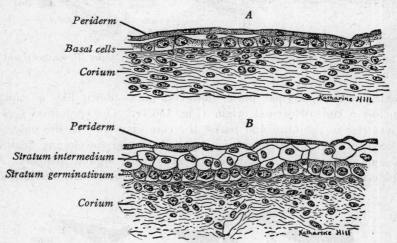

Fig. 155. Sections through human fetal skin. *A*, neck. *B*, chin. (From Arey after Prentiss.)

from the germinativum are transformed into a horny layer, the corneum. The underlying dermis is essentially a supporting layer of mesenchyme cells. It has generally been believed that the dermis was derived from the so-called dermatome, the most lateral region of the primitive somite. This idea has been questioned, however, and some investigators hold that the dermis originates from the somatic layer of the mesoderm, at least in part. In the dermis are formed blood vessels, connective tissue, bone, and muscle. The bony scales of fish are dermal in origin.

The corneum. It is this layer which gives rise to such horny derivatives as scales, feathers, and hair. Scales originate from regions of local growth in the corneum (Fig. 156A). They are found only among the amniota, where they are represented by structures (Fig. 156A), such as the scales of reptiles, or those found on the legs of birds, the tails of rats, etc. Among the birds, scales are largely replaced by feathers which originate in much the same manner as

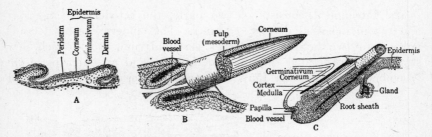

FIG. 156. Diagrams showing similar development in A, scale; B, feather; and C, hair. (After Kingsley.)

scales. The epidermal plate, however, grows down like a cup to enclose a core of dermal origin (Fig. 156B). The epidermal sheath gives rise to the quill and barbs, the core gives rise to the pulp, by means of which nutriment is supplied to the developing feather. Among the mammals, hair arises in a very similar fashion. An epidermal plate grows down into the dermis to form the hair bulb,

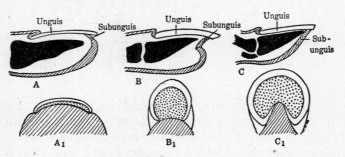

FIG. 157. Diagrams to show ectodermal primordia of A, nail, B, claw, and C, hoof. Above in sagittal sections; below ventral view. (After Kingsley.)

the proximal end of which invaginates to receive a mesodermal core, the hair papilla, while around the whole is a mesodermal hair sheath (Fig. 156C). The hair papilla, however, does not grow out into the center of the hair as does the pulp of the feather. Claws, nails, and hoofs arise from the union of two epidermal primordia like those of scales, a dorsal unguis and a ventral subunguis (Fig. 157).

The germinativum. The germinativum, in addition to producing the more superficial layers of the epidermis, gives rise to the glands of the skin (Fig. 158). Among the anamniotes, these glands are usually unicellular and produce the mucus which serves to diminish the friction of the skin against the water while swimming. Unicellular glands frequently aggregate to produce multicellular glands, such as the suckers or cement glands of the frog. The sebaceous (oil) and sudoriparous (sweat) glands of the mammals are also multicellular glands. The sebaceous glands are usually associated with hair follicles (Fig. 156C). The mammary glands of mammals are modified sudoriparous glands secreting the milk by which the new born are nourished through infancy.

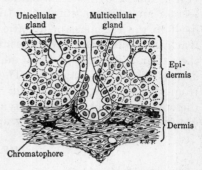

FIG. 158. Section of *Protopterus* skin to show glands. (After Kingsley.)

The dermis. Two types of pigmentation are to be distinguished in the integument. The first is produced by pigment secreted in the ectodermal epidermis, i.e., the melanin, of the frog tadpole. The second is produced by chromatophores, which are mesenchyme cells of the dermis or neural crest. These secrete pigment granules and form a layer immediately below the epidermis, some even wandering into the epidermis itself.

THE FROG

The epidermis of the frog develops cilia in stage 15 when the rotation of the embryo in its egg envelopes begins. These cilia are borne only on a particular type of rather large cell with clear protoplasm which is easily recognized. The rotation seen during gastrulation is probably due to the shifting of the center of gravity as the yolk mass is displaced. As development proceeds, the cilia disappear except on the tail, to which they are limited in stage 25. The jaws (Fig. 210) and oral combs of the tadpole are derivatives of the corneum and consist of rows of horny denticles forming replacement series. Cornification commences in stage 24. Lieberkind (1937), in a monograph on the amphibian adhesive organs, distinguishes two types of origin for the anuran oral sucker or cement gland, according to whether the suckers arise from one primordium or two. He set up also eight stages in its development which fit well with the stages observed in *Rana pipiens*. It appears first as a pigmented area in the epidermis on the ventral side of the head at stage 14. The epidermal cells thicken and form two U-shaped glands (Figs. 199, 205), one on either side of the stomodeal pit. They secrete an adhesive substance (mucus) by which the larva attaches itself to the egg mass or aquatic plants after hatching. The suckers reach their maximum development in stage 20, and begin to degenerate thereafter. The site of these glands is marked only by a pigmented area (Fig. 211) in stage 25. The pigmentation of the skin is derived from two sources, the melanin of the egg which is distributed to the epidermis, and the mesenchymal chromatophores (Fig. 214) which are found in the dermis. They appear for the first time in stage 21.

THE CHICK

The scales on the legs are typical reptilian scales and are derived from the corneum; they sometimes bear feathers in the young bird and so form a transition between scales and the characteristic avian feathers. The claws arise in the corneum from two primordia, a dorsal " claw plate " and a softer " claw sole." To prevent the sharp claws tearing the embryonic membranes, the concavity of the claw is filled with a pad known as the neonychium, derived from the corneum, which is lost after hatching. The beak arises from the corneum around the upper and lower margins of the jaws. The egg tooth is a horny prominence on the dorsal side of the upper jaw, appearing on the sixth day of incubation but not taking on its ultimate shape until the fourteenth. It serves to aid in breaking the shell and is lost after hatching.

MAN

The nails arise from nail plates and sole plates, of which the latter are rudimentary structures. They are covered during fetal life by the eponychium, consisting of the periderm and outer layers of the corneum. The hairs are arranged in patterns which have been interpreted as reminiscences of the ancestral scales. The first growth of hair is called the lanugo; it is cast off, except over the face, soon after birth. The mammary glands arise from two longitudinal thickenings of the epidermis, known as the milk ridge. In later development the gland resembles an aggregation of sudoriparous glands.

CHAPTER 15

NERVOUS SYSTEM

In the adult vertebrate the nervous system consists of the brain and spinal cord (central nervous system), their nerves (peripheral nervous system), and a semi-independent system of nerves and ganglia (sympathetic nervous system). Functionally these structures are associated with the sense organs on the one hand (receptors) and muscles or glands on the other (effectors). From the developmental point of view, the development of the nervous system is inextricably associated with some of the more concentrated sense organs, such as the nose, eye, ear, and lateral line system (when present).

Both the nervous system and the sense organs arise from specialized regions of the dorsal ectoderm, known respectively as the neural plate and the sense plates (placodes). Both the neural plate and the sensory placodes withdraw from the surface and become sub-epidermal by a process of invagination. In this connection it is interesting to note that the optic placode is incorporated into, and invaginates with, the neural plate so that, when the retina of the eye develops, it does so from the brain.

Neural tube. The origin of the neural tube is from the neural plate, which, as we have already seen (page 89), arises from cells which can be identified in the blastula stage, if not earlier. It will be remembered that this area lies next to the area of the presumptive chorda-mesoderm (Figs. 55, 62). It will be shown later (Chapter 17) that the presence of the chorda-mesoderm underneath the neural plate is necessary to bring about the formation of the neural tube. The method by which the tube is formed has been described in Chapter 5. The cavity of the tube remains open as the cerebrospinal canal. Its walls give rise to the brain and spinal cord.

Neural crest. When the neural folds meet in the midline to produce the neural tube (Fig. 159), the strip where they unite lies between the epidermis and the tube. This strip is the neural crest. It later divides into two strips, one on either side of the neural tube. The strips fragment to become the cerebrospinal ganglia, and from them move loose aggregates of cells which take part in the formation of the sympathetic ganglia, the suprarenal gland, and, in the amphibia, head mesenchyme, the visceral skeleton, and pigment.

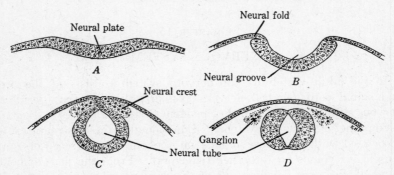

FIG. 159.   Diagrams to show origin of neural tube and crest.   *A*, neural plate.   *B*, neural groove and folds.   *C*, neural folds in contact.   *D*, neural tube.

Sensory placodes.   While these plates give rise mainly to sensory organs, they contribute also cells which are incorporated in cerebral and sometimes spinal ganglia.

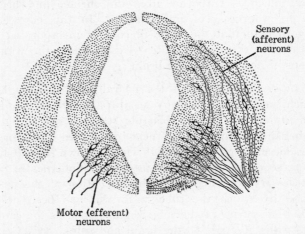

FIG. 160.   Diagrammatic section of neural tube and ganglia, to show origin of afferent and efferent neurons.

The neurons.   The inner lining of the neural tube, corresponding to the outer layer of the neural plate, is called the ependyma.   This is the center of cell proliferation.   Two types of cells are formed: the supporting cells, or spongioblasts; and the embryonic nerve cells, or neuroblasts (Fig. 160).   The neuroblasts migrate out of the ependyma and form an intermediate mantle layer in which they become transformed into neurons. These nerve elements have a prolongation at one end known as the axon or nerve fiber; at the other end are branched projections called dendrites. The axons grow out from the mantle layer into the outer layer of the cord, known as the marginal layer, where the medullary (myelin) sheaths which act as insulating coats are formed. Not all axons become medullated. In the ganglia, meantime, neurons and supporting cells are differentiated. These ganglionic neurons are bipolar, i.e., have two axons.

The bipolar neurons arising in the ganglia are sensory in nature, for they send out one process to a receptor, the other to the dorsolateral angle of the neural tube. They are also afferent, for the nervous impulses which they convey run from the receptor to the central nervous system. Some of the neurons originating in the tube itself send out their axons from the ventrolateral angle to some effector, and are therefore known as motor. They are efferent, for they convey nervous impulses from the central nervous system to the effector with which they are connected. The other neurons lie wholly within the walls of the tube and serve to connect afferent and efferent neurons.

The spinal cord. The spinal cord, or neural tube exclusive of the brain, retains its primitive characteristics. The cavity, or neurocoel, persists as the central canal. Between each pair of vertebrae the afferent and efferent neurons form a pair of spinal nerves which run out into the myotomes and hence have a metamerism equivalent to that of the myotomes, an important point in considering the homologies of the muscles. In the region of the pectoral and pelvic appendages, several of the segmental nerves combine to form the brachial and the sacral plexus, respectively. The development of the nerves will be taken up in a later section. The cord becomes surrounded by an envelope of mesenchyme known as the meninx, which in the higher vertebrates becomes divided into an inner pia mater and an outer dura mater.

In cross-section it can be seen that the spinal cord possesses an ependyma, mantle layer, and marginal layer. The roof and floor of the tube remain comparatively thin, but a multiplication of neurons in the dorsal and ventral angles of either side lead to a distinction between a dorsolateral alar plate (Fig. 161) (to which the afferent neurons send their axons) and a ventrolateral basal plate (from which the axons of the efferent neurons extend). Between the alar and basal plates there is a groove on the inner wall of each side. This is the sulcus limitans. In the marginal layers are the bundles of axons. Those on the dorsal side are from afferent neurons. Those of the lateral and ventral region serve to connect different regions of the cord itself or to connect these regions with the brain.

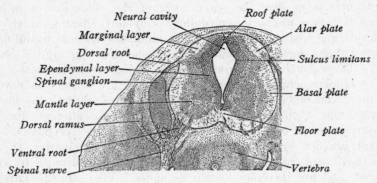

FIG. 161. Transverse section of human spinal cord at 6 weeks. ×30. (From Arey after Prentiss.)

The brain. In all vertebrate embryos the brain arises as a dilation at the anterior end of the neural tube, and here the neural folds come together earlier than in the cord. The first means of distinguishing

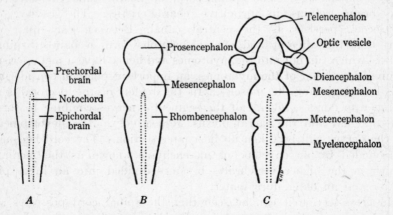

FIG. 162. Diagram to show origin of main divisions of the brain. *A*, before appearance of vesicles. *B*, at the three-vesicle stage. *C*, at the five-vesicle stage.

the parts of the brain is found in the relationship between brain and notochord. As the brain extends farther forward than the notochord, it consists at first of a prechordal and an epichordal portion (Fig. 162*A*). The prechordal portion soon bends ventrally around the tip of the notochord, thus giving rise to the first or cranial flexure. Three regions of local dilation (primary vesicles) now make their appearance (Fig. 162B). In the prechordal portion there is the fore-brain or prosencephalon; in the region of the cranial flexure, there is the mid-brain or mesencephalon. The hind-brain or rhombencephalon arises in the epichordal region. The primary vesicles are soon converted into the five definitive vesicles (Fig. 162C) through the

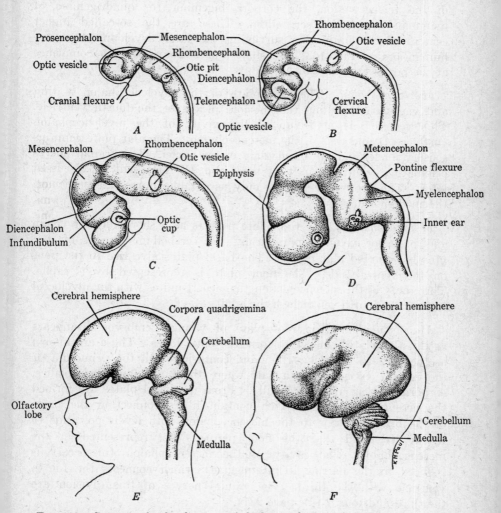

Fig. 163. Stages in the development of the human brain. *A*, 3-mm. embryo. *B*, 4-mm. embryo. *C*, 8-mm. embryo. *D*, embryo at 7 weeks. *E*, fetus of 3 months. *F*, fetus at 6 months. (*A–E* after Patten, *F* after Kollmann.)

division of the prosencephalon into the anterior telencephalon and posterior diencephalon, and through a similar division of the rhombencephalon into the anterior metencephalon and posterior myelencephalon which merges into the spinal cord.

Within the brain itself local aggregates of neurons form nuclei, either sensory or motor in function. Furthermore, on the dorsal surface there are three great enlargements, the cerebral hemispheres of the telencephalon, the corpora bigemina (or quadrigemina of mammals), and the cerebellum. These are the so-called higher centers of the brain. In surveying the later development of the human brain (Fig. 163), we shall find it convenient to commence at the posterior end.

Myelencephalon. The roof plate of the myelencephalon is thin and vascular, becoming the chorioid plexus of the fourth ventricle. This ventricle is made up of the cavity of the myelencephalon (myelocoel) and that of the metencephalon. The alar plate contains sensory nuclei and the basal plate motor nuclei. The cranial nerves originating from this part of the brain (V-XII) will be discussed later. The floor plate persists only as a raphe immediately beneath the median sulcus.

Metencephalon. The roof plate persists as a short anterior velum and posterior velum separated by the cerebellum formed by the greatly enlarged alar plates. The basal plates give rise to the pons on the ventral side. The floor plate is represented by a raphe. The cavity of the metencephalon (metacoel) unites with the myelocoel to form the fourth ventricle of the adult.

Mesencephalon. The roof plate of younger embryos disappears as the alar plates enlarge to form the optic lobes. These are known as the corpora bigemina (to avoid confusion with the primordia of the retina) except in mammals where there are four such bodies, corpora quadrigemina (colliculi). From the basal plates are formed the cerebral peduncles, which contain fibers connecting the parts of the brain anterior to the mesencephalon with levels posterior to it. It is stated that the floor plate is not represented in the mesencephalon. The cavity of the mesencephalon (mesocoel) is reduced to the narrow iter (aqueduct) which connects the fourth ventricle with the third. The cranial nerves of this division are the third and fourth (see page 227).

Diencephalon. This section of the brain has a thin roof plate which becomes the choroid plexus of the third ventricle, a name applied to the diacoel in the adult. No basal or floor plates exist, according to the latest investigations, so that the sides and floor of the diencephalon are formed by the alar plates. The most dorsal division of each alar plate is the epithalamus. In the posterior part of the diencephalon the epithalami on either side unite in the midline and give rise to an evagination known as the epiphysis. This becomes the pineal gland of the adult, presumably endocrine, but of unknown functions. It is not to be confused with the paraphysis, which in the lower vertebrates sometimes gives rise to a rudimentary or vestigial parietal or median eye. Ventral to the epithalamus on either side is the thalamus, separated by the thalamic sulci from the hypothalamus below. The hypothalamus forms the floor of the diencephalon. In this region, commencing at the posterior end and extending forward, are the following structures: a pair of mammillary bodies, a median swelling called the tuber cinereum, a depression known as the infundibulum to which the hypophyseal pouch (page 138) attaches itself, the optic chiasma arising from the crossing of the optic nerves, and, most anterior of all, the stalks of the optic vesicles from which the eyes arise (page 238). The thalami of the diencephalon contain many nuclei, including those which receive the afferent impulses from the optic nerves (II) and transmit impulses from one part of the brain to another.

Telencephalon. Like the diencephalon, this part of the brain is constructed solely from roof and alar plates. In the posterior part of the telencephalon the roof plate unites with that of the diencephalon to form the choroid plexus of the third ventricle. More anteriorly it is lost in the expansion of the alar plates. These give rise to three divisions of the telencephalon. Lowest is the corpus striatum continuous with the thalamus. Anterior and dorsal to the corpora striata come the olfactory lobes (rhinencephalon, archipallium) which receive the first cranial nerves. The rest of the sides and roof become the cerebral hemispheres (neopallium). These parts of the brain are distinguished by the movement of neuroblasts through the white medullated layer to form a thin superficial layer of neurons, the cortex of the cerebrum. The evagination of the cerebral hemispheres gives rise to two cavities (lateral ventricles).

Spinal nerves. It has been stated on an earlier page that, in addition to the neurons whose axons lie wholly within the brain and cord (Fig. 164), there exists afferent neurons whose cell bodies lie in the spinal ganglia and efferent neurons whose bodies lie in the cord itself. Both these groups may be subdivided further. Thus

there are two types of afferent neurons: the somatic afferent neurons
of the general type which convey impulses originating in the skin,
and visceral (splanchnic) afferent neurons of the general type which
convey impulses originating in the viscera. There are also special
types of both somatic and visceral afferent neurons which are found
only in the cranial nerves. The efferent neurons also fall into two

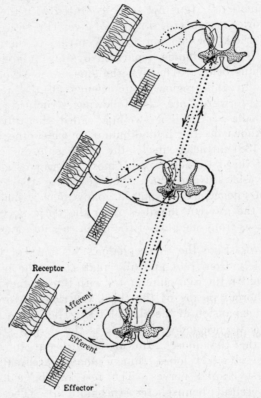

Receptor

Afferent

Efferent

Effector

FIG. 164. Diagram to show sections of the spinal cord at three different levels
with pathways of communicating neurons indicated by dotted lines.

groups, the somatic efferent neurons which stimulate skeletal (striped)
muscles and the visceral (splanchnic) efferent neurons which stimulate
smooth muscles and glands. Special efferent neurons are found in
the cranial nerves supplying the branchiomeric musculature.

The nerves are segmentally arranged bundles of afferent and
efferent neurons originally associated with the myotomes. The
afferent neurons arise in the ganglia, the efferent in the floor of the

spinal cord. Accordingly, a typical spinal nerve (Fig. 165) has two roots in the cord; a dorsal afferent root containing the ganglion, and a ventral efferent root which unites with the dorsal root to form the nerve trunk. The trunk soon divides into branches, each containing afferent and efferent neurons. These are called rami and supply the body wall, although one (the communicating ramus) connects with a sympathetic ganglion, derived from a spinal ganglion, through which the visceral afferent and efferent neurons serve the viscera.

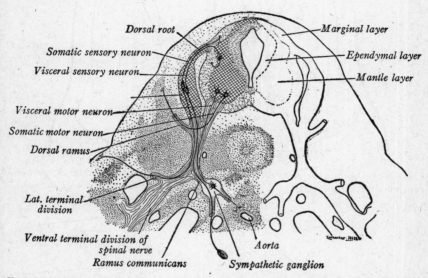

FIG. 165. Diagram to show the neuron components of a spinal nerve. Transverse section of 10-mm. human embryo. (From Arey after Prentiss.)

Origin of reflexes. It has been shown by Coghill that the development of behavior is closely paralleled by the development of the connections (synapses) between the neurons. Thus in the urodele, *Ambystoma,* the first reflex of the embryo, a bending away from a light touch on the skin, does not take place until an intermediate neuron in the spinal cord has established synaptic relations with the sensory tract on one hand and a floor plate cell which already has established a synaptic relation to the motor tract on the opposite side of the spinal cord (Fig. 166).

The cranial nerves. The cranial nerves, or nerves of the head region, contain not only splanchnic and somatic afferent and efferent neurons comparable to those of the spinal nerves, but also special afferent neurons from the nose, eye, ear, and lateral line system. There are also special efferent neurons to the branchiomeric muscles.

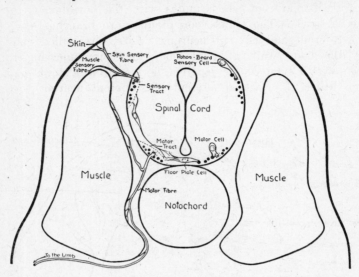

FIG. 166. Diagram to show in transverse section of *Ambystoma* larva, neurons concerned in earliest reflex. (From Coghill, *Anatomy and the Problem of Behavior.*)

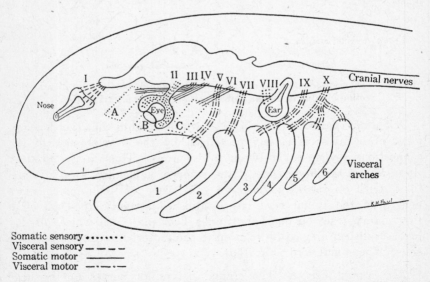

FIG. 167. Diagram to show relationships between cranial nerves and parts supplied. *A, B, C*, head somites. Arabic numerals, visceral arches. Roman numerals, cranial nerves.

There are ten cranial nerves in the anamniotes (Fig. 167), twelve in the amniotes (Fig. 171). To these should be added in all cases the terminal nerve, unknown when the cranial nerves were first classified.

0. *Terminal,* a ganglionated nerve from the vomeronasal organ (of Jacobson) entering the olfactory lobe with functions unknown, probably sensory. Its fibers are not myelinated.

I. *Olfactory,* a non-ganglionated special sensory nerve from the olfactory epithelium of the nose to the olfactory lobe. The cell bodies of this nerve originate in the nasal epithelium, and their fibers are not myelinated.

II. *Optic* (ophthalmic), a special sensory nerve from the retina of the eye to the floor of the diencephalon, where the fibers from the two eyes cross (optic chiasma). Each set of fibers then enters the brain and runs to the optic lobe on the opposite side of the brain to that on which the eye is located. The layer of cell bodies in the retina which gives rise to fibers of the optic nerve is known as the ganglion layer of the retina. The nerve fibers are myelinated. It is claimed that in some of the lower vertebrates efferent fibers are found in the optic nerve.

III. *Oculomotor* (motor oculi), a general somatic motor nerve (with some afferent fibers). Originating in the floor of the mesencephalon, it supplies all the muscles of the eyeball except the superior oblique and the lateral rectus.

IV. *Trochlear* (pathetic), like the third, a general somatic motor nerve (with some afferent fibers). It originates from the roof of the mesencephalon and supplies the superior oblique muscle of the eyeball.

V. *Trigeminal,* a mixed nerve. Its efferent neurons leave the side of the metencephalon at a level higher than the ventral roots of the spinal nerves. They are, therefore, to be described as special visceral efferent neurons, and they supply muscles originating in connection with the first visceral arch, later to become the jaw muscles.

The afferent neurons originate in the semilunar (Gasserian) ganglion and for the most part are general somatic in nature, although some special visceral afferent neurons have been described. In some lower vertebrates contributions from epibranchial placodes (Chapter 16) to the semilunar have been claimed.

VI. *Abducens.* This is a general somatic motor nerve, like III and IV (with some afferent fibers). It originates from the ventral side of the metencephalon and supplies the external rectus muscle of the eyeball.

VII. *Facial,* a mixed nerve. Its efferent neurons are of the special visceral type and supply the muscles originating in connection with the second visceral arch, many of which become the facial muscles.

The afferent neurons originate in the geniculate ganglion, which earlier forms a single ganglionic mass with the acoustic ganglion (VIII). This common primordium is designated the acousticofacial ganglion, and it is claimed that it receives contributions from the otic placode (page 241). This nerve has visceral sensory fibers connecting to the taste buds.

VIII. *Acoustic* (auditory). This is a special somatic sensory nerve, originating from the acoustic ganglion. The common origin of this with the geniculate ganglion and the contribution from the otic placode have been mentioned above. In the higher vertebrates the acoustic nerve is divided into a vestibular and cochlear (spiral) nerves, each with its own ganglion, which supply the semicircular canals and spiral organ (of Corti), as described in the chapter following.

IX. *Glossopharyngeal,* a mixed nerve. Its efferent neurons, of the special visceral motor type, arise from the sides of the myelencephalon and supply muscles of the pharynx derived from the third visceral arch and, in mammals, the salivary glands.

The afferent neurons arise from two ganglia, the superior and petrosal. They are of the visceral sensory type, supplying the region of the second and third visceral arches. Epibranchial placodes are said to contribute to the ganglia of the ninth nerve.

X. *Vagus* (pneumogastric), also a mixed nerve. Its efferent fibers, which in the lower vertebrates supply the branchiomeric muscles of the fourth, fifth, and sixth visceral arches, supply the pharyngeal and laryngeal musculature derived from those arches. They may then be described as special visceral motor neurons. Some fibers continue to the smooth muscles of the viscera; hence the older name " pneumogastric."

The afferent neurons arise from a number of ganglia, of which the first or jugular ganglion is the largest. The others are vestigial, but their presence lends confirmation to the theory that the vagus is composed of a number of originally separate nerves which might have supplied the more posterior visceral arches separately. The dorsal roots of the tenth cranial nerve pass through a nodose ganglion before they are distributed. This nerve supplies the lateral line organs of the anamniote vertebrates, and its ganglia may receive contributions from epibranchial placodes.

XI. *Spinal accessory.* This nerve is not one of the cranial nerves in the anamniotes, and is first included in the head by the reptiles. It is closely associated with the vagus. Only motor elements have been described, and these supply the head-turning muscles. They are said to arise from branchiomeric musculature, in which case the neurons are of the special visceral motor type.

XII. *Hypoglossal.* This is a motor nerve, whose roots originate from the side of the myelencephalon ventral to those of the vagus and accessory and are more nearly on the level of the ventral roots of the typical spinal nerves. They are then of the general somatic motor type. This nerve is included in the head of amniote vertebrates only, and supplies the muscles of the tongue. In the anamniotes this organ is supplied by the spinal nerves of the occipital region.

While there are no afferent neurons in the adult, the embryos of some mammals possess for a short time a vestigial ganglion (of Froriep).

Metamerism of the head. One of the burning questions in the phylogenetic period of comparative embryology was that of the metamerism of the head. It was generally assumed that the head represented the consolidation and specialization of a number of metameres. Some writers tried to work this out by calculating the original number of complete cranial nerves before dorsal and ventral roots separated or were lost. Others attempted to correlate the visceral arches with lost somites. Yet others studied the neuromeres, constrictions in the developing brain which in some vertebrates have rather constant numbers in the different regions of the brain. It must be admitted that so far these studies have not resulted in any generally accepted theory.

The sympathetic nerves. The brain, spinal cord, and cranial and spinal nerves are grouped by anatomists as the central nervous system. Associated with this is the sympathetic (autonomic) nervous system, consisting of nerves and ganglia and controlling the smooth muscles of the viscera and blood vessels, and some glands. This system arises from the neural plate, like the central nervous system, but from the lateral margins which become the neural crests. At the time when the neural crests are dividing into the cerebrospinal ganglia, some of the cells migrate inward toward the dorsal aorta, where they aggregate and multiply to form the chain ganglia. The chain ganglia on each side become connected by fore and aft extensions, which form the sympathetic trunks. They retain a connection with the cranial and spinal ganglia by means of the communicating rami, and send out nerves along the principal blood vessels.　From the chain ganglia, by secondary and tertiary migrations, arise the pre-

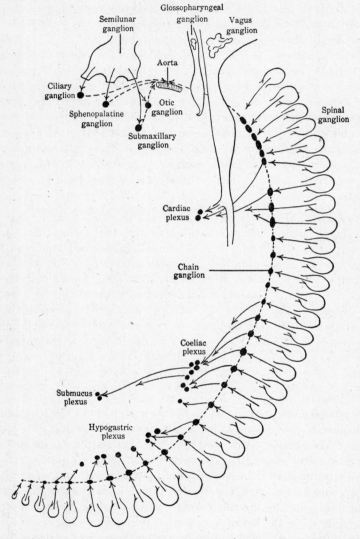

FIG. 168.　Diagram to show migrations of sympathetic ganglia in human development.　(After Streeter.)

vertebral and visceral ganglia.　In the head the four sympathetic ganglia (ciliary, sphenopalatine, otic, and submaxillary) arise from the semilunar ganglion of the fifth cranial nerve, and later acquire connections with the chain ganglia (Fig. 168).

It has already been noted (page 171) that some of the cells from the sympathetic ganglia (chromaffin cells) migrate to the vicinity of the mesonephros to form the suprarenal gland.

THE FROG

Central nervous system. The origin of the neural tube has already been described (page 105). There is no anterior neuropore, and the neurenteric canal is represented, if at all, by a pigmented streak where the neural folds closed over the blastopore. The divisions of the brain are poorly marked at first, but, assuming that the mesencephalon occupies the area where the cervical flexure over the anterior tip of the notochord is to be seen (Fig. 198), the relative positions of prosencephalon and rhombencephalon can be determined. In the embryo at the hatching stage (20) certain landmarks are apparent. On the roof of the brain (Fig. 204) the limits of the mesencephalon are marked by two constrictions with a swelling between. On the floor a thickening at a point just anterior to the tip of the notochord, and known as the posterior tubercle, marks the posterior end of the mesencephalon ventrally. In the prosencephalon, a definite evagination on the roof marks the primordium of the epiphysis. On its floor is a definite depression (optic recess) with one swelling behind (optic chiasma) and one in front (lamina terminalis), which was the original anterior end of the neural tube.

In the young tadpole stage (25) the differentiation of the grosser features of brain anatomy are well established (Fig. 169). The cervical flexure has been much reduced (Fig. 210). In the rhombencephalon there is a relatively small cerebellum, a well-developed choroid plexus, but the pons is scarcely developed, if at all. Corpora bigemina are apparent on the roof of the mesencephalon. The diencephalon has its choroid plexus on the dorsal side and a prominent epiphysis the cavity of which no longer connects with the diacoel. On the floor the trough-like infundibulum is partly constricted away from the diencephalon, and now is firmly attached to the hypophyseal portion. The optic chiasma is relatively larger than before, and the optic recess is clearly marked. The lamina terminalis extends upward and forward, beginning to form a partition which will separate the cerebral hemispheres internally as a longitudinal groove separates them externally at this time. The cerebral hemispheres never become very large in the frog, nor is the neopallium formed.

It should be noted that definite neuromeres do not appear in the developing brain.

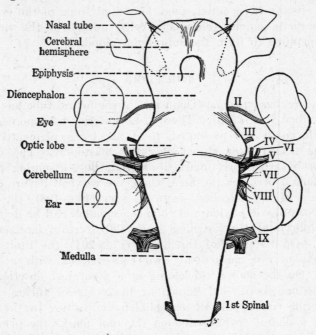

Fig. 169. Brain and sense organs of 11-mm. *Rana pipiens* embryo. From a wax plate reconstruction prepared by E. Phipps and E. Van Drasek. Dorsal view, ×50. (Note: Cranial nerve X, closely associated with IX, does not appear from this view.)

Peripheral nervous system. There are about forty pairs of spinal nerves formed in the tadpole, but only ten are retained after metamorphosis and the loss of the tail. Cranial nerves, ten pairs only, make their appearance. The ganglionated nerves are the first to be distinguished. Four ganglionic masses can be seen in the embryo at stage 20. The first of these gives rise to the semilunar ganglion of the fifth nerve and seems to receive a contribution from a placode which develops just external to it. The second becomes the acousticofacialis (VII and VIII), which receives a contribution from the auditory placode. The third forms the ganglion of the ninth nerves, and the fourth gives rise to that of the tenth. The two were at an earlier stage associated in a common mass (postotic), and each receives a contribution from an epibranchial placode.

The optic nerves are well developed at stage 20, but the olfactory nerves do not make an appearance until stage 25. The nerves of the eyeball muscles, III, IV, and VI, can be distinguished at stage 25, as the eye is a functioning organ at this time.

The ganglion cells which will form the sympathetic ganglia have reached their final positions at stage 25.

THE CHICK

Central nervous system. The neural folds are just meeting at the 24-hour stage (page 107). Between this time and the thirty-third hour, eleven neuromeres appear, of which three are absorbed by the prosencephalon, two by the mesencephalon, and six by the rhombencephalon. At 33 hours the most prominent part of the brain is the prosencephalon (Fig. 221), marked by the large optic

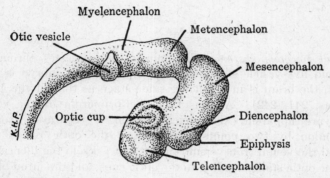

Myelencephalon

Otic vesicle

Metencephalon

Mesencephalon

Optic cup

Diencephalon

Epiphysis

Telencephalon

Fig. 170. Brain of the 72-hour chick embryo. Compare Fig. 233.

vesicles. On the floor a small infundibular evagination can be distinguished. By 48 hours (Fig. 227) there is a very well-developed cranial flexure and a small posterior tubercle extending inward at the tip of the curved notochord. The optic recess is a small one, and the epiphysis is a shallow evagination. At 72 hours (Figs. 170, 233) the division of the prosencephalon into telencephalon and diencephalon can be distinguished by a constriction in the roof between them. On the ventral side the boundary is marked by the anterior end of the optic recess. Another transverse constriction in the roof separates the diencephalon from the mesencephalon. The metencephalon at this time is distinguished from the myelencephalon only through the greater thickness in the roof of the former. In later days of incubation the cerebral hemispheres, corpora bigemina, cerebellum, and pons are developed. Two additional flexures occur, the cervical at the junction of myelencephalon and spinal cord, and the pontine in the floor of the myelencephalon at the level of the pons.

Peripheral nervous system. Thirty-eight pairs of spinal nerves are formed by the eighth day, according to Lillie. The ganglionated cranial nerves arise from three large ganglionic masses. The first is the primordium of the semilunar, the second is the acousticofacial, the third the postotic. At the 48-hour stage the postotic segment has given rise to the ganglia of the glossopharyngeal and vagus nerves. By 72 hours all the cranial nerves may be recognized except the trochlear and abducens, which do not appear until the sixth day, and the spinal accessory and hypogastric, which can be recognized on the fourth.

Sympathetic nervous system. The primordia of the sympathetic ganglia are in evidence during the fourth day of incubation.

MAN

Central nervous system. The human brain passes through the three- and five-vesicle stages, and by the time the embryo is 8 mm. in length the brain is in about the same stage as that of the 10-mm. pig (Figs. 241, 242). At this time the primordia of the cerebral vesicles are apparent. The telencephalon is separated from the diencephalon by two points of reference, the optic recess in the floor, and the velum transversum in the roof. From the diencephalon spring the optic stalks, leading to the optic cups, and the infundibulum, now in contact with the hypophysis as mentioned above. The posterior boundary of the diencephalon is indicated by the posterior tubercle arising from the brain floor. The epiphysis seldom appears at this stage. The mesencephalon is demarcated at its posterior end by the deep constriction of the isthmus. The metencephalon is distinguished from the myelencephalon by its thicker roof. The pons is not yet distinguishable. Cervical and cranial flexures have developed, but the pontine is still to be formed. In later stages the development of the human brain is marked by the great increase in size and complexity of the cerebral hemispheres of the telencephalon. The optic lobes are quadripartite (corpora quadrigemina), of which the two anterior lobes are especially associated with vision, the two posterior ones with hearing.

Peripheral nervous system. The spinal and cranial nerves (Fig. 171) are formed as in other vertebrates. In the 10-mm. pig, corresponding roughly to an 8-mm. human embryo, all the cranial nerves, with the occasional exception of the first, can be demonstrated.

Froriep's ganglion (XII) is distinguished only with difficulty from the accessory ganglia of XI.

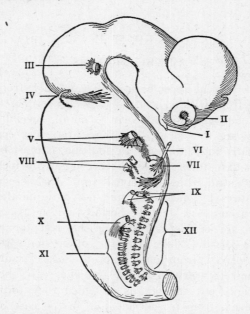

FIG. 171. Diagram to show origin of cranial nerves in man. (After His.)

Sympathetic nervous system. The ramus communicans of each spinal nerve (Fig. 244) leads to a sympathetic ganglion which can be seen by the time the stage is comparable to the development of a 10-mm. pig.

CHAPTER 16

SENSE ORGANS

The nervous system receives stimuli not only from outside the body but also from within, such as those concerning the tension of the muscles. For the reception of stimuli, special organs — the sense organs — are developed. Of these the most conspicuous are the eyes, the ears, and the nose. In addition, it must be remembered that the entire skin functions as a sense organ by means of special receptors, that stimuli are received from the viscera and other internal structures by means of free nerve terminations, and that the mouth contains taste buds, especially on the tongue. The free nerve endings are ectodermal as are the receptor corpuscles (of various types) of the skin. On the other hand the taste buds seem to be derived from endoderm, at least in amphibia. The actual receptors (sensory cells) of the eye, ear, and nose are of ectodermal origin, but the organs of which they form a part contain also elements from mesoderm, and, in the case of the ear, endoderm.

The eye, ear, and nose are alike in that they arise from localized thickenings known as placodes or sense plates, already mentioned in the preceding chapters. It is now generally recognized that these and other (epibranchial) placodes contribute to the building of many cranial ganglia. These placodes invaginate to form pits and in some, lens of the eye and inner ear, detach themselves completely from the surrounding ectoderm to become vesicles. The optic placode, which is the primordium of the retina, is incorporated, as we have seen in the preceding chapter, into the neural plate at the level of the prosencephalon. It is, therefore, carried into the neural tube and later evaginates from the prosencephalon with which the eye is permanently connected.

The nose. The nose arises as a pair of local thickenings of the ectoderm at the anterior end of the head (Fig. 172). These thickenings are hereafter known as the nasal (olfactory) placodes. Later they invaginate to form the nasal (olfactory) pits, which persist as the nose of all fish except the air-breathing dipnoi. Here also should be noted the fact that the cyclostomes are peculiar in the possession

236

of a single median nasal pit. Among the higher vertebrates, the
nasal pits acquire, by means differing in the various classes, openings
into the mouth or pharynx (Fig. 173). The olfactory epithelium
contains cells which greatly resemble ganglionic neuroblasts. These

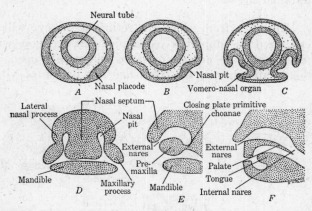

Fig. 172. Diagrams to show origin of nose. *A*, nasal placode. *B*, nasal pit. *C*,
vomero-nasal organ. *D*, connection between nasal pit and mouth. *E*, sagittal
section to show origin of primitive choanae. *F*, sagittal section to show origin of
internal nares.

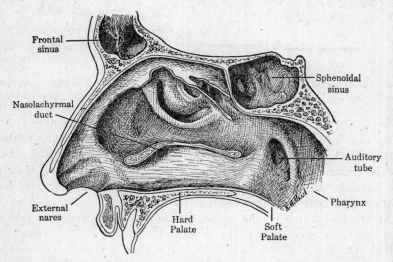

Fig. 173. Hemisection through human nose. (After Howden.)

become bipolar neurons which send their axons back into the
rhinencephalon of the fore-brain to become the first cranial nerve.

From each nasal pit on the median side an evagination gives rise to the vomeronasal organ (of Jacobson). This is thought to have some special olfactory function, particularly in aquatic vertebrates. It sends nerve fibers to join the olfactory nerve and is also connected with the terminal nerve.

The eye. The area from which the retina of the eye will develop can be recognized in amphibia as a pigmented region with long columnar cells while the neural folds are still widely open, and has in fact been located in the blastula stage by means of vital dyes.

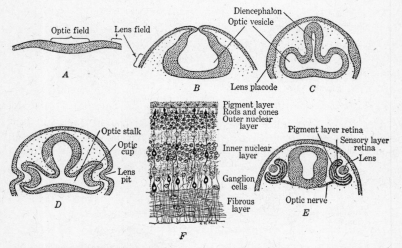

Fig. 174. Diagrams to show origin of eye. *A*, optic field of neural plate. *B*, optic vesicle early. *C*, optic vesicle, late. *D*, optic cup. *E*, sensory and pigment layers of retina. *F*, details of retina.

After the closure of the neural folds this field is located on the ventral side and at the ventrolateral angles of the fore-brain (Fig. 174). As the retina evaginates from the fore-brain, a pair of optic vesicles are formed. In each of these vesicles a constriction in the proximal portion results in the formation of the optic stalks.

At the point where the optic vesicle approaches the ectoderm, two reactions take place: (1) a local thickening of the ectoderm, called the lens placode, from which the lens of the eye develops; and (2) an invagination of the optic vesicle whereby this vesicle is transformed into a two-layered optic cup. This invagination continues into the optic stalk to produce a groove called the choroid fissure.

The lens. The lens placode invaginates to form the lens pit, which then withdraws still further from the surface and becomes closed in by the union of its external lip to form the lens vesicle. The lens vesicle becomes solid by the elongation of the cells on the internal side which later assume a clear transparent appearance.

The optic cup. The inner layer of the cup becomes the sensory portion of the retina, the outer layer the pigmented portion (tapetum). The sensory layer of the retina soon becomes stratified. The layer of cells farthest from the cavity of the optic cup, corresponding to the ependyma and mantle layer of the neural tube, later gives rise to an outer layer of cells which form the rods and cones and an inner layer of bipolar cells (Fig. 174*F*). These, in turn, communicate with large ganglion cells, making up the ganglion layer. The axons from the ganglion-layer cells grow out into the fibrous layer lining the cavity of the cup and corresponding to the marginal layer of the neural tube. On reaching the fibrous layer, the axons converge towards the optic stalk and turn inward at that point to grow down the wall of the stalk and become the optic nerve. In the pigmented layer of the retina, melanin is secreted. Meantime the cavity of the optic cup becomes filled with a clear fluid secreted by the surrounding cells, which later becomes viscous and forms the vitreous body (humor).

The envelopes of the eyeball. Around the optic cup and stalk, a layer of mesenchyme accumulates. This layer later differentiates into an inner delicate layer called the choroid, which contains pigment and capillaries and may be compared with the pia mater of the brain, and an outer dense layer known as the sclera, which may be compared with the dura mater of the brain. The external portion of the sclera over the lens makes contact with the epidermis and becomes transparent to form the cornea (Fig. 175). The epidermis over the eye forms the conjunctiva. In some vertebrates, sclerotic cartilage, or even bone, is formed, the vestige of an optic capsule. The edge of the choroid, together with the marginal retina, gives rise to the iris, a circular curtain surrounding the opening of the cup which is called the pupil of the eye. The muscles of the iris are apparently of ectodermal origin. The iris divides the space between the lens and the cornea into two chambers, an anterior and a posterior chamber, which are filled with a fluid, the aqueous humor. The muscles of the eye arise comparatively late. It will be recalled that in the elasmobranch these muscles arise from three short-lived preotic somites. In all other vertebrates they are formed from condensations of the head mesenchyme.

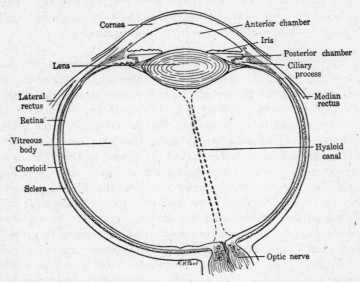

FIG. 175. Horizontal section of human eye. (After Howden.)

The ear. The vertebrate ear consists of the vestibule or equilibratory organ and the cochlea or organ of hearing. Three parts

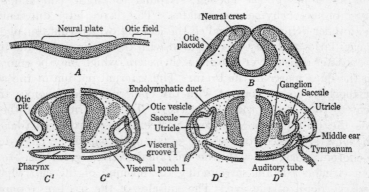

FIG. 176. Diagrams to show origin of ear. *A*, relation between neural plate and otic field. *B*, otic placode. *C¹*, otic pit. *C²*, otic vesicle (otocyst). *D¹*, division of inner ear. *D²*, relation between inner and middle ear.

of the ear are distinguished (Fig. 176). The inner ear, common to all vertebrates, giving rise to the vestibule and the cochlea, arises from an ectodermal otic (auditory) placode. The middle ear appears for the first time in the amphibians, and is derived from the endodermal first visceral pouch. The outer ear, found only in the amniotes, is an ectodermal derivative of the first visceral groove. In mammals an outgrowth from the mandibular and hyoid arches, is known as the pinna.

The inner ear. This originates from the otic placode, which invaginates to form an otic (auditory) pit (Fig. 176) and later closes over to withdraw from the epidermis as the otic (auditory) vesicle or otocyst. In some vertebrates (elasmobranchs) the vesicle retains its connection with the exterior by means of a hollow stalk, the endolymphatic duct. Usually this connection is lost and the endolymph duct of the adult is a new formation. The vesicle divides into a ventral saccule and a dorsal vestibule or utricle. The saccule gives rise to the endolymph duct and the lagena, which in mammals becomes the coiled cochlea or organ of hearing, while the utricle gives rise by constriction to three semicircular canals, each with a dilation at one end, the ampulla. The sensory epithelium is restricted to the lagena and ampullae. The cavity of these structures is known as the membranous labyrinth, and contains a fluid, the endolymph. Concretions, the otoliths, may appear in the endolymph of the vestibular portion. Around this labyrinth the otic capsule, or skeletal labyrinth, is formed. This later ossifies to give rise to the otic bones of the skull. The skeletal labyrinth contains a fluid known as the perilymph. In those vertebrates which possess a middle ear, two openings are formed in the skeletal labyrinth, the fenestra rotunda, closed by a membrane, and the fenestra ovale, into which the stapes projects. The acoustic nerve, which is ganglionated, divides into a vestibular and a cochlear nerve, each with its separate ganglion.

The middle ear. The middle ear arises from the first visceral pouch, which constricts into a proximal auditory (Eustachian) tube and a distal tympanic cavity. It is separated from the exterior by the tympanic membrane, a persistent closing plate formed from ectoderm and endoderm. Through the tympanic cavity there is a chain of bones (auditory ossicles) connecting the tympanum with the fenestra ovalis. In anurans and sauropsids, this chain of auditory ossicles consists of the columella, a rod originating in part from the roof of the tympanic cavity and in part from the wall of the otic capsule (stapedial plate). This bone has been compared to the hyomandibular cartilage of the elasmobranch and to the stapes of the mammal. In mammals three auditory ossicles are found. The stapes originates from the second visceral arch, the malleus and incus from the first. These have been compared to the articular and quadrate bones of reptiles respectively. The muscles of the middle ear, tensor tympani and stapedial muscles, arise from the mesoderm of the mandibular and hyoid arches, respectively, and are innervated by the trigeminal and facial nerves.

The outer ear. The external ear consists of the external auditory meatus, derived from the first visceral groove. In crocodiles and some birds (owl) a flap of skin partially protects the external auditory meatus. Only mammals develop a pinna, which arises from tubercles on the mandibular and hyoid arches. It is composed of mesoderm and ectoderm, contains muscles, and is strengthened by cartilage. The innervation is from the facial nerve.

The lateral-line system. This is a diffuse sensory organ consisting of sense buds arranged in rows over the head and body of aquatic anamniotes. Its function apparently is to detect slow vibrations in the water. The origin of the lateral-line system is a lateral thickening of the sensory ectoderm which later breaks up into separate epibranchial placodes. These are found in the embryos of the amniotes but soon degenerate. The lateral-line system is of particular interest inasmuch as the lateral thickening referred to is in some cases continuous with the otic placode which gives rise to the ear. The principal nerve supplying the lateral-line system is the facial, although trigeminal, glossopharyngeal, and vagus often contain lateral-line components.

THE FROG

The nose. The nasal placodes appear in the frog embryo at stage 16 as two thickenings in the sense plate. They begin invaginating in the following stage (17) and by hatching time (stage 20) have formed two circular pits (Fig. 208). In stage 21, these pits grow back towards the mouth into which they open at stage 23. At stage 25 the vomeronasal organ forms an evagination on the mesial side of each nasal tube (Fig. 214).

The eye. The retinal (optic) field (Fig. 177) may be distinguished in the neural plate in stage 14, and by stage 16 optic vesicles (Fig. 199) are well developed. The lens placode can be seen in stage 18, is invaginating in stage 19, and has become a vesicle (Fig. 205) in stage 20. During these stages the invagination of

the optic cup is accomplished. In stage 20 the cornea of the eye
is transparent and, after this, the inner cells of the lens fill the
cavity of this structure. The division of the retina into a cellular
and fibrous layer is apparent in stage 22, and by stage 25 all the
layers of the retina, including the rods and cones, are finally established
(Fig. 211).

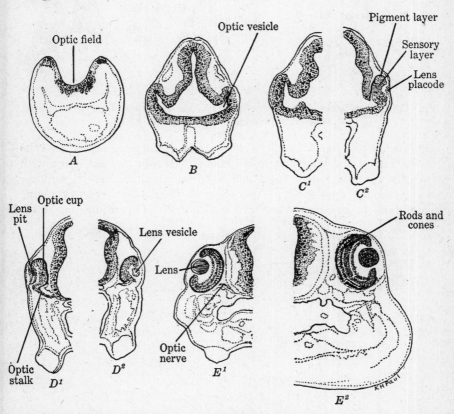

FIG. 177. Sections of frog embryos to show origin of eye. *A*, stage 14. *B*, stage
16. *C¹*, stage 17. *C²*, stage 18. *D¹*, stage 19. *D²*, stage 20. *E¹*, stage 23. *E²*,
stage 25. ×28.

The ear. The auditory placode (Fig. 178) may be distinguished
as a thickening in stage 15 and commences to invaginate in the stage
following. A vesicle, still adhering to the overlying ectoderm
(Fig. 200) is formed in stage 17. In stage 22 an endolymphatic duct
is formed by a dorsomesial invagination from each vesicle, and an
oblique partition indicates the beginning of the separation of utricle

from saccule. The lateral horizontal semicircular canal (Fig. 212) is being constricted from the utricle in stage 24 and, in the stage following, the dorsal anteroposterior canal appears. The tubotympanic cavity arises from the first visceral pouch, which in the frog

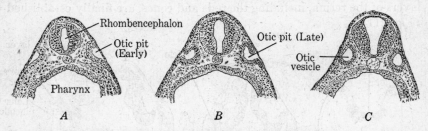

FIG. 178. Three stages in the development of the inner ear of the frog embryo. A, stage 15. B, stage 16. C, stage 17. ×20.

is vestigial and has no cavity. From this rudiment a strand of cells grows dorsad and later acquires a lumen. It loses its connection with the pharynx and moves backward to the ear region where it acquires a secondary connection with the pharynx (Fig. 179). The tympanic membrane is apparently entirely ectodermal. The columella, which

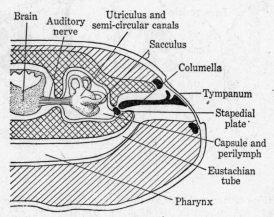

FIG. 179. *Rana pipiens*, diagram to show the parts of the ear. Schematic cross-section through head.

connects the tympanum with the inner ear, arises from two primordia: the inner stapedial plate, which is a part of the otic capsule; and a cartilage derived from the palatoquadrate bar.

Lateral-line organs. The lateral-line organs arise from the fragmentation of the placode which contributes to the tenth cranial nerve.

Similar epibranchial placodes appear on the head and are innervated by the seventh, ninth, and tenth nerves. They are larval sense organs and disappear at metamorphosis.

THE CHICK

The nose. The nasal placodes are first seen in the chick after 60 hours of incubation, and in the 72-hour chick they have invaginated to form pits (Fig. 237). During the fifth day the pits are divided into anterodorsal and posteroventral portions, the first remaining at the surface as the external nares while the second are carried into the roof of the mouth to become the posterior nares (primitive choanae). In the second week of development, the growth of the palate carries the posterior nares back to enter the pharynx as the secondary choanae. A vestigial vomeronasal organ appears but does not persist until hatching.

The eye. The optic vesicles (Figs. 221, 223) are prominent in the 33-hour chick and have invaginated to form cups (Figs. 227, 229) at 48 hours. The lens has become a vesicle at this stage but is still open to the exterior. At 72 hours the cells of the inner wall are elongating (Fig. 236).

The ear. In the chick of 33 hours, the auditory placodes (Fig. 224) are visible and at 48 hours they have invaginated to form pits (Fig. 229). By 72 hours they are constricted almost wholly from the overlying ectoderm (Figs. 233, 235) as the auditory vesicles (otocysts). There is still a narrow canal connecting them to the exterior. This is the primordium of the endolymphatic duct, which in later stages will shift its position to the median surface of the vesicle. The semicircular canals arise as outpocketings of the otocyst prior to its separation into utricle and saccule. The cochlea is more highly developed than in the frog. The tubotympanic cavity arises from the first visceral pouch. The tympanum is formed from ectoderm and endoderm and includes a middle layer of mesenchyme. The columella arises from a stapedial plate and hyomandibular cartilage. The external auditory meatus is short, and no pinna is developed.

MAN

The nose. The human nose arises as a pair of nasal placodes which become pits (Figs. 245). These obtain an opening into the mouth by the rupture of the thin epithelium separating them from it. The openings into the mouth (primitive choanae) are carried backward by the formation of the palate until they open into the pharynx as the permanent choanae or posterior nares. Thus the nasal passages represent the cavities of the nasal pits plus part of the original cavity of the mouth. A poorly developed vomeronasal organ appears in each nasal pit but usually disappears before birth.

The eyes. An optic field has been recognized in the region of the fore-brain before the neural tube has closed, and the evagination of the optic vesicles is also precocious. In the stage comparable to the 10-mm. pig embryo the optic cup (Fig. 244) and choroid fissure have formed, the cellular and fibrous layers of the retina can be distinguished, and the lens is a hollow vesicle.

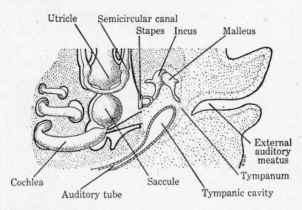

Utricle   Semicircular canal
Stapes   Incus   Malleus
External auditory meatus
Tympanum
Cochlea   Saccule   Tympanic cavity
Auditory tube

Fig. 180.   Diagram of the parts of the human ear in a fetus of three months.
(After Arey.)

The ear. The inner ear arises early as an auditory placode which invaginates to form first a pit and then a vesicle (Fig. 243). The vesicle loses its connection to the exterior, but the endolymphatic duct arises from the vesicle in the region where the connection formerly existed. Towards the end of the second month the cochlea commences the coiling, which is so characteristic of the mammalian ear (Fig. 180). The middle ear arises from the first visceral pouch (with a possible contribution from the second). The external auditory meatus originates from the first visceral groove and the pinna from elevations on the first and second visceral arches.

CHAPTER 17

EXPERIMENTAL EMBRYOLOGY

Recent progress in vertebrate embryology has resulted so largely from the application of the experimental method that even the beginning student must acquaint himself with some of the methods used and the results so far obtained. Within the limits of this book only a few of the important fields in which the experimental method has been employed can be mentioned, and the student must be referred to more extended treatises for further information concerning this relatively new and important branch of embryology.

The amphioxus and the frog have long been used by experimental embryologists, and more recently successful methods have been devised for the experimental study of the developing egg of the hen. *Triton,* in Germany, and *Ambystoma,* in this country, are urodele amphibia whose eggs have been particularly favorable for experimental embryology. The eggs of mammals, difficult to obtain, and, so far, impossible to orient during the early stages of embryology, have been employed to a lesser extent.

The experimental embryologist alters the conditions under which the egg develops in the hope of determining the factors involved in particular developmental processes. It is appropriate to conclude the study of embryology with a short account of some of the experiments which bear directly on the organization of the fertilized egg, on differentiation during cleavage, the formation of the germ layers and neurulation, and on the direct effects of environmental factors upon development.

THE ORGANIZATION OF THE FERTILIZED EGG

The fertilized egg, as we have seen, is the product resulting from the union of two germ cells, the egg and the sperm. It contains two pronuclei, of maternal and paternal origin, respectively, as well as a mass of cytoplasm which is almost exclusively maternal in origin. The nuclei contain the parental contributions of genes, the units which together determine the hereditary characters of the developing individual. How the genes produce their effects is not known, but it is certain that they must act directly upon the cytoplasm. Accordingly we may turn first to experiments dealing with the nuclei of the fertilized egg, and, second, to those concerned with the organization of the cytosome itself.

Nuclear organization. The fact that the fertilized egg has the diploid number of chromosomes and of genes, while the two gametes have the haploid number, naturally leads to the question whether the diploid number is necessary to continued development. A considerable number of experiments bear directly upon this question.

Artificial parthenogenesis. The frog's egg can be induced to develop by puncture with a finely pointed glass needle (Loeb and others). These artificially parthenogenetic eggs have given rise to tadpoles and frogs. One would expect that such embryos would possess the haploid number of chromosomes. Actually haploid, diploid, and even triploid embryos are produced. Apparently the first cleavage division is delayed while the chromosome number is doubled by a nuclear division. It is suggested that triploid embryos result from the extrusion of but one of the four nuclei formed in meiosis while the remaining three unite into one. The fact that males, females, and hermaphroditic individuals are formed suggests that the diploid individuals are genetic females, some of which undergo sex reversal.

Artificial parthenogenesis has also been accomplished in the lamprey and in the rabbit egg. Pincus reports the birth of a normal living female rabbit from an egg activated by low temperature.

Gynogenesis. Sperms of the amphibian *Triton*, treated to an appropriate dosage of radium emanations, have their nuclei injured in such a way that they are unable to form normal pronuclei (Hertwig). But they retain their mobility and are able to penetrate the egg and induce development. The sperm head remains in the cytoplasm and passes to one or another of the developing blastomeres, but takes no part in mitosis and ultimately degenerates. The number of chromosomes in the larval cells is usually haploid, although redoubling may occur. The development of a new individual from a nucleus exclusively maternal is known as gynogenesis.

Androgenesis. On the other hand, haploid individuals may be produced with a paternal nucleus only, androgenesis. Eggs of *Triton* have also been irradiated to kill the egg nucleus and then fertilized with normal sperms. These eggs develop with the haploid number of chromosomes, showing that either maternal or paternal pronucleus is adequate for development.

Merogony. This term is applied to the development of individuals from enucleate fragments of eggs which have been fertilized by normal sperms. A similar result can be obtained in telolecithal vertebrate

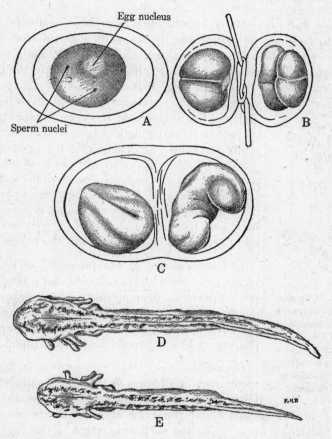

Fig. 181. The experimental production of haploid larvae in *Triton*. *A*, fertilized egg with two sperm nuclei. *B*, same after constriction separating part of egg with diploid nucleus (right) from part with haploid nucleus formed by supernumerary sperm (left). *C*, showing relatively more advanced diploid embryo (right) and less advanced haploid embryo (left). *D*, diploid larva. *E*, haploid larva. (After Spemann.)

eggs, such as those of *Triton*, where several sperms normally enter the egg. After the entrance of the sperm, it is possible to constrict the egg into halves, by means of a fine hair loop, in such a way that the female pronucleus lies in one half (Fig. 181). This half will eventually have the diploid number of chromosomes, for a sperm pronucleus will conjugate with the egg pronucleus. The other half will have only the haploid number. Both halves will develop into larvae, one of which will have haploid and the other diploid nuclei.

Species hybrids. Many experiments have been made in the attempt to fertilize the egg of one species with a sperm from another species. Often as in the teleost fish (Moenkhaus), both pronuclei take part in the subsequent cleavage, although frequently the chromosomes from the two pronuclei (Fig. 182) form separate groups on the mitotic spindle (gonomery). But in other cases Hertwig has shown that the male pronucleus takes no part in subsequent cleavages, so that the embryo really develops parthenogenetically (gynogenesis).

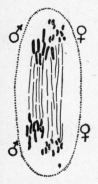

Natural interspecific hybrids in both plant and animal kingdom are more common than formerly believed. Usually these interspecific hybrids are infertile, such as the mule and many types of hybrid bony fish, but they often grow to larger size and are more active (hybrid vigor) than the parents.

FIG. 182. Chromosomes in anaphase of first cleavage of a hybrid fish, *Menidia* egg and *Fundulus* sperm, illustrating gonomery. (After Moenkhaus.)

The equivalence of the pronuclei. The experiments mentioned above indicate that a single set of genes, paternal or maternal, is adequate for the development of an egg. It must be recognized, however, that the experimental haploid animals are frequently less vigorous than normal diploid forms.

Organization of the cytoplasm. It has been mentioned in Chapter 3 that the fertilized egg of many animals had markings such as the yellow crescent of the ascidian and the gray crescent of the amphibian. These particular areas lie on the surface or crust of the egg (cortex, ectoplasm). When studied by the methods of descriptive embryology, including the use of vital stains, the prospective fate of these areas was established. Similarly, in the egg of the echinoderm, the use of the dark-field microscope has shown that the area surrounding the vegetal pole appeared in a different color from that of the animal pole. Experiments showed that these areas gave rise to endoderm and ectoderm respectively. Ectodermalization or endodermalization could be augmented by removing parts of the egg from the appropriate regions or by the use of chemicals which produced the same effects. Although the factors located in these areas are as yet unknown, the word " field " is applied to the organization comprising these organizing factors. The area possessing such a field is referred to as a " field district."

Polarity. The primary expression of the egg's organization is the polarity already impressed upon it in the ovary (page 30). That this polarity is itself not due to gravity is shown by the fact that frog eggs which are kept in motion during early development give rise to normal embryos (Morgan, Kathariner). But polarity is not immutable, for many experiments in which the eggs of frogs have been made to develop in an inverted position (Born, Pflüger, Morgan) show that the yolk streams down through the egg, and cleavage begins in the relatively yolk-free region which was formerly the vegetal pole. There seems to be good reason to suppose that the polar axis represents a metabolic axial gradient (Child), for when dilute solutions of lethal chemicals, e.g., potassium cyanide, are applied to the frog's egg (Bellamy), disintegration begins at the animal pole and continues toward the vegetal pole, which is the last part of the egg to be affected.

Bilaterality. The animal pole marks the anterior end of the developing amphibian embryo. Its dorsal side is marked by the gray crescent. The gray crescent often, but not always, appears on the side of the egg opposite the point where the sperm entered. In urodeles, in fact, the gray crescent makes its appearance prior to the entrance of the sperm. And in parthenogenetic eggs (when development is initiated by puncture) the point of entrance of the needle seems to have no constant relation to the subsequent bilaterality of the egg. This would indicate (Huxley and de Beer) that the egg has an underlying bilaterality of its own.

Asymmetry. The vertebrate embryo is not, strictly speaking, bilaterally symmetrical. A third axis or gradient from one side to the other (usually left to right) is often apparent, as seen in the development of the opercular opening on the left side of the tadpole, the fact that the chick heart develops on the right side, and that the head turns to the right in torsion. The stomach in all vertebrates is twisted to the left of the midline, and many other examples might be mentioned. When this asymmetry is reversed we have the phenomenon known as situs inversus, and this condition can be reproduced experimentally. For example, it has been shown by Spemann that, when two blastomeres which would ordinarily produce the right and left sides of an embryo are separated by a hair loop, the left-hand blastomere gives rise to a normally asymmetrical embryo, while the right-hand blastomere gives rise either to an embryo with normal asymmetry or to one with situs inversus.

These few examples of experiments on the fertilized egg indicate that the egg is a complex system with a definite organization indicated by its three axial gradients corresponding to its three spatial dimensions, viz., an anteroposterior gradient (polarity), a dorsoventral gradient, and frequently a left-right gradient.

ORGANIZATION OF THE EMBRYO DURING CLEAVAGE

Cell-lineage studies seemed to indicate that the dividing egg is becoming a mosaic of blastomeres, each set apart from the others to form a specific portion of the embryo. Roux (1888) was the first to realize that this might be tested experimentally. He destroyed one of the ½-blastomeres of the frog's egg and observed that the other gave rise to a ½-embryo, which later regenerated the missing portion.

Later investigators devised a number of methods by which blastomeres could be separated from each other, by shaking them, cutting them apart with fine needles, constricting them with fine threads, or placing them in artificial calcium-free sea water. Blastomeres of marine eggs in this medium separate immediately, and when returned to normal sea water continue their development without further separation (Herbst).

Regulation and mosaic eggs. The results of their experimentation seemed to indicate that in some eggs, e.g., those of the amphioxus (Fig. 183), either of the ½-blastomeres might, when separated, give rise to complete embryos (Wilson). These were called regulation eggs and were said to have indeterminate cleavage. In others, such as *Styela* (Conklin) or the mollusc *Dentalium* (Wilson), the ½-blastomeres give rise only to ½-embryos (Fig. 183). These were called mosaic eggs and were said to have determinate cleavage.

Experiments on frog's eggs had been inconclusive until an improved technique made it possible to separate blastomeres of the two-cell stage completely (Schmidt, 1930, 1933). These experiments show that each of the ½-blastomeres can give rise to a complete and perfect larva, provided only it contains some of the gray crescent region. If, on the other hand, the egg is so constricted that the first cleavage divides it into an animal and a vegetal half, the animal half, containing the gray crescent, gives rise to a complete embryo, while the vegetal half, lacking this region, is unable so to organize itself (Fig. 184). This seems to indicate that Roux's results were due to the presence of the injured blastomere inhibiting complete development on the part of the uninjured blastomere. In this connection it is interesting to note that Witschi (1927) has described a case in which two eggs were found in a single chorion. Each of them was flattened on the side next to its neighbor and in later development showed deficiencies in the corresponding region.

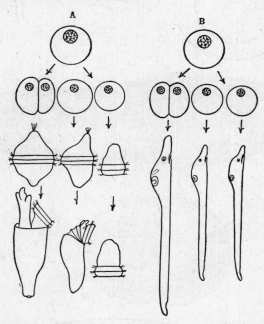

Fig. 183. Diagram to show the fate of isolated blastomeres from mosaic and regulation eggs. *A*, mosaic egg of *Dentalium*. At left, a complete embryo produced by entire egg: at right, partial embryos produced by the ½-blastomeres when artificially separated. *B*, regulation egg of *Amphioxus*. At left, embryo produced by entire egg; at right, perfect dwarf embryos produced by ½-blastomeres. (After Wilson.)

A beautiful demonstration that it is the cytoplasm and not the nucleus which is concerned with differentiation during cleavage is afforded by an instructive experiment of Spemann. If the egg is tied off before cleavage so that the nucleus is confined in one of its halves (Fig. 185), all cleavage planes will be restricted to that half until eventually a cleavage plane, in this case at the fourth cleavage, coincides with the plane of constriction. The nucleus which enters the previously enucleate half is naturally one which would serve a $\frac{1}{16}$-blastomere. If the loop is now tightened until the two halves are completely separated, the portion containing this single nucleus will

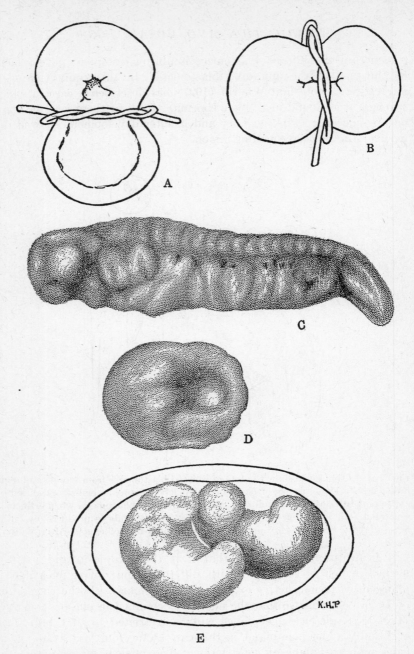

FIG. 184. Embryos arising from separated ½-blastomeres of the newt's egg. *A*, the ligature separates the dorsal and ventral halves of the embryo. *B*, the ligature separates the right and left halves. *C*, perfect embryo arising from dorsal ½-blastomere. *D*, mass of cells arising from ventral ½-blastomere. *E*, two perfect embryos arising from right and left ½-blastomeres. (After Spemann.)

give rise to an embryo like the one from the portion containing the fifteen nuclei and exactly like one arising from a complete fertilized egg.

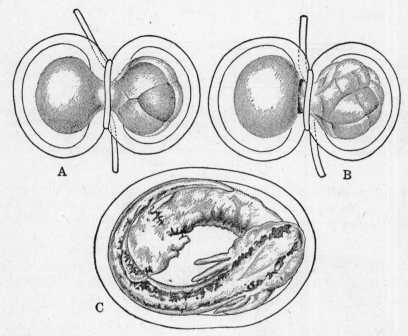

FIG. 185. Experiment demonstrating equality of nuclei formed during cleavage (*Triton*). A ligature has been tied around the fertilized egg restricting the nucleus to the right-hand portion. *A*, 16-cell stage, one nucleus passing into left-hand portion. *B*, ligature tightened to separate the two portions. *C*, perfect embryos formed by the separate portions. The nucleus of a $\frac{1}{16}$-blastomere equivalent to that of a complete zygote. (After Spemann.)

Pressure experiments. Further examples of the regulative power of some eggs may be seen in pressure experiments. If the eggs of the frog are placed between glass plates during cleavage, the third cleavage planes will be meridional instead of latitudinal, and the fourth cleavage plane is latitudinal (Fig. 186). Now if the eggs are released, their later development will be quite normal even though the blastomeres are occupying positions unlike those which they hold ordinarily.

Double embryos. Still another example may be seen in the eggs of *Triton*. If these are freed from the egg envelopes, the blastomeres

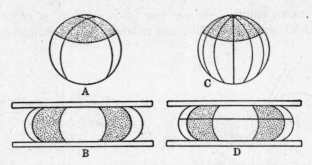

FIG. 186. Diagram to show new relationship of blastomeres in frog's egg resulting from pressure during cleavage. *A*, normal 8-cell stage. *B*, 8-cell stage formed under pressure. *C*, normal 16-cell stage. *D*, 16-cell stage formed under pressure. Cells normally in animal hemisphere shown in stipple. (Suggested by a diagram in Wells, Huxley, and Wells.)

at the two-cell stage assume a dumb-bell shape. Mangold discovered that, by placing one embryo in the two-cell stage over another (Fig. 187), a double embryo resulted almost exactly similar to a single embryo in the four-cell stage and would develop as such, provided only that the gray crescent regions of the two fell in the same plane. Otherwise double monsters resulted.

FIG. 187. Double embryo arising from fusion of 2-cell stages of *Triton alpestris* (above and below) and *Triton taeniatus* (right and left) when laid over each other crosswise. Note that a new cleavage is under way in all blastomeres. (After Mangold and Seidel.)

Monovular twins and monsters. The extreme plasticity of the vertebrate egg as seen by the fact that either two separate individuals or duplicate monsters may be formed from the complete or partial separation of blastomeres suggests an explanation of identical twins and the duplicate monsters which play so large a part in the study of teratology. It is generally accepted that identical, as distinguished from fraternal, twins are the product of a single fertilized egg which has divided completely during early embryology, whereas the duplicate monsters, ranging from Siamese twins to monsters in which one individual is but a parasite upon the body of the other, result from incomplete separation. These identical twins are always of the same sex. Ordinary or fraternal twins (triplets, etc.) are supposed to be the product of separate eggs which ovulated and were fertilized at about the same time. Such twins are frequently of different sexes. In this connection we might mention the free-martin, a sterile female twinned with a male, not infrequent among cattle, and supposed to result from one of two eggs which develop a common chorion and therefore a common blood stream. It is supposed that a male hormone circulating in the common blood stream inhibits the normal development of the female twin, so resulting in the production of the sterile free-martin (Lillie).

ORGANIZATION OF THE EMBRYO DURING GERM-LAYER FORMATION

The amphibian embryo is remarkably hardy, and during the early stages of development will endure very severe operations. The work of Harrison in this country and of Spemann in Germany has resulted in the perfection of a method of removing portions of an embryo (microdissection) and grafting them into a new environment, where they will continue development. The embryo from which the portion is removed is known as the donor; the removed portion is called the graft (transplant); and, when the portion removed is transplanted into another embryo, the second embryo is termed the host.

The accompanying diagram (Fig. 188) will bring out some of the methods which have been developed in transplantation experiments. Thus the graft may be transplanted into another portion of the same embryo (homoplastic transplantation).[1] It may be transplanted into another embryo of the same species (heteroplastic transplantation). It may even be transplanted into an embryo of another species or genus (xenoplastic transplantation).

Another method which has brought interesting results is transplanting the removed portion into a nutrient medium and allowing it to develop there under sterile conditions (explantation). This is also known as cultivation " in vitro," which means in glass. Another ingenious technique is transplanting the graft into a cavity of another embryo and allowing it to develop there. The example shown in the diagram is of a bit of embryonic tissue transplanted into the eyeball of a tadpole, which acts as a nutrient chamber. Hoadley and others have developed a technique of grafting chick-embryo tissue from a donor to the chorio-allantois of a host. Such a technique is called interplantation (implantation).

---

[1] Some investigators use autoplastic = homoplastic; homoplastic = heteroplastic; and heteroplastic = xenoplastic.

When considering the results of these experiments, we must realize that they fall into three classes. The first, which is concerned with the fate of a particular portion of the embryo when explanted or interplanted, may be called isolation experiments. The second, which

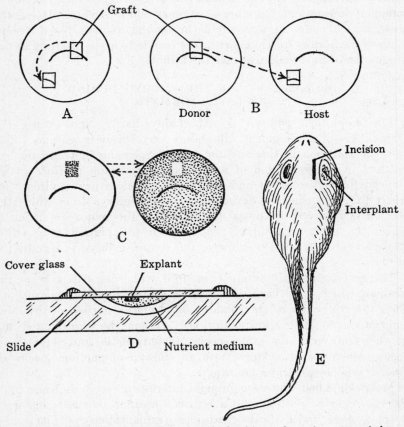

Fig. 188.   Diagrams to show different methods of transplantation, etc.   A, homoplastic transplantation.   B, heteroplastic transplantation (both donor and host of same species).   C, xenoplastic transplantation (donor and host of different species).   D, explantation (in vitro).   E, interplantation.   (Based on a diagram of Dürken.)

is concerned with the fate of an embryo from which a particular portion is removed, may be called defect experiments. The third, which is concerned with the fate of a particular portion of an embryo which has been transplanted into a host and also with the effects produced by the transplant upon the host, may be called recombination experiments.

Plasticity (dependent differentiation). In the amphibian egg, which is of the regulation type, it has been demonstrated that the presumptive organ regions of the blastula (and until about the middle of gastrulation) are quite plastic, i.e., can be transplanted into other localities and will give rise to the organs appropriate to the new locality. Thus, material which is presumptive epidermis can be transplanted into a region where it will become neural plate, mesoderm, or even endoderm. Presumptive mesoderm is more refractory. When transplanted it tends to invaginate, but within the mesodermal area small groups of cells can be interchanged freely. The presence

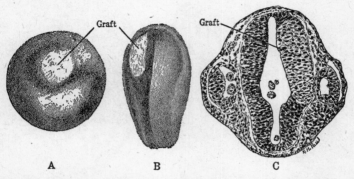

A   B   C

Fig. 189. Xenoplastic transplantation. Here *T. cristatus* (light) is the donor and *T. taeniatus* (dark) is the host. *A,* after transplantation. *B,* the transplant developing in the neural plate (region of the brain). *C,* section in later stage showing transplant developing in fore-brain. (After Spemann.)

of yolk apparently prevents the large cells of endoderm from conforming to the pattern of surrounding cells. In the chick, however, the endodermal cells show a high degree of plasticity.

Very instructive experiments are those in which material is transferred from a species with heavy pigmentation (*Triton taeniatus*) to one with light pigmentation (*Triton cristatus*). Here the graft preserves its racial character of pigmentation while otherwise conforming to the development of the host. Figure 189 illustrates such an example of xenoplastic transplantation. The light-colored graft from *T. cristatus* has developed into part of the neural tube of the host, where it stands out by reason of its light color. In the reciprocal transplantation (Fig. 190), the dark graft from *T. taeniatus* has given rise to the right external gills of the host.

With the exception of the chorda-mesodermal field district (the gray crescent area, or marginal belt) and the endodermal field district, in which the phenomenon of plasticity exists only within the area itself, it may be said that the possibilities of any group of blastomeres are greater than their presumptive fate. This is expressed in another way by saying that differentiation potency is greater than differentiation fate.

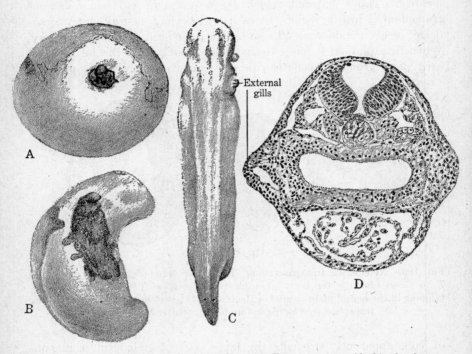

External gills

FIG. 190. Xenoplastic transplantation between *Triton taeniatus* (dark), the donor, and *Triton cristatus* (light), the host, to show early plasticity. *A*, immediately after transplantation. *B*, the transplant developing in the gill region. *C*, the gills of the transplant relatively more advanced. *D*, section through *C* in the gill region. (After Spemann.)

The loss of plasticity (self-differentiation). After gastrulation is well under way, this plasticity seen in earlier stages is lost. The various regions of the embryo have become determined and thenceforth will give rise only to the structures normally developing from them. From now on it is a real mosaic. Figure 191 shows an embryo in which the various organ fields are determined. If a bit of tissue is removed from the eye field and transferred to the flank of another embryo (Fig. 192), it will give rise only to an eye, even in its new and abnormal environment.

Similar experiments have been carried on with the chick (implantation on chorio-allantois), and it has been proved that the eye field, ear field, limb buds, and other regions will develop and give rise only to the respective organs.

Very striking results have been obtained by implanting portions of rat embryos on the chorio-allantois of the chick, and a considerable amount of self-differentiation has been demonstrated.

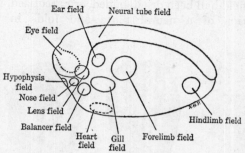

Fig. 191. Diagram of an amphibian embryo, showing organ fields as determined by transplantation experiments. (After Huxley and de Beer.)

The chorda-mesodermal field. The area which first manifests the property of self-differentiation is the gray crescent region. This area when transplanted always undergoes involution and develops notochord and mesoderm. But what is more striking it always induces the layer of cells immediately overlying it to form a neural plate,

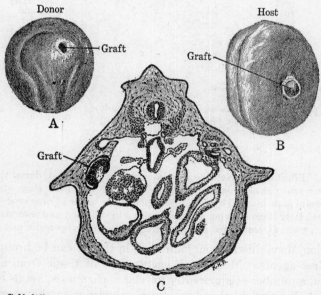

Fig. 192. Self-differentiation in the toad *Bombinator*. *A*, donor in early neurula stage showing region from which graft was taken. *B*, host in late neurula stage. *C*, section through later embryo of host, showing graft forming optic cup in region normally occupied by pronephros. (After Spemann.)

folds, and tube. For this reason the area was originally called the "organizer" (organizator, organizing center).

It was later shown that when material from the chorda-mesodermal field had been dried, boiled, or narcotized, it could still evoke the formation of a neural plate and folds in the ectoderm overlying it.

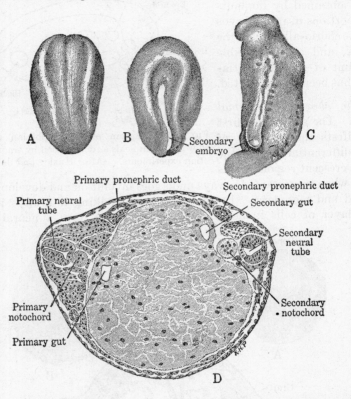

Fig. 193. Effect of transplanting chorda-mesodermal field. *A*, dorsal view of host (*Triton taeniatus*) in neurula stage. *B*, right side view at same stage showing secondary neural plate induced by dorsal lip region of the donor (*Triton cristatus*) shown in white. *C*, later stage showing primary embryo in side view and secondary embryo in dorsal view. *D*, transverse section through *C*. (After Spemann and Mangold.)

Evocation, then, differs from induction, in that it can be brought about by lifeless agents. Many such agents, bits of tissue from adult animals and a number of apparently unrelated chemicals, act as evocators. We must distinguish, therefore, three properties in the chorda-mesodermal field. First, its self-differentiating ability, that is to say, the fact that this area is the first to have its fate determined. Second, its inductive ability, in that it can induce the tissue around it to respond to and become part of the pattern which it is developing. Third, the fact that it contains substances which are sufficiently stable to resist physical and chemical treatments and yet evoke a response in near-by areas.

Competence. In later development subfields (Fig. 191) are segregated in the larger fields, until the property of plasticity has disappeared and the fates of the different parts of the embryo are strictly determined. The mechanism of this process is still obscure, but experimental embryologists are convinced that it is a progressive one, in which there are two main factors or sets of factors. One factor is the ability (competence) of a portion of the embryo to respond to an induction, the other the presence of an inductor. For example, in some species of frogs (e.g., *Rana fusca*) the lens of the eye will not form if the prospective primordium of the retina is removed in the neurula stage. In another species (*Rana esculenta*) the lens forms even if the retinal primordium has been removed. The question arises as to whether the failure of the lens to form in *R. fusca* was due to the lack of an inductor or the lack of competence. It was settled by grafting over the developing optic vesicles the belly skin of the same species and, in other embryos, the belly skin of a toad. The frog skin did not form a lens but the toad skin did, thus showing that the failure was due to lack of competence.

ENVIRONMENTAL FACTORS IN DEVELOPMENT

Many experiments have been carried on in the attempt to find the definite results produced on the developing embryo by changes in the environment. These investigations have established normal limits of temperature, etc., within which development can be completed. Within these limits, although development may be altered as to rate, etc., it is nevertheless carried on to a successful outcome. Beyond these limits the alterations are so profound as to produce monsters or cause death. Among the factors susceptible to experimental control are gravity, heat, light, the chemical constitution of the environment, and food.

Gravity (and centrifugal force). It has been remarked (page 251) that the original polarity of the egg is not due to any effect of gravity. In telolecithal eggs, however, gravity may have some effect on the course of development. Thus frog's eggs when forcefully inverted may give rise to duplicate monsters. The hen's egg if not rotated at regular intervals fails to hatch.   It has been shown (Dareste, 1877) that this is due to the failure of the yolk sac to complete its development.   It adheres to the allantois and cannot be retracted into the body as in normal development.

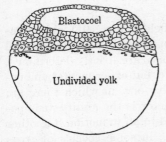

FIG. 194. Vertical section through blastula of a frog's egg following centrifuging.   (After Hertwig.)

The influence of gravity may be shown in an exaggerated manner by prolonged centrifuging. It was found by O. Hertwig that, if the frog's egg is centrifuged during cleavage, the yolk is so concentrated in the vegetal hemisphere that the cleavage planes fail to cut through it and the end result is meroblastic cleavage suggestive of that seen in the chick (Fig. 194).

Heat. The rate of development is directly affected by temperature. This is well shown in the development of the frog's egg.   In this the range, or difference between the upper and lower limiting temperatures, over which normal development is possible is over 20° C. (Moore, 1939). Within this range, which in *Rana pipiens* extends from approximately 8° C. to 28° C., development proceeds more rapidly at higher temperatures and more slowly at lower temperatures.   The times assigned to the stages (Shumway, 1940) used in this book are based on development at 18° C.

For the hen's egg, Kaestner determined the optimum temperature for normal development to be between 35° and 39° C. (95°–102° F.). The maximum temperature tolerated is 43° C., the minimum 28° C. (20°–21° C., Edwards).

Eggs of either frog or hen which have been exposed to extreme heat or cold and then returned to the optimum temperature often develop abnormally.   A common type of monster is one in which neural plate and notochord are split (spina bifida).

Very striking results have been obtained by subjecting the eggs of the frog or the hen to a temperature gradient, that is, controlling the temperature so that one side is hotter or colder than the other. If the gradient runs along the polar axis, and the greater heat is applied to the animal pole, the result is that the embryos and larvae have overlarge heads; if the higher temperature is applied to the vegetal pole, the head region is subnormal.   When the temperature gradient is applied laterally, the development of the heated side proceeds more rapidly than that of the cooled side.

It may be concluded that, within the limits of toleration, development is accelerated by increased temperatures and retarded by decreased temperatures.

Light and other forms of radiation. In spite of a considerable number of experiments designed to determine the effects of definite intensities and wavelengths of light upon the developing embryo, the results are as yet too inchoate to be discussed in an elementary textbook.

Ultraviolet light, X-rays, and radium emanations in extreme dosage cause the cessation of development. In smaller dosage, they bring about anomalies (abnormalities in structure caused by disturbances in development). It should be remembered that the work of Müller and others indicates that these agents accelerate the rate of mutation of *Drosophila* genes, and so induce genetic point mutations as well as developmental anomalies.

Chemical composition. The chemical composition of the surrounding medium affects profoundly the nature of development. The embryo cannot develop without oxygen, for it cannot live without respiration. It has been pointed out by Morgan that frog's eggs in the very center of the egg mass often develop abnormally (spina bifida, etc.). And it has long been known that the hen's egg ceases development if the pores of the shell are closed by water glass, varnish, or other agents.

Water, too, is an essential. The growth of the embryo depends upon the absorption of water, and all embryos must undergo their development within a watery medium. Even the terrestrial embryo has its private pond in the amnion. A slowing up in the rate of development, accompanied by abnormalities and a large percentage of deaths, results from incubating hen's eggs in a desiccator. The percentage of water in the frog's egg increases steadily during the first two weeks of development.

A very striking series of experiments was carried on by Herbst on the development of the sea urchin in artificial sea waters which had been made up omitting one after another of the elements found in normal sea water. Jenkinson, summarizing the evidence, says: " The experiments which we have been considering are unique of their kind, and it is impossible to exaggerate their importance. For, whatever may be the ultimate explanation of the facts, there can be no doubt whatever that the most complete demonstration has been given of the absolute necessity of many of the elements occurring in ordinary sea water, its normal environment, for the proper growth and differentiation of the larva of the sea urchin. Nor is this all. Some of the substances are necessary for one part or phase of development, some for another, some from the very beginning, others only later on. Thus potassium, magnesium, and a certain degree of alkalinity are essential for fertilization, chlorine and sodium for segmentation, calcium for the adequate cohesion of the blastomeres, potassium, calcium, and the hydroxyl ion for securing the internal osmotic pressure necessary for growth, while without the sulph-ion and magnesium the due

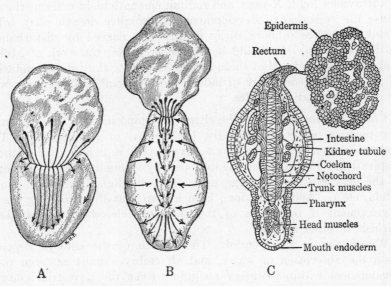

FIG. 195. Exogastrulation in *Triton*. *A*, *B*, exogastrulae showing direction of displacements during exogastrulation. Compare Fig. 56. *C*, section of later exoembryo. (After Holtfreter in Huxley and de Beer.)

differentiation of the alimentary tract and the proper formation of the skeleton cannot occur; the secretion of pigment depends on the presence of some sulphate and alkalinity, the skeleton requires calcium carbonate, cilia will only beat in an alkaline medium containing potassium and magnesium, and muscles will only contract when potassium and calcium are there."

The addition of chemicals to the medium has resulted in many interesting disturbances in development. We can call attention here to two only. In the sea urchin it was found that the addition, of lithium salts to sea water caused the embryo to undergo a very curious form of gastrulation, in which the endoderm and mesoderm were evaginated instead of being invaginated (Herbst). Such an embryo is called an exogastrula.

Holtfreter (1933) induced exogastrulation in the egg of *Triton* by removing the egg envelopes and placing the developing egg in weak Ringer's salt solution. In the cases where development continued for some length of time (Fig. 195), it was discovered that the embryo developed in two parts, an ectodermal portion with no differentiation, connected by a narrow isthmus to a mesendodermal portion in which differentiation proceeded, but in an abnormal fashion. The embryo is inside-out. The mesendodermal portion of the exoembryo develops a typical notochord, somites, kidney, gonad, a heart (empty), and a digestive tube, in which all the typical regions are indicated, including visceral pouches. These results confirm those of transplantation and explantation experiments discussed in an earlier section.

Food, hormones and vitamins. The amount and kind of food supplied to the developing young naturally affect the subsequent development. Thus, if frog tadpoles are fed on an exclusively vegetarian diet, the intestine becomes much longer than when an exclusively meat diet is offered. Specific foods often result in equally definite changes in the body. Thus Gudernatsch discovered that frog tadpoles fed on thyroid tissue grew less rapidly but underwent metamorphosis much more rapidly than the controls.

Later investigations indicate that the effects of thyroid are due to a hormone formed by this gland (thyroxin), which is a definite factor in bringing about amphibian metamorphosis (Fig. 196). The thyroid is but one of several endocrine glands which have been shown to be important factors in development either by feeding experiments, by transplantation of glandular tissue, or by extirpation of the gland from a young embryo.

The pituitary gland, often called the master gland of the vertebrate body, secretes a number of hormones. The follicle-stimulating hormone and luteinizing hormone have already been mentioned (page 128). In mammals a lactogenic hormone controls the enlargement of the mammary glands. Other hormones secreted by the pituitary gland are important in stimulating the development and activity of such endocrine glands as the thyroid, adrenal, and the gonads. Still another, the so-called growth-promoting hormone, stimulates the growth of the embryo in later stages. It must not be thought that this last-named secretion is wholly responsible for growth, because this phenomenon commences before the appearance of the pituitary gland, and, in tadpoles, the extirpation of the gland does not inhibit further growth.

The gonads form the so-called sex hormones, male sex hormone in the testis, and female sex hormone in the ovary. These have most important effects on the later development of the sex organs of the individual. Lillie's theory as to the origin of the free-martin, a sterile female intersex in cattle, has been mentioned (page 257). Witschi has created artificial Siamese twins in amphibia by cutting off a portion of the embryos in an early stage and grafting the two cut surfaces

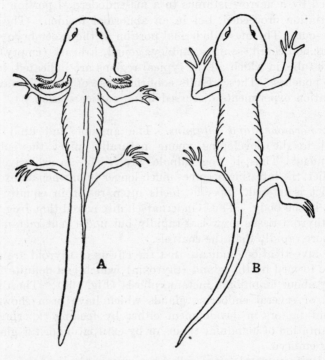

FIG. 196.   Metamorphosis in *Ambystoma*.   *A,* before metamorphosis.   *B,* after metamorphosis.   (After Dürken.)

together. Individuals united side-by-side are called parabionts; those united end-to-end are termed telobionts. If both members of the pair are of the same sex development proceeds normally, but if it turns out that one was a genetic female and the other a genetic male, the female is underdeveloped sexually, apparently due to the more powerful effect of the male sex hormone. Several investigators have shown that sex hormones can be transmitted across the placental barrier, but at the time of writing free-martins have not been successfully produced through the direct action of purified male sex hormones.

The rôle of the vitamins in the metabolism of the embryo is too little understood at the present time for us to do more than allude to this subject. Vitamin E is often called the antisterility vitamin because its absence from the diet results in loss of the reproductive power. Adamstone (1931) in this laboratory has shown that the chick embryo produced by hens on a vitamin-E-free diet dies early in development, after extensive disturbances in the blood-vascular system.

CHAPTER 18

ATLAS OF VERTEBRATE EMBRYOS

As the chapter heading indicates, the reader will find here illustrations to portray the anatomy of representative stages in the development of the frog, chick, and pig, as these are commonly studied in the laboratory. They have been referred to often in previous chapters, but the student will find it an advantage to go over them again for the mental exercise of comparing transverse with sagittal and frontal sections, and also sections of all kinds with transparent whole mounts. He should remember that these sections are not idealized but are exactly the same kind of material as that he will encounter in the laboratory. On the other hand, since all embryos vary slightly in the stage of their development and the method of preparation employed, the student will never encounter sections exactly like those here portrayed. They are labeled extensively but not completely, and they should be considered, at most, a starting point for intensive individual work in the laboratory.

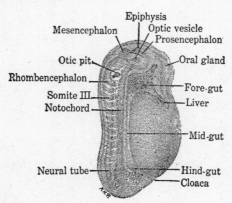

FIG. 197. 3-mm. frog embryo, viewed from right side as a transparent object. (Stage 17.) ×15.

NOTE. The frog embryos illustrated belong to the species *Rana pipiens.* All references in the text, in the absence of specific statements to the contrary, are to *R. pipiens* and based on personal examination of embryos raised in the laboratory from identified adults of this species. Embryos of other species of *Rana* will differ from those described and figured here.

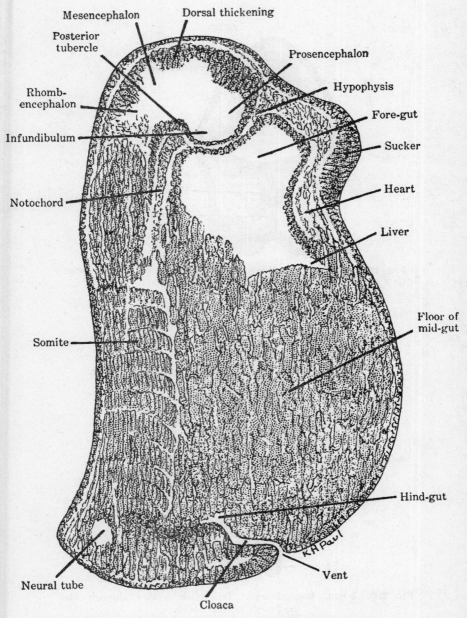

Fig. 198. 3-mm. frog embryo. Sagittal section. ×50.

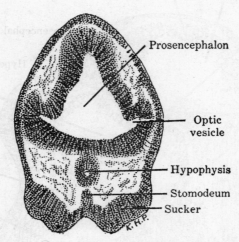

Fig. 199. 3-mm. frog embryo. Transverse section through optic vesicle. ×50.

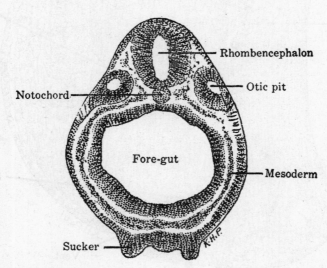

Fig. 200. 3-mm. frog embryo. Transverse section through otic (auditory) vesicle. ×50.

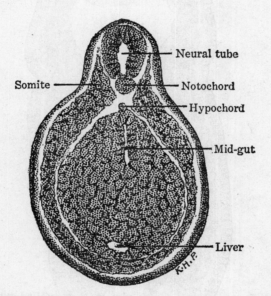

Neural tube

Somite

Notochord

Hypochord

Mid-gut

Liver

K.H.P.

FIG. 201. 3-mm. frog embryo. Transverse section through mid-gut and liver. ×50.

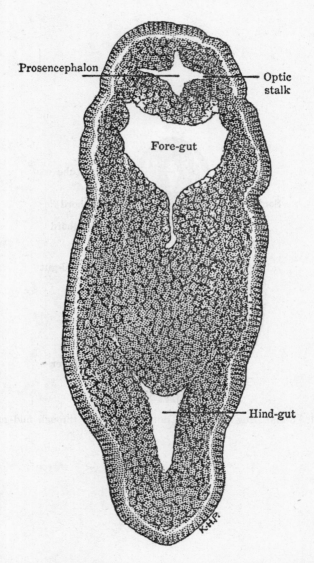

Fig. 202. 3-mm. frog embryo. Frontal section through optic stalks, liver, and hind-gut. ×50.

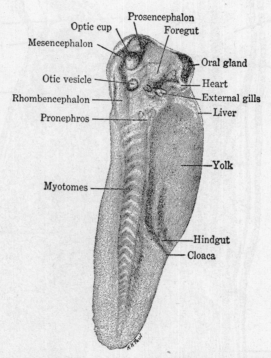

Fig. 203. 6-mm. frog larva (just hatched). Transparent preparation, viewed from right side. (Stage 20.) ×15.

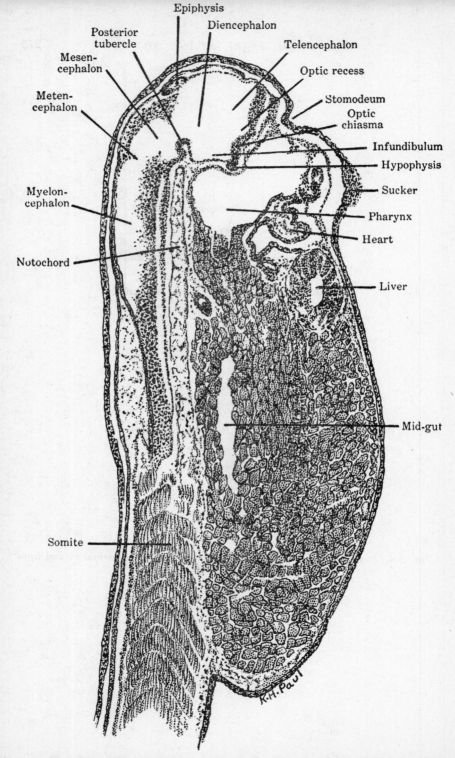

Fig. 204. 6-mm. frog larva. Sagittal section, anterior portion. ×50

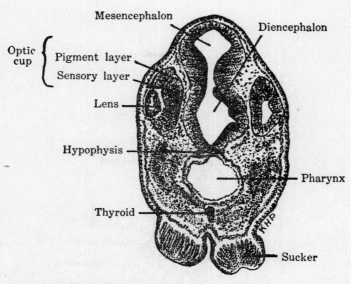

FIG. 205. 6-mm. frog larva. Transverse section through optic cup. ×50.

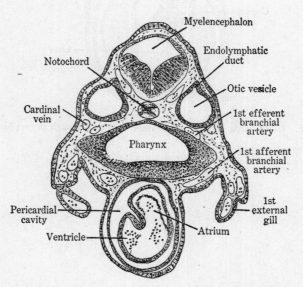

FIG. 206. 6-mm. frog larva. Transverse section through otic vesicle. ×50.

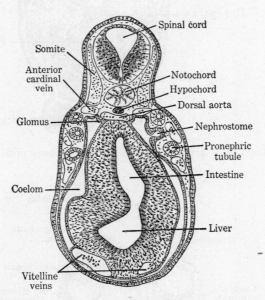

FIG. 207.   6-mm. frog larva.   Transverse section through pronephros.   ×50.

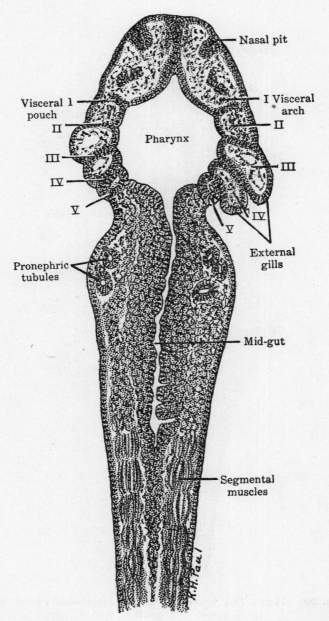

FIG. 208. 6-mm. frog larva. Frontal section through nasal pit and visceral pouches. ×50.

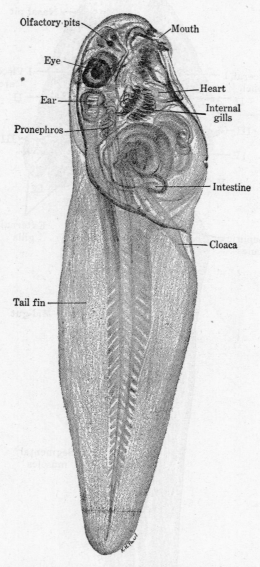

FIG. 209.   11-mm. frog larva.   Transparent preparation viewed from right side.   (Stage 25.)   ×15.

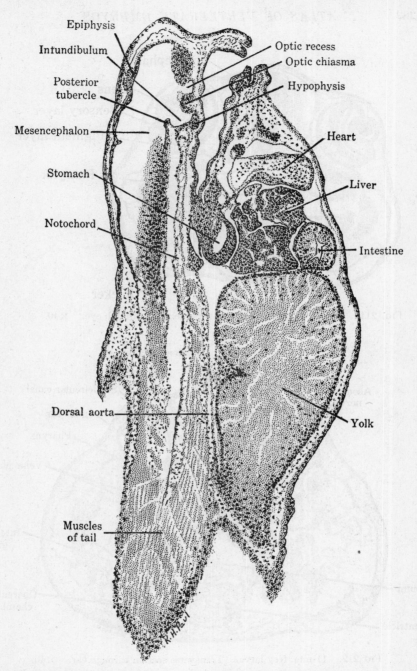

Epiphysis

Intundibulum

Posterior
tubercle

Mesencephalon

Stomach

Notochord

Optic recess

Optic chiasma

Hypophysis

Heart

Liver

Intestine

Dorsal aorta

Yolk

Muscles
of tail

Fig. 210.   11-mm. frog larva.   Sagittal section, anterior part.   ×40.

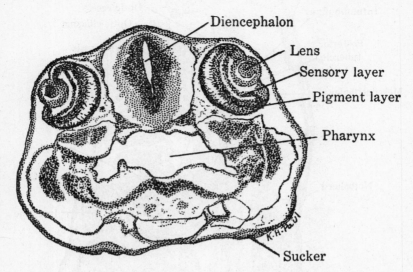

FIG. 211.   11-mm. frog larva.   Transverse section, through eye.   ×40.

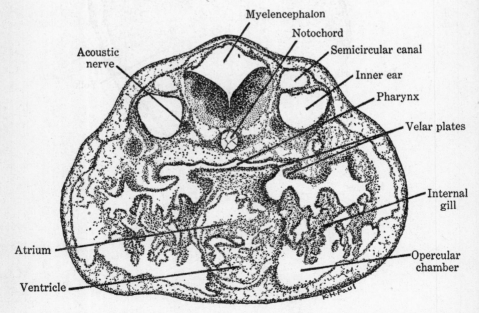

FIG 212.   11-mm. frog larva.   Transverse section through ear.   ×40.

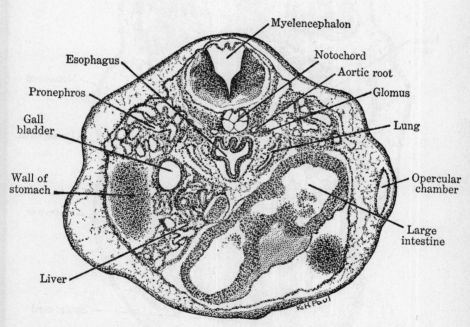

Fig. 213. 11-mm. frog larva. Transverse section through pronephros. ×40.

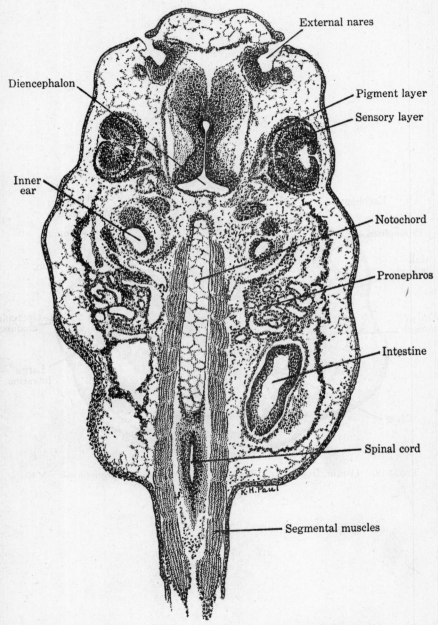

FIG. 214.   11-mm. frog larva.   Frontal section through nose, eye, and ear.   ×40.

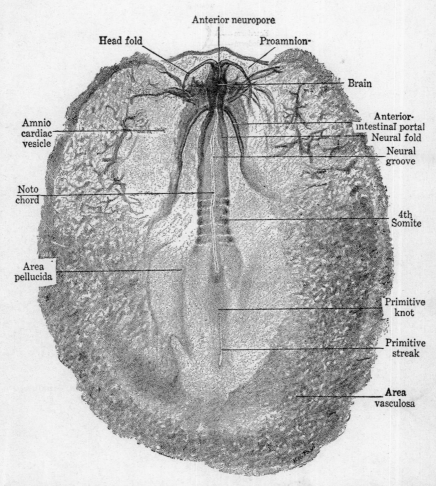

Anterior neuropore

Head fold

Proamnion

Brain

Amnio cardiac vesicle

Anterior-intestinal portal

Neural fold

Neural groove

Noto chord

4th Somite

Area pellucida

Primitive knot

Primitive streak

Area vasculosa

Fig. 215. 24-hour chick embryo. Cleared preparation from dorsal side. ×25.

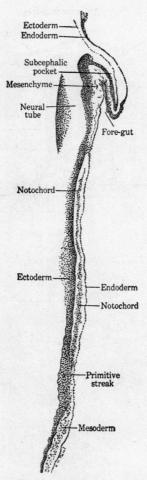

FIG. 216. 24-hour chick embryo. Sagittal section. ×37½.

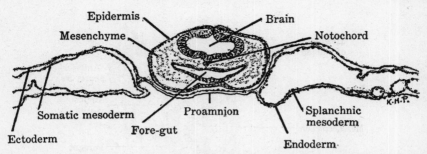

FIG. 217. 24-hour chick embryo. Transverse section through brain region. The neural folds have met but are not yet fused together. ×50.

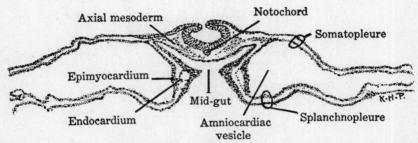

FIG. 218. 24-hour chick embryo. Transverse section through region of intestinal portal. ×50.

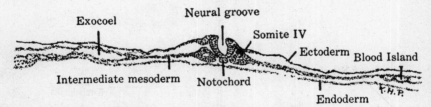

FIG. 219. 24-hour chick embryo. Transverse section through fourth somite. ×50.

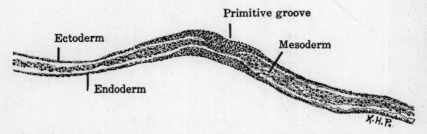

FIG. 220. 24-hour chick embryo. Transverse section through primitive streak. ×50.

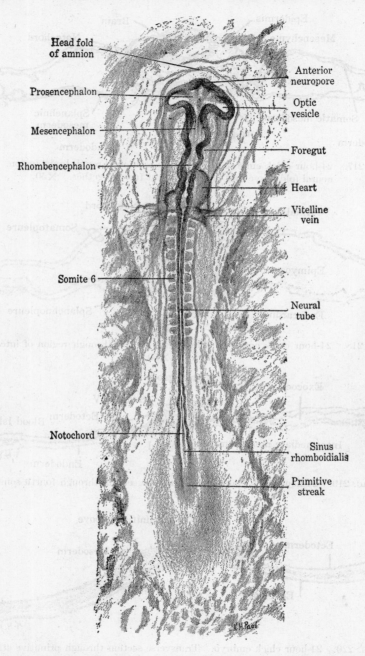

Head fold
of amnion

Prosencephalon

Mesencephalon

Rhombencephalon

Somite 6

Notochord

Anterior
neuropore

Optic
vesicle

Foregut

Heart

Vitelline
vein

Neural
tube

Sinus
rhomboidialis

Primitive
streak

FIG. 221. 33-hour chick embryo. Cleared preparation from dorsal view. ×25.

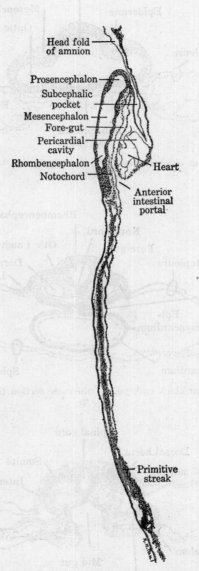

Head fold
of amnion

Prosencephalon

Subcephalic
pocket

Mesencephalon

Fore-gut

Pericardial
cavity

Rhombencephalon

Notochord

Heart

Anterior
intestinal
portal

Primitive
streak

Fig. 222.   33-hour chick embryo.   Sagittal section.   ×25.

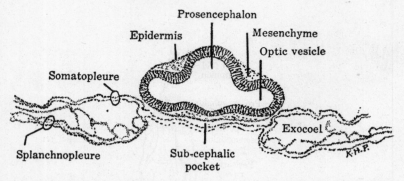

FIG. 223.   33-hour chick embryo.   Transverse section through optic vesicles.
×50.

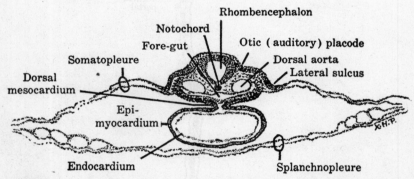

FIG. 224.   33-hour chick embryo.   Transverse section through otic placodes.
×50.

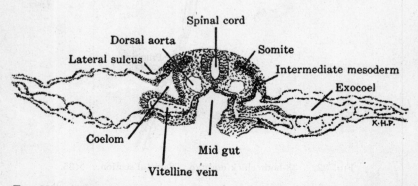

FIG. 225.   33-hour chick embryo.   Transverse section through vitelline veins.
×50.

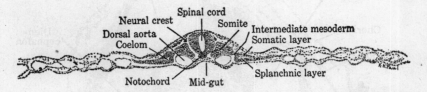

Fig. 226. 33-hour chick embryo. Transverse section through sixth somite. ×50.

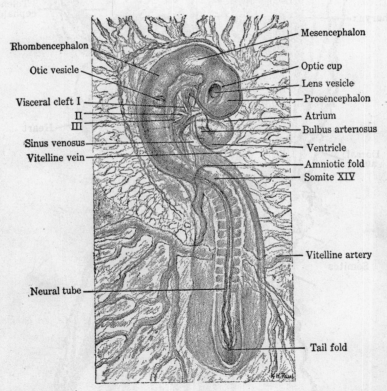

Fig. 227. 48-hour chick embryo. Transparent preparation from dorsal view (head from right side). ×15.

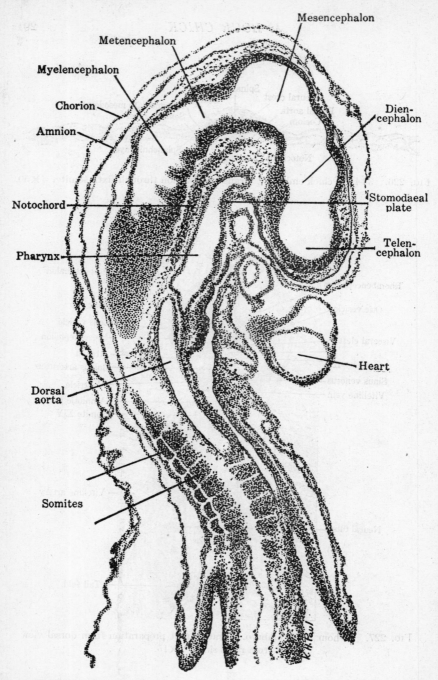

FIG. 228. 48-hour chick embryo. Head in sagittal section, somite region in frontal section due to torsion. ×50.

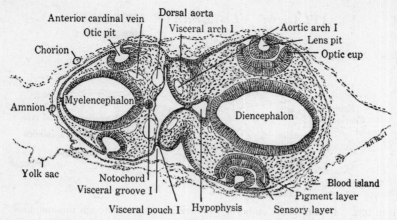

FIG. 229. 48-hour chick embryo. Transverse section through otic pit and optic cup. ×50.

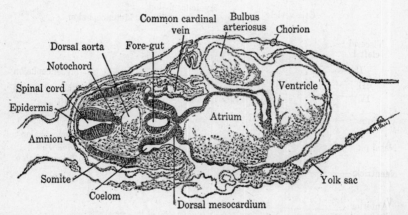

FIG. 230. 48-hour chick embryo. Transverse section through heart. ×50.

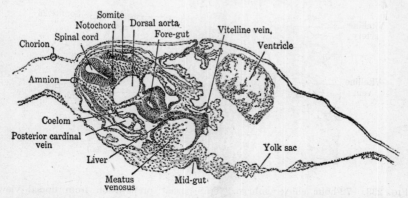

FIG. 231. 48-hour chick embryo. Transverse section through liver. ×50.

293

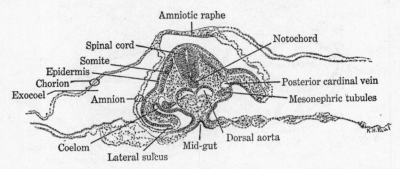

FIG. 232. 48-hour chick embryo. Transverse section through mesonephros. ×50.

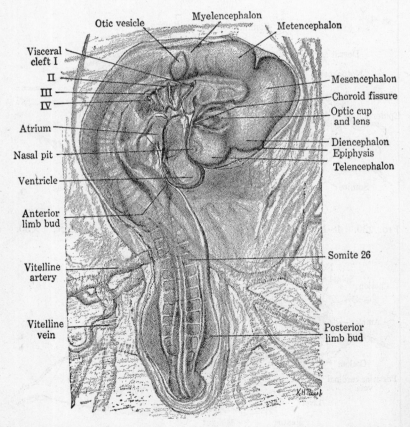

FIG. 233. 72-hour chick embryo. Transparent preparation from dorsal view, head seen from right side. ×15.

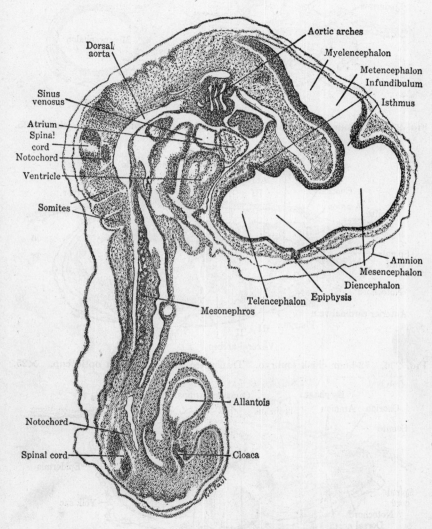

Fig. 234. 72-hour chick embryo. Sagittal section. ×25.

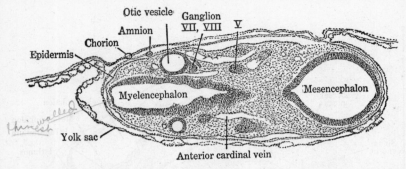

Otic vesicle
Ganglion
VII, VIII   V
Amnion
Chorion
Epidermis
Myelencephalon
Mesencephalon
Yolk sac
Anterior cardinal vein

Fig. 235. 72-hour chick embryo. Transverse section through otic vesicle. ×25.

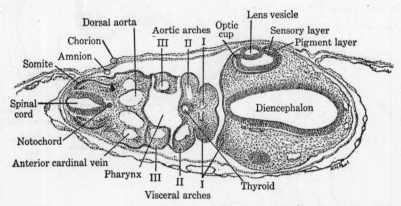

Dorsal aorta
Aortic arches
III   II   I
Optic cup
Lens vesicle
Sensory layer
Pigment layer
Chorion
Amnion
Somite
Spinal cord
Diencephalon
Notochord
Anterior cardinal vein
Pharynx   III
II   I
Thyroid
Visceral arches

Fig. 236. 72-hour chick embryo. Transverse section through optic cup. ×25.

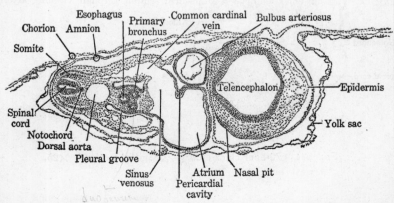

Esophagus
Primary bronchus
Common cardinal vein
Bulbus arteriosus
Chorion   Amnion
Somite
Telencephalon
Epidermis
Spinal cord
Yolk sac
Notochord
Dorsal aorta
Pleural groove
Sinus venosus
Atrium
Pericardial cavity
Nasal pit

Fig. 237. 72-hour chick embryo. Transverse section through heart and lung. ×25.

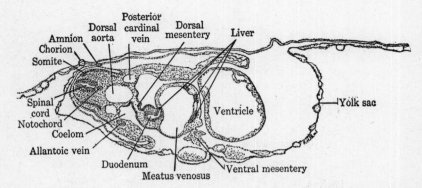

FIG. 238. 72-hour chick embryo. Transverse section through liver. ×25.

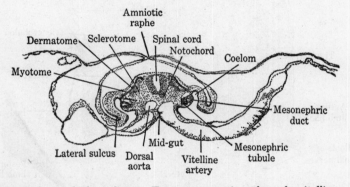

FIG. 239. 72-hour chick embryo. Transverse section through vitelline arteries leaving body. ×25.

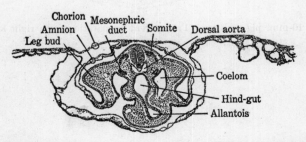

FIG. 240. 72-hour chick embryo. Transverse section through allantois. ×25.

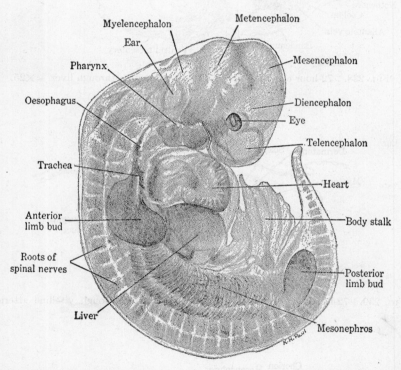

Fig. 241.   10-mm. pig embryo.   Transparent preparation from right side.   ×11.

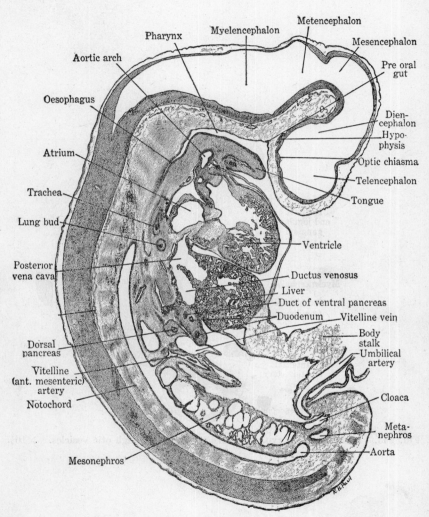

Fig. 242. 10-mm. pig embryo. Sagittal section. ×16½.

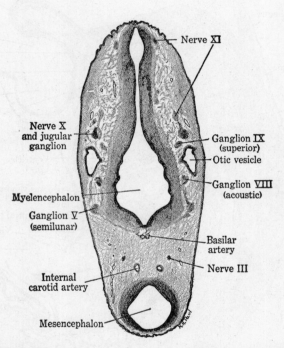

Fɪɢ. 243.   10-mm. pig embryo.   Transverse section through otic vesicles.   ×16½.

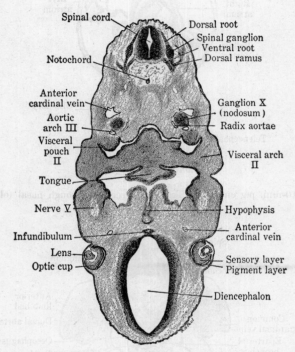

Spinal cord
Dorsal root
Spinal ganglion
Ventral root
Dorsal ramus
Notochord
Anterior cardinal vein
Ganglion X (nodosum)
Aortic arch III
Radix aortae
Visceral pouch II
Visceral arch II
Tongue
Nerve V
Hypophysis
Infundibulum
Anterior cardinal vein
Lens
Optic cup
Sensory layer
Pigment layer
Diencephalon

FIG. 244. 10-mm. pig embryo. Transverse section through optic cup. ✕16½.

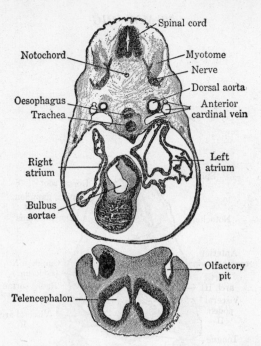

Fig. 245. 10-mm. pig embryo. Transverse section through nasal (olfactory) pit. ×16½.

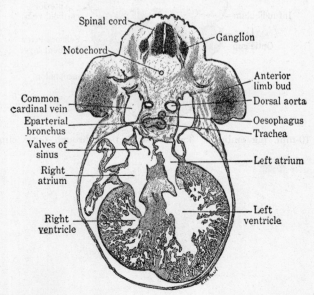

Fig. 246. 10-mm. pig embryo. Transverse section through sinus venosus. ×16½.

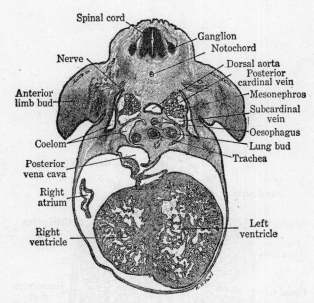

Fɪɢ. 247. 10-mm. pig embryo. Transverse section through lung buds. ×16½.

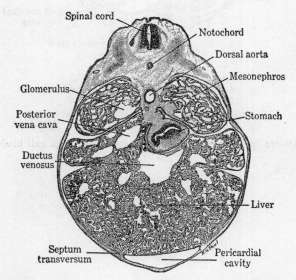

Fɪɢ. 248. 10-mm. pig embryo. Transverse section through stomach. ×16½.

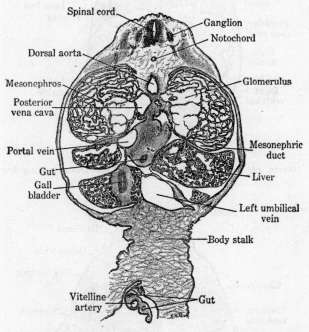

Fig. 249.   10-mm. pig embryo.   Transverse section through gall bladder.   ×16½.

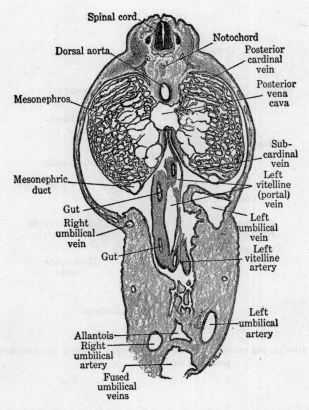

Spinal cord

Dorsal aorta

Mesonephros

Mesonephric
duct

Gut

Right
umbilical
vein

Gut

Allantois

Right
umbilical
artery

Fused
umbilical
veins

Notochord

Posterior
cardinal
vein

Posterior
vena
cava

Sub-
cardinal
vein

Left
vitelline
(portal)
vein

Left
umbilical
vein

Left
vitelline
artery

Left
umbilical
artery

Fig. 250. 10-mm. pig embryo. Transverse section through umbilical stalk in
region of intestinal loop. $\times 16\frac{1}{2}$.

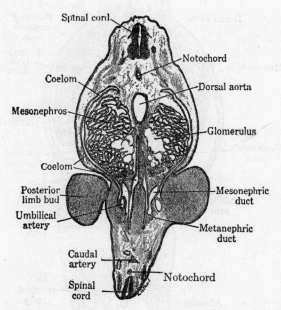

Fig. 251.   10-mm. pig embryo.   Transverse section through metanephric duct and posterior limb buds.   ×16½.

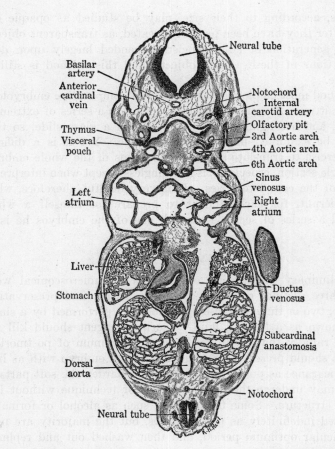

Fig. 252. 10-mm. pig embryo. Frontal section through aortic arches and ductus venosus. ×16½.

CHAPTER 19

EMBRYOLOGICAL TECHNIQUE

Embryos, according to their size, may be studied as opaque objects or, after they have been properly treated, as transparent objects. The older generation of embryologists depended largely upon delicate dissections of these minute objects, and this method is still of great value.

The method most employed in the study of comparative embryology is that of cutting a preserved egg or embryo into a series of extremely thin slices, and arranging these in order upon a glass slide, so that they may be examined under the microscope. Yet it is a difficult mental exercise to translate sections into terms of the whole embryo, for the single section, especially, is meaningless except when interpreted as a part of the complete series. It is very helpful, therefore, when facilities permit, for each student to prepare for himself a whole mount and a series of sections through one of the embryos he is to study.

FIXATION

The preliminary preparation of material for microscopical work involves three distinct operations: killing, fixing, and preservation. In practice, two or three of these operations are performed by a single reagent known as a " fixing fluid." Such a reagent should kill the embryo so rapidly that it will undergo the minimum of postmortem changes; it should preserve the structures of the embryo with as life-like an appearance as possible; and it should harden the soft parts so that they may undergo the later processes of technique without loss of form or structure. Some fixing fluids, such as alcohol or formalin, may be used indefinitely as preservatives, but the majority are used for a particular optimum period, and then washed out and replaced by alcohol.

THE FROG

The frog's egg, *before* hatching, is best fixed by Smith's fluid.

Potassium bichromate	0.5 gram
Glacial acetic acid	2.5 cc.
Formalin	10.0 cc.
Distilled water	75.0 cc.

1. Cut the egg masses into small pieces of about twenty-five eggs each, and submerge them in a dish of Smith's fluid for 24 hours. A quantity equal to ten times the volume of the eggs should be used.

2. Rinse the eggs in water and wash with a 5 per cent aqueous solution of formalin until no more free color comes out. The eggs may be kept indefinitely in this fluid. If it is desired to remove the egg membranes, proceed as follows:

3. Wash in water for 24 hours, changing the water several times.

4. Place the eggs in eau de Javelle, diluted with three times its volume of water, and shake gently from time to time during a period of 15 to 30 minutes until the membranes are almost dissolved and will shake off.

5. Rinse in water and run through 50 per cent and 70 per cent alcohol, an hour to a day each, and preserve in 80 per cent alcohol.

After hatching, larvae are best fixed in Bouin's fluid.

Picric acid, saturated aqueous solution	75 cc.
Formalin	25 cc.
Glacial acetic acid	5 cc.

1. Larvae are left in this fluid 1 to 18 hours, according to size.

2. After rinsing in 50 per cent alcohol, wash in 70 per cent alcohol, to which has been added a few drops of lithium carbonate, saturated aqueous solution, until the yellow color is extracted, and preserve in 80 per cent alcohol.

THE CHICK

The chick embryo must be removed from the shell, albumen, and yolk before fixation. As the early stages are more difficult to handle, it is advisable to practice this operation on embryos of 72 hours' incubation and then work backward toward the stages of the first day.

1. Place the egg in a dish 3 inches high and 6 inches in diameter, two-thirds full of normal saline solution, warmed to 40° C.

Sodium chloride	0.75 gr.
Water	100.00 cc.

2. Crack the shell at the broad end with the flat of the scalpel, and pick away the pieces of shell until an opening slightly larger than a half dollar has been made. Remove the outer and inner shell membranes. Invert egg beneath the surface of the salt solution and allow the contents to flow out. The blastoderm, containing the embryo, will rotate until it is uppermost. With fine-pointed scissors, cut rapidly a circle of blastoderm, about the size of a quarter, with

the embryo at the center. With blunted forceps, pull the blastoderm and adherent vitelline membrane away from the yolk and albumen, waving it gently beneath the surface of the salt solution to remove all yolk.

3. Submerge a Syracuse watch glass in the salt solution and float the embryo into this. Remove the watch glass carefully from the large dish and examine the embryo with a dissecting lens. If the vitelline membrane has not yet separated from the blastoderm, it should be removed at this time with fine-pointed forceps and needles. Make sure that the embryo lies dorsal side up, as it did when the egg was opened.

4. Slide a cover glass under the embryo, and remove all salt solution with a pipette, taking care that the embryo lies in the center of the cover glass. Lift the cover glass by one corner so that the overhanging edges of the blastoderm fold under and place it in a dry watch glass on a piece of thin absorbent tissue paper. Add at once a few drops of F.A.A. fixing fluid, prepared immediately before using.

Formalin	2 parts
Alcohol (85%)	17 parts
Glacial acetic acid	1 part

While the embryo is becoming attached to the cover glass, remove the yolk, albumen, and pieces of shell from the dish of salt solution to a slop jar, reheat the salt solution to 40° C., and prepare another embryo. Three embryos of each stage are to be prepared.

5. After 5 minutes, drop the cover glass, embryo side up, into a small stender dish of F.A.A. and leave for 4 hours.

6. Wash in 70 per cent alcohol for 30 minutes and preserve in 80 per cent alcohol or stain at once.

THE PIG

Embryos of 6 mm. body length and over are easily located in the uterine wall. Slit open the uterus and remove the embryo with fine-pointed forceps and a horn spoon, taking pains not to rupture the membranes. Place at once in Bouin's fluid. Embryos of 10 mm. body length should be fixed for 4 hours. Rinsing and preserving are done as for the frog or chick. Larger embryos should have the body cavity slit open to admit the fixing fluid. Fetal pigs of 6 inches or more should be injected through the umbilical artery with formalin (20 per cent aqueous solution). This solution is also injected into the body cavity and cranium, after which the fetus is submerged in the same medium for a week and preserved in 6 per cent formalin.

WHOLE MOUNTS

It is very helpful to have some embryos mounted entire for comparison with the serial sections. In making these whole mounts, the embryos are stained, cleared, and mounted, i.e., transferred to a final medium for preservation and examination on the slide beneath a cover glass.

THE FROG

Frog eggs and embryos may be mounted as opaque objects with the natural pigmentation, or they may be cleared and stained as transparent mounts.

Opaque whole mounts. Most of the older methods of preparing opaque whole mounts have not been permanent enough to justify their inclusion in this section. In the 1940 meeting of the A.A.A.S. demonstrations of material mounted in a plastic (methyl methacrylate) were shown which hold promise of more permanent preparations. Directions for experimentation along these lines may be obtained from companies manufacturing these chemicals.

Transparent stained mounts.

1. Bleach the embryo, until white, in hydrogen peroxide. About one week is required for this purpose. Embryos that have been preserved in 80 per cent alcohol should first be passed through 70 and 50 per cent alcohol to water, an hour or more in each fluid. Embryos in formalin must be rinsed in water for one hour.

2. Stain in dilute borax carmine four days or more.

> Borax, 4 per cent aqueous solution .... 100 cc.
> Carmine .... 1 gr.
> Boil until dissolved and add alcohol, 70 per cent .... 100 cc.
> To dilute, take 5 cc. of the borax carmine and 95 cc. of 35 per cent alcohol and add a crystal of thymol.

3. If overstained, remove the surplus color with hydrochloric acid (1 per cent solution in 70 per cent alcohol) after passing through water and 50 per cent alcohol, an hour each. If acid has been used, several changes of alcohol during the hour are recommended.

4. Run up through 80, 95, and 100 per cent alcohol, an hour each, and place in xylene (xylol) until transparent.

5. Prepare a mounting diagram by drawing an outline of a slide on a piece of cardboard and on this lay off an outline of the cover glass to be used. Place a clean slide on the diagram, and, just inside

the right and left margins of the cover-glass outline, put a small piece of broken coverslip as a support. Place a few drops of Canada balsam, or clarite, dissolved in xylene, between the supports, place the embryo in position, and lower a clean cover glass gently. Try to avoid the formation of air bubbles. If these appear later, they may be removed by a needle which has been heated or dipped in xylene. A little fresh balsam or clarite may be run into the cavity.

THE CHICK

Total mounts may be stained either with the borax carmine or with Mayer's hemalum.

Hematoxylin	1 gr.
Distilled water	1000 cc.
After this has dissolved, add	
Sodium iodate	2 gr.
Alum	50 gr.
(Does not keep well)	

1. Run the embryo from the 80 per cent alcohol down to water through changes of 70 and 50 per cent alcohol, an hour each.

2. Stain in borax carmine, undiluted, over night, or in hemalum 1 to 3 hours. Either stain may be diluted still further and the staining period prolonged. In the author's laboratory the schedule demands a 4-day staining period, and 5 per cent solutions of the borax carmine or hemalum are used. The borax carmine is preferred for whole mounts, the hemalum for material which is to be sectioned.

3. Destain, if necessary, in acid alcohol until the desired color is obtained. Embryos stained with hemalum will turn red in the acid alcohol, and the blue color must be restored by washing them in running water or, after washing in neutral 70 per cent alcohol, placing them in alkaline alcohol (1 per cent ammonia in 80 per cent alcohol).

4. Run up the alcohols, 80, 95, and 100 per cent, half an hour each. Pour off half the 100 per cent alcohol and add an equal amount of xylene. When the diffusion currents disappear, transfer to pure xylene and leave until the embryo is transparent. In rainy weather, or when 100 per cent alcohol cannot be obtained, phenol-xylene (phenol crystals, 25 gr. and xylene 75 cc.) may be substituted.

5. Remove the embryo from the cover glass (if it has not already detached itself) and trim the surrounding blastoderm to the form of an oblong or circle. Arrange a clean slide on the mounting diagram, as described for the frog, place broken bits of cover slip for support, and mount the embryo in Canada balsam or clarite with the same side uppermost as when the egg was opened. Put the slide away

where it may lie flat and free from dust until the balsam has hardened. This will take at least a week, after which the slide may be cautiously cleaned and studied. The process may be hastened by drying the slide in a paraffin oven.

THE PIG

Embryos up to 10 mm. body length may be prepared as whole mounts by staining in dilute borax carmine, destaining until only a trace of color persists, and mounting in Canada balsam. The time spent in each alcohol should be at least an hour for the larger embryos.

SERIAL SECTIONS

In the preparation of serial sections of an embryo, the fixed material is (1) embedded in a suitable matrix and (2) sliced into extremely thin sections, which are (3) mounted in serial order upon slides. The embryo may be stained before or after sectioning.

Embedding. There are two principal methods of embedding, in paraffin or in celloidin. For especially delicate objects, the best results are obtained by a combination of these methods, the embryo being first impregnated with celloidin in order to avoid the shrinkage (about 10 per cent) caused by paraffin embedding, and the block of celloidin then immersed in paraffin so that ribbons of serial sections may be cut. In spite of the shrinkage caused by paraffin, the necessity of having the sections adhere to each other to form a ribbon (page 315) has resulted in the almost universal use of paraffin sections.

Embedding in paraffin. In preparing the first few embryos for sectioning, it is advisable to stain, dehydrate, dealcoholize, and clear as if for a total mount. Later, the staining may be omitted until after the sections are affixed to the slide.

1. After clearing in xylene, which should be done in a warm place, for example, the low-temperature oven at about 40° C., pour off half the xylene and add an equal amount of paraffin chips. In the author's laboratory a paraffin of about 55° C. melting point, obtained by mixing commercial paraffin with parawax, is used. The parawax, unfortunately, varies in melting point, so that the formula is empirical. A rubber paraffin, Tissue mat, now on the market, is better for frog embryos. The embryo may be left in this xylene paraffin for two days.

2. If the mixture has hardened it should again be melted in the low-temperature oven. Fill a clean stender dish with melted paraffin,

transfer the embryo to this, and place in the high-temperature oven at about 56° C. (or one degree above the melting point of the paraffin used) for not more than 2 hours. The xylene-paraffin should be thrown in the slop jar. Take care not to get any xylene in the high-temperature oven or paraffin used for the final embedding.

3. Smear the interior of a small watch glass with a 10 per cent aqueous solution of glycerin (or vaseline), and fill with fresh melted paraffin. Transfer the embryo to this, making any necessary adjustments in position with a heated needle. Place the embryo dorsal side up, and note the position of the head. Cool the surface of the paraffin by blowing on it gently until it is congealed. Then plunge it immediately into a dish of cold water or waste alcohol and leave it there for 5 minutes. Mark the block for identification. Objects may be left in paraffin indefinitely.

4. On removing the block of paraffin from its container, examine for the following flaws:

a. Air bubbles, if they are not near the embryo, may be removed with a hot needle. Otherwise it is better to trim the block close to the embryo, put it into melted paraffin, and re-embed.

b. Milky streaks are due to the presence of xylene. These will crumble during sectioning, so that it is best to re-embed if they occur near the embryo.

c. If the paraffin has " fallen " in the center, it is because the surface was cooled too long before the block was immersed in the water. If any part of the embryo is exposed, it must be re-embedded.

Sectioning after paraffin embedding. Before sectioning your first embryo, be sure you understand the mechanism of the microtome (there are many varieties, of which the rotary type is best adapted to beginning students) and have practiced the technique on a block of paraffin. There are three standard planes of sectioning corresponding to the axes of the body (Fig. 253).[1] Transverse sections are obtained by cutting the cephalic end of the body first, with the knife entering the left side. Sagittal sections are made by cutting the right side first, with the knife entering the ventral surface. Frontal sections are made by commencing at the dorsal surface, the knife entering the left side. It is best to begin with transverse sections.

[1] In transverse sectioning of embryos having a marked torsion of the head, as in the 72-hour chick embryo, it is best to cut the cephalic end first, *but with the knife entering the ventral side* of the blastoderm. This procedure permits a closer trimming of the paraffin block, which will then yield a ribbon with a compact series of sections that may be mounted on fewer slides.

1. Attach the paraffin block to the object-carrier of the microtome in the proper manner to obtain the type of section desired. This is done by heating the surface of the carrier until it will just melt paraffin, pressing the block against it in the desired orientation, and lowering into a dish of cold water. A little melted paraffin may be poured around the base of the block and this again cooled to secure additional support.

2. Place the object-carrier in the microtome and, after orienting the block with respect to the knife, trim it so that the end of the block is a perfect rectangle with one of the longer sides parallel to

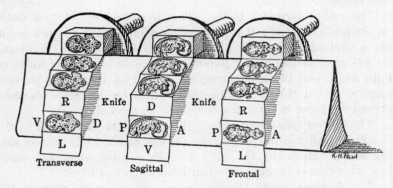

FIG. 253. Diagram to show method of orienting embryo with reference to microtome knife according to type of section desired.

the knife edge. If one of the angles is cut off slightly there will be a series of indentations in the ribbon, which will assist in orienting the sections on the slide.

3. If microtome knives are not available, place a new safety-razor blade (Autostrop type) in the holder provided, allowing the edge to project between a sixteenth and an eighth of an inch. Screw the holder in the knife-carrier so that the edge of the blade is tilted inward about 10° from the perpendicular.

4. Set the regulator for 20 microns (thousandths of a millimeter).

5. Run the feed screw as far back as it runs freely; do not force it.

6. Advance the knife-carrier until the edge of the blade just clears the block.

7. Release safety catch and turn the wheel steadily until the knife begins to cut the block. Cut slowly, making necessary adjustments to the block and knife until you are cutting a perfectly straight ribbon without wrinkles or splits. The principal causes of trouble and their remedies are:

a. The ribbon curls to right or left. This happens because (1) the block is thicker on the side away from which the ribbon curls, or (2) the knife is duller on the side toward which the ribbon curls. Remedy: (1) trim the sides of the block parallel; (2) shift the knife to one side.

b. The sections curl and the ribbon is not continuous. This is due to (1) too much tilt of the knife, (2) too hard a grade of paraffin, or (3) too cold a room. Remedy: (1) lessen tilt of knife; (2) re-embed in softer paraffin; (3) move microtome to warmer place, light an electric light or micro-bunsen burner near microtome, or cut thinner sections.

c. The ribbon wrinkles badly. This is caused by (1) too little tilt to the knife, (2) too soft a grade of paraffin, (3) too warm a room, or (4) a dull or dirty knife. Remedy: (1) increase the tilt of the knife; (2) re-embed in harder paraffin; (3) move to a cooler room, or cool the knife and block by dropping alcohol on them and blowing vigorously, or cut thicker sections; (4) clean knife edge with cloth moistened in xylene or shift to a new place on the knife.

d. The ribbon splits lengthwise. This is due to (1) a nick in the knife, (2) a bubble in the paraffin, or (3) dirt on the knife edge or side of the block. Remedy: (1) shift to new cutting edge; (2) paint surface with thin celloidin; (3) clean knife edge and block.

e. The sections refuse to ribbon; they fly apart or cling to the knife or the block. This is due to the electrification of the sections caused by unfavorable atmospheric conditions. Many remedies have been suggested; usually it is advisable to wait for more favorable conditions.

8. Remove the ribbon in 6 inch lengths with a camel's-hair brush and arrange these in order, shiny side down, in a cardboard box cover. Avoid air currents of all kinds. The ribbons may be put away in a dust-free place if the room is not too warm. It is better to affix them to slides as soon as possible.

Affixing paraffin sections to the slide.

1. Prepare a mounting diagram by laying off the outline of a slide as before, but enclose in this the outline of a long cover glass (24 by 50 mm. approximately) and leave space for a label on the right-hand side.

2. Clean a slide thoroughly by washing with acid alcohol and then distilled water. Place this over the mounting diagram and brush over the surface above the outline of the cover glass with the following dilute solution of egg albumen:

Egg albumen, beaten and skimmed .... 50 cc.
Glycerin .... 50 cc.
Filter and add thymol .... a crystal
Dilute 2 drops of this to distilled water .... 25 cc.

3. Cut the ribbon into lengths about 20 per cent shorter than the length of the cover glass. Using the wet brush from which most of the albumen solution has been squeezed, pick up these lengths and arrange them on the albumenized slide so that the sections will follow each other like the words on a printed page. The shiny side of the ribbon should be next to the slide. Great care should be taken to lower the ribbon slowly so as to prevent the formation of air bubbles beneath it.

4. Carefully warm the slides on a warming plate or a piece of plate glass, previously heated in the paraffin oven, until the sections are expanded and perfectly smooth. If bubbles appear beneath the ribbon, prick them with a hot needle while the ribbon is still soft and hot. Drain off the surplus water, carefully realign the sections, mark the slides with a glass-marking crayon, and set them away in the low-temperature oven to dry, at least two days. They may be kept indefinitely in this condition if not exposed to dust.

Staining serial sections. When the embryo has been stained before sectioning, it is necessary only to remove the paraffin, replace with Canada balsam or clarite, and cover, if the stain proves to be satisfactory. Sometimes, however, it is advisable to strengthen or weaken the stain or to add a contrasting dye.

To examine stain. Before proceeding further, the quality of the stain should be examined by placing the slide, section side toward you, in a Coplin staining jar of xylene. After 5 minutes, wipe the *back* of the slide dry with a paper towel and examine immediately under a microscope. CAUTION: xylene evaporates *very* rapidly. Get the slide back in the jar of xylene as fast as possible. If satisfactory mount at once (see below).

To strengthen a weak stain.
1. Xylene, 5 minutes.
2. Xylene and absolute alcohol (equal parts), 5 minutes.
3. Absolute alcohol, 5 minutes.
4. 95 per cent, 80 per cent, 70 per cent alcohol, 1 minute each.
5. Distilled water, 1 minute.
6. Stain, undiluted, as required.
7. Distilled water, 1 minute.

8.   70 per cent, 80 per cent, 95 per cent alcohol, 1 minute each.
9.   Absolute alcohol, 5 minutes.
10. Xylene and absolute alcohol (equal parts), 5 minutes.
11. Xylene, 5 minutes.

To weaken an intense stain.
Steps 1–4 as above.
5.   Acid 70 per cent alcohol, as required.
6.   Rinse in 70 per cent alcohol, 1 minute.
7.   Alkaline 70 per cent alcohol, 5 minutes.
Steps 8–11 as above.

To counterstain. In order to differentiate the parts of the embryo more sharply, it is often desirable to add a second stain contrasting with the first. The stains that have been employed in the previous exercises are nuclear dyes; that is, when extracting by acid alcohol, the color will persist in the nucleus after it has been washed out of the cytoplasm. The second stains affect the cytoplasm and should contrast in color with the nuclear stain employed. After borax carmine, a blue stain (indigo-carmine, saturated solution in distilled water) or a green stain (indigo-carmine prepared as above and mixed with saturated aqueous solution of picric acid in equal parts) is useful. After hemalum a 0.1 per cent solution of eosin in 95 per cent alcohol is good.

1.   Run down the alcohols to the stage corresponding to the medium in which the counterstain is dissolved (water for indigo-carmine and picro-indigo-carmine; 95 per cent alcohol for eosin).
2.   Stain (5 minutes for indigo-carmine and picro-indigo-carmine; 10 seconds for eosin).
3.   Run up the alcohols to xylene and mount.

To mount sections after stain is satisfactory. Wipe back and sides of slide dry with paper toweling. Add about three drops of Canada balsam or clarite. Place tip of needle (or forceps held in left hand) to left of area to be covered. Dip left end of cover slip in benzene, rest it against needle, and lower gently with fingers of right hand. This should be practiced several times before trying to cover sections. It must be done rapidly so that xylene will not evaporate before sections are covered.

Staining with Heidenhain's hematoxylin. This is one of the most important embryological stains.

1.   Remove the paraffin from the sections and run down the alcohols to distilled water. N.B. If embryo has been stained before sectioning,

the color must be removed by acid alcohol, and the acid neutralized before proceeding.

2. Four per cent aqueous solution of iron alum, one hour to over night.

3. Rinse in distilled water and place in 0.5 per cent aqueous solution of hematoxylin, same time as in the iron alum.

4. Rinse in distilled water and return to the iron alum until sections are a pale gray. Check from time to time by rinsing in distilled water and examining under microscope to see that the desired structures are still visible. N.B. Many investigators prefer to destain in a saturated aqueous solution of picric acid, neutralizing with running water until gray color is restored.

5. When the embryo is sufficiently destained, wash in running water for 20 minutes, or in distilled water, with frequent changes, for 2 hours.

6. Run up the alcohols, clear, and mount.

Fuchsin and picro-indigo-carmine. This polychromatic stain is especially fine for organogeny.

1. Remove the paraffin and run down the alcohols to distilled water.

2. Stain in basic fuchsin, saturated aqueous solution, 20 minutes.

3. Rinse in distilled water and place in picro-indigo-carmine for 5 minutes.

Picric acid, saturated aqueous solution	50 cc.
Indigo-carmine, saturated aqueous solution	50 cc.

4. Pass rapidly through 70, 95, and absolute alcohol into xylene-alcohol. The green dye is extracted most rapidly by the 70 per cent alcohol, the red by the absolute. Only experience will teach the right time allowance for each alcohol.

5. Clear in xylene and mount.

TECHNICAL RECORDS

Not the least important part of technique is the keeping of exact records covering every technical operation. For each embryo there should be a card, giving the following data:

1. Kind of embryo and stage of development.
2. Method of fixation, time and date.
3. Bulk staining, time and date.
4. Method of embedding, time and date.
5. Plane and thickness of sections and date.

6. Slide staining, time and date.
7. Method of mounting and date.
8. Name of preparator.

EMBRYOLOGICAL DRAWINGS

Free-hand drawings of microscopic objects can only approximate an accurate representation. However, great pains should be taken to secure at least accurate proportions, neat and clean-cut lines, and complete labels. Accurate outlines can be secured by the aid of the camera lucida, various types of projection apparatus, or micro-photography.

Equipment. The student will need a hard lead pencil (4H), a medium pencil (HB), and blue, red, and yellow pencils, and an eraser.

Free-hand drawing.

1. Lay off the space to be occupied by the drawing, by placing four dots at the corners. Rule in two lines, intersecting at right angles in the center of this space. These will represent the dorsoventral and the dextrosinistral axes, if the drawing is to be of a transverse section.

2. Measure the corresponding axes of the sections by means of the ocular micrometer (see below), multiply by the desired magnification of the drawing, and lay off these magnified measurements on the cross lines already drawn. The following magnifications are recommended: for the 24-hour chick, 60 ✕; for the 33-hour chick, 50 ✕; for the 48-hour chick, 40 ✕; for the 72-hour chick, 30 ✕; for the 10-mm. pig, 20 ✕.

3. Draw in a careful outline of the section and of the internal structures, paying particular attention to the proportions, which should be measured with the ocular micrometer and laid off on the axes at the proper magnification.

4. On one side of the dorsoventral axis, all structures should be colored in accordance with the following scheme: ectoderm, blue; mesoderm, red; and endoderm, yellow.

5. Label all structures represented in the section, using broken lines at right angles to the long axis of the paper to connect the label with the structure indicated.

6. Identify the drawing fully, by means of a serial number, the species, and stage of development, the number given to the series, slide, and section, the type of sections, and the amount of magnification. Example: No. 23, Chick, 48 hours, Series 1102, Slide 2, section 28, transverse section 50 ✕. If a drawing has already been made of the total embryo or a total mount, indicate on this, by means of a

heavy ruled line, the position of the section just drawn, and number this line with the serial number of the section.

Micrometry. The unit of measurement in microscopy is the micron (μ). It is the one-thousandth part of a millimeter. Measurement of microscopic objects is performed with the aid of micrometers, of which there are two types, the stage micrometer and the ocular micrometer. The former is a glass slide, in the center of which, under a cover glass, is a line, usually 2 mm. long, divided into 200 equal parts, each of which, therefore, is equivalent to 10 μ. The ocular micrometer is a glass disc, placed in an ocular at the level of the ocular diaphragm, on which is engraved a scale, with arbitrary subdivisions. Some oculars are furnished with a draw tube so that the upper lens of the system may be focused more sharply upon the scale. The value of the divisions indicated on the scale varies according to the amount of magnification of the real image, and so must be obtained for each objective independently, according to the following method:

1. Arrange the microscope as before, taking particular care to secure the proper tube length.

2. Focus the eye lens on the ocular micrometer scale by means of the ocular draw tube. Focus the objective on the stage micrometer.

3. Make the lines of the stage micrometer parallel with those of the ocular micrometer, and determine the value of the divisions of the ocular micrometer in terms of those of the stage micrometer. Thus, if it requires 10 spaces of the ocular micrometer, and the latter is equal to 0.1 mm., then the value of a single space of the ocular micrometer for that particular objective and at that particular tube length is 0.01 mm. or 10 μ. Determine the value of the ocular micrometer for each objective in the same way.

Abbé camera lucida. This is an attachment which reflects the light from the drawing board, by means of a mirror, to a silvered prism, whence the light is reflected to the eye, superimposed on the image of the object which is transmitted through a small hole in the silvered surface of the prism directly above the ocular of the microscope (Fig. 254).

1. Attach the camera to the draw tube of the microscope in such a way that the mirror projects to the right, and the opening in the prism lies above the center of the ocular.

2. Extend the mirror arm to its greatest length and set the mirror at an angle of 45°. The mirror arm must be parallel to the drawing board.

3. Try various combinations of objectives and oculars until an image of the desired magnification appears on the paper. Magnifications intermediate to those obtainable in this way may be secured by varying the tube length or by raising or lowering the drawing board. If the stage of the microscope interferes with the drawing, the mirror should be set at an angle of 40° or 35° and the drawing board tilted toward the microscope at an angle of 10° or 20°, respectively, by means of wooden wedges. If the image is stronger than the reflection of the pencil point, a smoked glass may be replaced beneath the prism, or the aperture of the iris diaphragm may be reduced. If the reflection of the pencil is stronger than the image, smoked glass may be placed at the side of the prism or the amount of light falling on the paper reduced by means of a screen.

4. Draw in the outlines of the sections and the larger internal structures. The details may be added free hand.

5. Remove the slide and substitute a stage micrometer. Trace in part of the scale by means of which both the magnification of the drawing and the absolute size of the object may be computed readily.

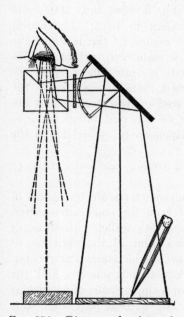

Fig. 254. Diagram showing principle of the Abbé camera lucida. Path of image seen in microscope shown in broken lines, that on drawing paper shown in unbroken lines. (From Gage.)

Projection apparatus. Where many drawings are to be made, as in the case of reconstructions, some form of apparatus by means of which the image of the section may be projected directly upon the paper is very helpful. There are many types of projection apparatus, directions for the use of which may be obtained with the instruments. A photographic enlarger can be used very successfully.

Microphotography. The photography of minute objects with the aid of the microscope is of great assistance in embryology. However, the methods are so difficult, the apparatus so complex, expensive, and delicate, and the process requires so much technical knowledge and skill, that microphotography has been considered a field too advanced for the beginning student. In recent years the motion-picture camera has been adapted for use with the microscope, and excellent results have already been obtained.

RECONSTRUCTION

After an embryo has been sectioned, it is sometimes necessary to reconstruct some part of it from the sections. There are two important methods: graphic reconstruction, in which a geometric projection of a sagittal section, for example, might be made from transverse sections; and plastic reconstruction, in which magnified replicas of each section are made of wax and piled together so as to make an enlarged model of the object to be studied. A complete series of sections of uniform thickness and accurate orientation is required for either type of reconstruction, and an outline drawing of the embryo before sectioning is of great assistance.

The graphic method (*of His*). This method can best be described by giving practical directions for a particular problem, e.g., to prepare a geometrical sagittal projection 20 × of the neural tube of a 10-mm. pig embryo from a series of transverse sections 20 μ in thickness.

1. From the lateral view of the embryo drawn before sectioning, make an outline drawing 20 ×.

2. Draw a median line corresponding to the cephalocaudal axis, the length of which, in this case, should be 200 mm.

3. Count the number of sections in the series, in this case, 500.

4. Locate the position of each transverse section which you have drawn on the median line of the outline. Thus if the most anterior section drawn was the fiftieth of the series of 500 sections, it would be located at a point one-tenth of the total length of the axis (200 μ), or 20 mm. from the cephalic end.

5. Theoretically, each section is at right angles to the median line, but this angle may be greater or less as a result of variations in technique. Study each drawing of a cross-section in connection with the drawing of the total embryo and determine the angle made by that section with the cephalocaudal axis of the embryo. Draw in, at each point located on the median line, a cross line at the proper angle so determined. These lines represent the dorsoventral axes of the transverse sections. Their lengths should correspond with those of the dorsoventral axes of the drawings of the transverse sections previously made at the same magnification, 20 ×.

6. Plot in on each section-plane line (dorsoventral axis) the dorsal and ventral boundaries of the neural tube as determined from

measurements of the drawings already made. Interpolate by direct measurement and magnification of these points on intervening sections.

7. Sketch in the contours of the neural tube by connecting up the points which have just been plotted. Compare the drawing with a sagittal section of an embryo in the same stage of development.

Plastic reconstruction. This method also will be indicated by practical directions for the reconstruction of a particular organ, in this case, a model 50 × of the heart of a 10-mm. pig, from a series of transverse section, 20 μ in thickness.

1. Prepare a number of wax plates of the proper thickness. In this case, if every section is to be reconstructed, the thickness of the plates must be 50 × 20 μ, or 1 mm. Nearly as good results can be obtained by reconstructing every second section and making the plates twice as thick. The wax is prepared according to the following formula:

Beeswax	6 parts
Paraffin, 56° C. m.p.	4 parts
Rosin, white lump	2 parts
Mix and melt.	

Pour 130 grams of this wax into a pan with an inside measurement of 500 × 280 mm., into which boiling water has been poured to a depth of 15 mm. This amount of wax will make a plate 1 mm. in thickness. Bubbles in the wax may be removed by playing the flame of a Bunsen burner over the surface as it is cooling. As the surface hardens, cut the edges free from the sides of the pan. When the wax has set but is still malleable, roll up the plate and remove it to a soapstone slab, where it is unrolled and allowed to cool.

2. With the help of a camera lucida or projection apparatus, prepare outlines 50 × of the heart in all the sections in which it is found. Number the drawings consecutively and note the serial number of the sections drawn, so that it will be possible to check the drawings later if necessary. Note also whether the right and left sides of the drawing actually correspond with the right and left sides of the embryo or whether this condition is reversed. This is very important, as a mistake at this point would render the reconstruction valueless.

3. Transfer the drawings to the wax plates by means of carbon paper. Place the wax plates on a sheet of glass, and cut out the parts to be preserved with a sharp scalpel, leaving bridges of wax to connect the parts which would otherwise be separated. These

bridges are best made in the form of arches bending towards the outside of the section.

4. Pile the sections in order, taking care to avoid the reversal of right and left sides, and to get an accurate fit. It is best to group the sections in piles of ten. A steady pressure of the hand will be sufficient to cause the sections to adhere to each other. The bridges may be cut away and stout pieces of wire substituted. Heat the wire at each end and press into position. After the wire is set, the wax bridges are cut away and the edges of the piece smoothed with a heated scalpel or aluminum modeling tool.

5. When all the sections have been combined in groups of ten, these groups should be united and the completed model smoothed in the same way. Such models may be painted or dissected, and mounted on wooden supports as desired. They are quite permanent if not exposed to high temperatures. Plaster of Paris molds and casts may be made from them in the customary manner.

BIBLIOGRAPHY

To list all the books and journals consulted in the preparation of this book would increase its size unduly. The following references are classified in the hope that they may be of service to students who desire to obtain more information in special fields than can be given in an introductory book.

ATLASES

Duval, M. 1884. Atlas d'embryologie.
Goette, A. 1874. Atlas zur Entwickelungsgeschichte der Unke.
Keibel, F. (ed.) 1897–1938. Normentafeln zur Entwicklungsgeschichte der Wirbeltiere.
Kohlmann, J. 1907. Handatlas der Entwickelungsgeschichte des Menschen.
Long, J. A. 1937. A Stereoscopic Atlas of the Chick.

BIBLIOGRAPHIES
(See also bibliographies in other references cited.)

Biological Abstracts, commencing with literature of 1926.
Concilium Bibliographicum, card index, commencing with literature of 1896.
Minot, C. S. 1893. A Bibliography of Vertebrate Embryology. Mem. Boston Soc. Nat. Hist., 4:487–614.

COLLATERAL TEXTBOOKS

Huettner, A. F. 1941. Fundamentals of Comparative Embryology of the Vertebrates.
McEwen, R. S. 1931. Vertebrate Embryology, 2nd Ed.
Richards, A. 1931. Outline of Comparative Embryology.
Wieman, H. L. 1930. An Introduction to Vertebrate Embryology.

COMPARATIVE INVERTEBRATE EMBRYOLOGY

Dawydoff, C. 1928. Traité d'embryologie comparée des invertébrés.
Korschelt, E., and Heider, K. 1902–1910. Lehrbuch der vergleichenden Entwicklungsgeschichte der wirbellosen Tiere.
Korschelt, E., and Heider, K. 1936. Vergleichenden Entwicklungsgeschichte der Tiere.
MacBride, E. W. 1914. Textbook of Embryology, Vol. 1., Invertebrates.

COMPARATIVE VERTEBRATE EMBRYOLOGY

Brachet, A. 1935. Traité d'embryologie des vertébrés, 2nd Ed.
Chiarugi, G. 1929–1935. Trattato di Embriologia.
Hertwig, O. (ed.) 1906. Handbuch der vergleichenden und experimentallen Entwickelungslehre der Wirbeltiere. 6 volumes.
Jenkinson, J. W. 1913. Vertebrate Embryology.
Kellicott, W. E. 1913. Chordate Development.

Kerr, J. G. 1919. Textbook of Embryology, Vol. 2., Vertebrates Exclusive of Mammals.

EXPERIMENTAL EMBRYOLOGY

Allen, E. (ed.) 1939. Sex and Internal Secretion, 2nd Ed.
Bertalanffy, L. von, and Woodger, J. H. 1933. Modern Theories of Development.
Brachet, A. 1931. L'oeuf et les facters de l'ontogénèse.
Brambell, F. W. R. 1930. The Development of Sex in Vertebrates.
Child, C. M. 1915. Individuality in Organisms.
Child, C. M. 1941. Patterns and Problems of Development.
de Beer, G. R. 1934. Introduction to Experimental Embryology, 2nd Ed.
Dalcq, A. M. 1938. Form and Causality in Early Development.
Duesberg, J. 1926. L'oeuf et ses localisations germinales.
Dürken, B. 1932. Experimental Analysis of Development (trans).
Fauré-Fremiet, M. E. 1925. La cinétique du développement.
Huxley, J. S., and de Beer, G. R. 1934. The Elements of Experimental Embryology.
Jenkinson, J. W. 1909. Experimental Embryology.
Jenkinson, J. W. 1917. Three Lectures on Experimental Embryology.
Korschelt, E. 1927–1931. Regeneration und Transplantation.
Morgan, T. H. 1927. Experimental Embryology.
Morgan, T. H. 1934. Embryology and Genetics.
Needham, J. 1931. Chemical Embryology.
Newman, H. H. 1923. The Physiology of Twinning.
Ruffini, A. 1925. Fisiogenia.
Russell, E. S. 1930. The Interpretation of Development and Heredity.
Schleip, W. 1929. Die Determination der Primitiventwicklung.
Spemann, H. 1938. Embryonic Development and Induction.
Waddington, C. H. 1936. How Animals Develop.
Waddington, C. H. 1940. Organizers and Genes.
Weiss, P. 1930. Entwicklungsphysiologie der Tiere.
Weiss, P. 1939. Principles of Development.
Windle, W. F. 1940. Physiology of the Fetus.

GERM CELLS AND CHROMOSOMES

Cowdry, E. V. (ed.) 1924. General Cytology.
Kellicott, W. E. 1913. General Embryology.
Sharp, L. W. 1934. Introduction to Cytology, 3rd Ed.
Wilson, E. B. 1925. The Cell in Development and Heredity, 3rd Ed.

HISTORY OF EMBRYOLOGY

Castaglioni, A. 1941. A History of Medicine.
Cole, F. C. 1930. Early Theories of Sexual Generation.
Locy, W. A. 1915. Biology and Its Makers, 3rd Ed.
Mayer, A. W. 1939. The Rise of Embryology.
Needham, J. 1931. Chemical Embryology, Vol. 1.
Needham, J. 1934. History of Embryology.
Nordenskiold, E. 1928. The History of Biology.
Russell, E. S. 1916. Form and Function.
Singer, C. S. 1931. The Story of Living Things.

LABORATORY MANUALS

Adamstone, F. B., and Shumway, W. 1939. A Laboratory Manual of Vertebrate Embryology.

Boyden, E. A. 1933. A Laboratory Atlas of the Pig Embryo.

Lillie, F. R., and Moore, C. R. 1919. A Laboratory Outline of Embryology.

Vecchierello, H., and Worden, J. L. 1935. A Laboratory Manual of Vertebrate Embryology.

Waite, F. C., and Patten, B. M. 1918. An Outline of Laboratory Work in Vertebrate Embryology, Part I. The Chick. 1925. Part II. The Pig.

Wieman, H. L., and Weichert, C. K. 1930. A Laboratory Manual for Vertebrate Embryology.

Experimental Embryology

Adams, A. E. 1941. Studies in Experimental Zoology.

Rugh, R. 1941. Experimental Embryology.

MONOGRAPHS, EMBRYOLOGICAL SERIES

Carnegie Institution of Washington. Contributions to Embryology, Vols. 1–29.

SPECIAL VERTEBRATE EMBRYOLOGIES

Amphioxus

Conklin, E. G. 1932. The embryology of Amphioxus. Jour. Morphol. 54:69–151.

Conklin, E. G. 1933. The development of isolated and partially separated blastomeres of Amphioxus. Jour. Exp. Zool. 64:303–375.

Frog

Marshall, A. M. 1893. Vertebrate Embryology.

Morgan, T. H. 1897. The Development of the Frog's Egg.

Pollister, A. W., and Moore, J. A. 1937. Tables for the normal development of *Rana sylvatica*. Anat. Rec. 68:489–496.

Shumway, W. 1940. Stages in the normal development of *Rana pipiens*. I. External form. Anat. Rec. 78:139–147.

Wright, A. H. 1914. North American Anura.

Ziegler, H. E. 1902. Lehrbuch der vergleichenden Entwickelungsgeschichte der niederen Wirbeltiere.

Chick

Lillie, F. R. 1919. The Development of the Chick, 2nd Ed.

Patten, B. M. 1929. The Early Embryology of the Chick, 3rd Ed.

Man

Arey, L. B. 1940. Developmental Anatomy, 4th Ed.

Keibel, F., and Mall, F. P. 1910. Human Embryology.

Pig

Lewis, F. T. 1902. The gross anatomy of a 12 mm. pig, Am. Jour. Anat., 2: 211–226.

Minot, C. S. 1911. A Laboratory Textbook of Embryology, 2nd Ed.

Patten, B. M. 1931. The Embryology of the Pig, 2nd Ed.

Wallin, E. 1917. A teaching model of a 10 mm. pig embryo, Anat. Rec., 5:17–45.

TECHNIQUE

Belling, J. 1930. The Use of the Microscope.

Conn, H. J. 1940. Biological Stains, 4th Ed.

Gage, S. H. 1941. The Microscope, 17th Ed.

Guyer, M. F. 1936. Animal Micrology, 4th Ed.

Lee, A. B. 1937. The Microtomist's Vade-Mecum, 10th Ed.

McClung, C. A. 1937. Handbook of Microscopical Technique, 2nd Ed.

Mueller, J. F. 1935. A Manual of Drawing for Science Students.

Norman, J. R. 1923. Methods and technique of reconstruction. Jour. Roy. Microsc. Soc. 1923:37–56.

GLOSSARY

This glossary includes the technical vocabulary of vertebrate embryology as used in the text but does not include terms used in classification and comparative anatomy. Technical words employed in cytology, genetics, and experimental embryology are distinguished by the abbreviated name of the particular science in parentheses, e.g. (*Cyt.*). Synonyms are included with the definition but not indicated separately. For cross-references to synonyms, see Index.

ABERRATION. (*Cyt.*) Irregularity in the number or constitution of the chromosomes, producing modifications in development. *See* Mutation.

ACROSOME. A body at the apex of the vertebrate sperm. *Syn.*, perforatorium.

ADNEXA. Extra-embryonic structures produced during development and discarded before the adult condition is attained, e.g., yolk sac.

AGGLUTINATION. (*Exp.*) A reaction in which sperms collect in a clump under the influence of egg-water (fertilizin).

ALBUMEN. A tertiary egg envelope secreted by the wall of the oviduct in amniote animals and used as a foodstuff.

ALLANTOIS. An extra-embryonic sac formed in the development of the amniota.

ALLELE. (*Gen.*) One of two genes located at the same locus in homologous chromosomes but inducing alternative expressions of a particular character. *Syn.*, allelomorph.

AMITOSIS. A form of cell division in which no chromosomes appear. *Syn.*, direct division.

AMNIOCARDIAC VESICLE. A region of the coelom in the anterior part of the chick embryo contributing to the pericardial cavity and the amniotic cavity.

AMNION. An extra-embryonic sac enclosing the embryo, found only in the amniota.

AMNIOTA. Reptiles, birds, and mammals.

AMNIOTIC RAPHE. The point where the amniotic folds meet and fuse. *Syn.*, sero-amniotic, chorio-amniotic raphe.

AMPLEXUS. The sexual embrace assumed by amphibians during the breeding season.

ANAMNIOTA. Cyclostomes, fish, and amphibia.

ANAPHASE. (*Cyt.*) That phase of mitosis in which the chromatids (daughter chromosomes) are separating from each other.

ANASTOMOSIS. The union of two parts of a branching network, e.g., blood vessels.

ANDROGENESIS. (*Exp.*) The development of an egg which contains paternal chromosomes only.

ANESTRUM. The period following estrus in the female mammal.

ANGIOBLAST. A term applied collectively to all cells participating in the formation of the blood vascular system.

ANIMAL (POLE or HEMISPHERE). The region in which the polocytes are formed. *Syn.*, apical (pole or hemisphere).

APPENDIX TESTIS. A portion of the Müllerian duct persisting in the adult male mammal.

ARCUALIA. Small blocks of connective tissue formed from the sclerotome and taking part in the formation of vertebrae.

AREA OPACA. A region of the chick blastoderm immediately surrounding the area pellucida. Here the yolk is in close connection with the cells of the blastoderm.

AREA PELLUCIDA. The inner region of the chick blastoderm in which the body of the embryo develops. Here the yolk is separated from the cells of the blastoderm by a cavity.

AREA VASCULOSA. A region of the area opaca in which the vitelline blood vessels develop.

AREA VITELLINA. A region of the area opaca surrounding the area vasculosa.

ASTER. (*Cyt.*) A group of fibers extending radially from a centrosome during mitosis.

ATRIOPORE. An aperture from an atrial chamber. *Syn.*, spiracle.

ATTACHMENT POINT. (*Cyt.*) The region of a chromosome which is the first to move towards the centrosome in the anaphase. Point where chromosomal spindle fiber is attached. Presumably free from genes. *Syn.*, kinetochore, chromocenter, centromere.

AUTOSOME. (*Cyt.*) Any chromosome except the X- or Y-chromosome.

AUXOCYTE. (*Cyt.*) A germ cell just prior to the meiotic divisions. *Syn.*, meiocyte, cyte.

AXIAL FILAMENT. The contractile element in the tail of a sperm.

AXIAL MESODERM. The region of the mesoderm nearest to the notochord. *Syn.*, epimere.

BALANCER. Paired structures on the head of a urodele embryo which are used as adhesive organs in place of suckers.

BLASTEMA. A group of cells prior to their organization into a definite tissue.

BLASTOCOEL. A cavity associated with the blastula. *Syn.*, segmentation cavity.

BLASTOCYST. The type of blastula peculiar to mammals.

BLASTODERM. The sum total of blastomeres before gastrulation. Especially the living part of the hen's egg from which the embryo and all its membranes are derived (Lillie).

BLASTODISC. The disc-shaped mass of protoplasm lying on the yolk in the extreme type of telolecithal egg. *Syn.*, germinal disc.

BLASTOMERE. A cell arising in the cleavage of the egg, prior to gastrulation.

BLASTOPORE. The aperture connecting the gastrocoel with the exterior. Closed by the yolk plug in amphibia. Represented by primitive streak in the amniota.

BLASTULA. A spherical or disc-shaped embryonic stage marking the end of cleavage and just prior to gastrulation.

BLOOD ISLAND. An isolated area of mesenchyme in the splanchnic mesoderm which will become a blood vesicle, one of the primordia of the vascular system.

BRANCHIAL. Having to do with the gills.

BRANCHIOMERY. A form of metamerism associated with the visceral arches.

CELL LINEAGE. The study of the blastomeres, their origin and fate in later development. *Syn.*, cytogeny.

CENTROSOME. (*Cyt.*) A small body characteristic of the cell and occupying the center of the aster during mitosis (Boveri, 1888). Centriole used as synonym by many cytologists who define centrosome as centriole plus clear substance immediately surrounding it.

CEREBROSPINAL. Pertaining both to the brain and the spinal cord.

CERVICAL. Pertaining to the neck, e.g., cervical flexure.

CHALAZA. Twisted albumen, the " strings " seen in white of egg.

CHEMOTAXIS. Movement in response to a chemical stimulus.

CHIMERA. An individual which has two different sets of genes represented in different parts of the body, usually rising from chromosomal aberrations after fertilization of the egg.

CHONDRIFICATION. The process of forming cartilage.

CHONDRIOBLASTS. Cartilage-forming cells.

CHONDROCRANIUM. That part of the skull originally cartilaginous.

CHORDA MESODERM. That part of the embryo which will give rise to the notochord and the mesoderm.

CHORDA NEURAL CRESCENT. A region in the protochordate egg from which is derived the notochord and the neural plate.

CHORIO-ALLANTOIS. A membrane formed by the fusion of the wall of the chorion and that of the allantois.

CHORION. (1) An extra-embryonic sac external to and enclosing the amnion and allantois. Found only in amniota. *Syn.*, serosa, false amnion.

(2) An egg envelope formed by the cells of the ovarian follicle.

CHOROID. Used with reference to delicate vascular membranes e.g., choroid layer of the eye, choroid plexus of the brain, etc.

CHROMATID. (*Cyt.*) A half-chromosome. One of the four parts of a tetrad (McClung, 1900).

CHROMATIN. (*Cyt.*) Nuclear material readily stained with basic dyes.

CHROMATOPHORE. A cell containing a mass of pigment granules.

CHROMIDIA. (*Cyt.*) Cytoplasmic granules with the staining reactions of chromatin.

CHROMOMERE. (*Cyt.*) A distinguishable region of a chromosome.

CHROMONEMA. (*Cyt.*) A slender thread of chromatin which becomes the core of a chromosome during mitosis.

CHROMOSOME. (*Cyt.*) A mass of chromatin, containing matrix and one or two chromonemata, apparent during mitosis.

CLEAVAGE. The division of the fertilized egg into blastomeres. *Syn.*, segmentation.

CLEAVAGE PATH. The path taken by the pronuclei during fertilization from the point where they meet to their position in readiness for the first cleavage division.

CLEIDOIC. The type of egg characteristic of reptiles, birds, and oviparous mammals, protected by a shell (Needham, 1931).

COELOBLASTULA. Spherical type of blastula with a central blastocoel (Haeckel).

COELOM. The body cavity formed by the separation of the somatic and splanchnic layers of mesoderm.

COLLECTING TUBULE. Part of nephric tubule leading to nephric duct.

COMPETENCE. (*Exp.*) The ability of an embryonic area to respond to the action of an evocator.

CONCRESCENCE. The coming together of parts of the embryo which were originally separate.

COPULATION PATH. The path taken by the male or the female pronuclei in their approach towards each other.

CORONA RADIATA. A layer of follicle cells surrounding the human egg at ovulation.

CORPUS LUTEUM. A yellow substance secreted in the vesicular follicle following ovulation in mammals.

COTYLEDON. A brush-like group of villi characteristic of the chorion in some mammals, e.g., the cow.

CRANIAL. Pertaining to the head.

CROSSING OVER. (*Gen.*) A mutual exchange of corresponding regions between two chromosomes in synapsis.

CRYPTS. Depressions, such as those in the uterine wall for the reception of chorionic cotyledons.

CUMULUS OÖPHORUS. The mass of cells immediately surrounding the mammalian egg in the vesicular follicle.

CYTE. The germ cell just prior to meiosis, either oöcyte or spermatocyte.

CYTOKINESIS. (*Cyt.*) The phenomena displayed in the cytosome during mitosis.

CYTOLOGY. The study of cells.

CYTOPLASM. The material of the cell exclusive of the nucleus.

CYTOSOME. The body of the cell exclusive of the nucleus.

CYTOTROPHODERM. The region of the trophoderm characterised by the presence of typical cells.

DECIDUA. That portion of the uterine wall cast off at parturition.

DECIDUA BASALIS. The portion of the decidua which contributes to the formation of the placenta.

DECIDUA CAPSULARIS. The portion of the decidua immediately investing the chorion.

DECIDUA VERA. The portion of the decidua neither basalis nor capsularis.

DECIDUATE. A type of placentation characterized by the destruction of maternal tissue.

DELAMINATION. Separation by splitting, involving division, migration, and rearrangement of cells.

DENTAL PAPILLA. The mesodermal portion of a tooth primordium.

DERMATOME. That portion of a somite which contributes to the dermis of the skin.

DERMOCRANIUM. That portion of the skull which does not pass through a cartilaginous stage in development. *Syn.*, membranocranium.

DETERMINATE. A type of cleavage in which the blastomeres have not the potentiality of producing a complete embryo. *Syn.*, mosaic type.

DETERMINATION. (*Exp.*) The mode of development in which an embryonic area will develop only in a particular way under any conditions in which development is possible.

DEUTOPLASM. Lifeless material in the egg cytoplasm used as food.

DIACOEL. The cavity of the diencephalon. *Syn.*, third ventricle.

DIESTRUM. The period intervening between estrus and the following proestrum in polyestrous mammals.

DIFFERENTIATION. The act of becoming different. The appearance of unlike parts and regions in the embryo.

DIGAMETY. The condition of having two different kinds of sperm (or eggs) according to the number or kind of sex chromosomes represented.

DIPLOID. The number of chromosomes characteristic of somatic cells. Two complete haploid sets.

DISCOBLASTULA. A disc-shaped blastula characteristic of telolecithal eggs, e.g., the hen's egg (Haeckel).

DIVERTICULUM. A blind outpouching from a tubular structure.

DOMINANCE. (*Gen.*) Mendel's principle that, when two allelic genes are present in the same fertilized egg, the effects of but one of them will be evident.

DOMINANT. (*Gen.*) A gene whose effects are apparent even in the presence of its allele.

DUCTUS ARTERIOSUS. A persisting portion of the sixth aortic arch serving as a connection between the pulmonary artery and the dorsal aorta, characteristic of the mammalian fetus.

DUCTUS VENOSUS. A vein running through the liver connecting the umbilical vein with the hepatic vein, characteristic of the mammalian fetus.

DYAD. A chromosome composed of two chromatids.

ECTODERM. The outermost germ layer. *Syn.*, epiblast.

ECTODERMALIZATION. (*Exp.*) A modification of normal development by which a greater proportion of the embryo gives rise to ectoderm at the expense of the other germ layers.

Egg envelope. Material enveloping the egg, but not part of the egg cell, e.g., vitelline membrane, albumen, etc.

Egg jelly. The egg envelope secreted by the wall of the oviduct around the amphibian egg.

Egg tooth. A horny structure developed on the beak of the chick before hatching.

Ejaculation. The emission of sperms from the body.

Embryo. Any stage in the development of the fertilized egg. Usually restricted to stages incapable of obtaining food from external sources. In human embryology restricted to the period between the second week and the second month.

Embryonic disc. The region of the mammalian embryo where the ectoderm and endoderm are in close contact, comparable to the area pellucida of the chick.

Embryonic knob. The inner cell mass of the mammalian blastocyst.

Embryonic shield. That region of the blastoderm which will give rise to the body of the embryo in fish.

Embryotroph. The material obtained from breaking down maternal tissue by the mammalian embryo prior to the establishment of the placental circulation.

Enamel organ. The ectodermal portion of the tooth primordium.

Endocardium. That part of the splanchnic mesoderm giving rise to the inner lining layer of the heart.

Endoderm. The innermost germ layer. *Syn.*, entoderm, hypoblast.

Endodermalization. (*Exp.*) A modification of normal development by which a greater proportion of the embryo gives rise to endoderm at the expense of the other germ layers.

Enterocoel. The mesodermal coelomic pouch characteristic of the amphioxus. *Syn.*, coelomic pouch, gut pouch.

Entypy. A type of gastrulation seen in rodents where the elongate embryonic knob is covered with endoderm which is, therefore, external to the ectoderm of the amnion.

Eparterial bronchus. An unpaired lung bud.

Epiboly. A mode of gastrulation characterized by the fact that the ectoderm grows out over the endoderm.

Epibranchial placode. A placode formed in the region external to the gills which contributes to the formation of the lateral line organs and certain cranial nerves. *Syn.*, suprabranchial placode.

Epicardium. That part of the splanchnic mesoderm forming the outer layer of the heart.

Epichordal brain. That portion of the brain lying dorsal to the notochord. *Syn.*, dentencephalon.

Epididymis. Part of the mesonephros persisting to carry sperms from the mammalian testis.

Epigenesis. The theory that development proceeds from the simple to the complex, opposed to the theory of preformation.

EPIMERE. That portion of the mesoderm lying adjacent to the notochord and from which the somites are formed. *Syn.*, axial mesoderm.

EPIMYOCARDIUM. The epicardium and the mesoderm which will form the muscle cells of the heart wall.

EPITHELIAL BODIES. Structures arising from the endoderm of the visceral pouches, e.g., thymus, parathyroids.

EPONYCHIUM. That part of the skin overlying the nails during fetal life.

EPOÖPHORON. A structure comparable to the epididymis characteristic of the female mammal.

EQUATION DIVISION. (*Cyt.*) A meiotic division in which the chromatids composing the daughter chromosomes are identical. Contrast reduction division.

EQUATORIAL PLATE. (*Cyt.*) The metaphase chromosomes as viewed at right angles to the axis of the spindle.

ESTRIN. A hormone formed in the ovarian follicles.

ESTROUS CYCLE. A periodic series of changes in the mammalian uterus culminating in its preparation for the implantation of the fertilized egg.

ESTRUS. The period in which the uterus is prepared for implantation.

EVOCATOR. (*Exp.*) An agent, not necessarily living, or part of the embryo, which calls forth a developmental reaction from a competent embryonic area.

EXOCOEL. A cavity produced by the separation of the somatic and splanchnic layers of mesoderm beyond the limits of the embryonic body. *Syn.*, extra-embryonic coelom.

EXOGASTRULA. (*Exp.*) A type of gastrula produced experimentally in which the mesendoderm is not enclosed by the ectoderm.

EXPLANTATION. (*Exp.*) The development of part of an embryo removed into a nutrient medium. *Syn.*, in vitro culture.

EXTRA-EMBRYONIC. Not a part of the embryonic body.

FERTILIZATION. The entrance of a sperm (or sperms) into an egg thereby inducing development.

FERTILIZATION CONE. A mass of cytoplasm extending from the surface of the egg and engulfing the sperm.

FERTILIZATION MEMBRANE. A membrane apparently lifted away from the surface of the egg when fertilization is complete. In some cases evidently the vitelline membrane.

FERTILIZIN. A substance secreted by the mature egg before fertilization (Lillie).

FETUS. A mammalian embryo which has attained the recognizable characters of the species.

FIELD. (*Exp.*) The complex of physicochemical agents determining the pattern of development in a given area of the embryo.

FIELD DISTRICT. (*Exp.*) The region in which a field normally exercises its activities.

FLEXURE. Bending, e.g., the cranial flexure, a characteristic bend of the brain over the tip of the notochord.

FOLLICLE. A mass of cells forming an envelope; e.g., the one enclosing the ovarian egg. The vesicular (Graafian) follicle is characteristic of the mammalian egg before ovulation.

FORAMEN OVALE. An oval opening in the bony labyrinth of the ear. *Syn.,* foramen vestibuli.

FORE-BRAIN. The more anterior of the three primary vesicles of the brain.

FORE-GUT. The more anterior portion of the digestive tube.

FOVEA. A small unpigmented spot on the surface of the frog's egg under which the nucleus is located prior to fertilization.

FREE-MARTIN. A sterile female developed along with a male twin with which it shares a common chorion, e.g., in cattle.

GAMETE. A mature germ cell, ovum, or sperm.

GAMETOGENESIS. The development of the germ cells.

GARTNER'S CANAL. Persistent remains of the mesonephric duct in female mammals.

GASTREA. A hypothetical extinct animal supposed to be the evolutionary stage comparable to the vertebrate gastrula (Haeckel).

GASTROCOEL. The cavity of the gastrula. *Syn.,* archenteron.

GASTRO-HEPATIC OMENTUM. Part of the ventral mesentery persisting as a connection between the stomach and liver.

GASTRULA. A stage in embryology in which the germ layers are separated from each other.

GASTRULATION. The process by which the gastrula is formed.

GENE. (*Gen.*) A minute body, located in the chromonema, whose presence, absence, or modification induced definite effects in development. "The unit of heredity."

GENETICS. The study of heredity.

GENIC BALANCE. (*Gen.*) The theory that the development of the individual, particularly with respect to the determination of sex, is due to the relative proportion of the kinds of genes represented as well as to the different kinds of genes.

GENITAL. Having to do with reproduction.

GENITAL RIDGE. An elevation along the mesial side of the mesonephros caused by the multiplication of the gonia. The primordium of the gonad.

GENITAL TUBERCLE. A ridge at the base of the phallus, the primordium of the labioscrotal swellings in mammals.

GENOTYPE. Individuals with similar gene complexes.

GERM. The beginning of a new individual. Often used for early stages in development, i.e., during cleavage.

GERM CELL. Egg or sperm or any cell ancestral to these.

GERM LAYER. One of the layers of cells separated during gastrulation or later.

GERM LINE. The genealogy of the germ cells during the development of an individual. *Syn.,* germ track, Keimbahn.

GERM PLASM. The germ cells in the body of an individual taken collectively.

GERM WALL. The advancing boundary of the blastoderm as it grows around the yolk.

GESTATION. The act of carrying the unborn young.

GILL PLATE. A thickening of the ectoderm in the embryo posterior to the sense plate in which the visceral grooves are formed.

GLAND FIELD. An area of the fore-gut floor which takes part in the formation of the tongue.

GOLGI BODY. (*Cyt.*) A body of a material in the cytoplasm demonstrable with silver nitrate or osmium tetroxide; often associated with others in a network. *Syn.*, dictyosome.

GONAD. Ovary or testis. *Syn.*, germ gland.

GONE. One of the four cells arising from the two meiotic division (Sharp, 1934).

GONIUM. A germ cell in the gonad prior to the meiotic divisions. Oögonium or spermatogonium.

GONOMERY. A phenomenon visible in the egg fertilized by sperm of a different species when the two sets of chromosomes remain distinct during cleavage divisions.

GRADIENT. (*Exp.*) A gradual variation in a given direction; e.g., axial gradient, i.e., variation along the egg axis from animal pole to vegetal pole.

GRAFT. (*Exp.*) A portion of one embryo transplanted to a different position in the same individual or in a different individual. *Syn.*, transplant.

GRAY CRESCENT. A crescentic area on the surface of the frog's egg appearing after fertilization. It is in this area that the dorsal lip of the blastopore is formed.

GYNANDROMORPH. An individual showing female characteristics in one part of the body and male characteristics in another.

GYNOGENESIS. (*Exp.*) The development of an egg which contains maternal chromosomes only, although development is initiated by the action of a sperm.

HAPLOID. The number of chromosomes characteristic of the gamete in any particular species. *Syn.*, monoploid.

HEAD FOLD. In the amniota, a fold which marks the elevation of the head above the blastoderm or embryonic disc.

HEAD FOLD OF THE AMNION. The fold of the amnion which envelops the head of the embryo.

HEMIPLACENTA. The chorion plus the yolk sac and/or the allantois which serves as an organ to supply nutrition to the uterine young of marsupials.

HEMOBLAST. The earliest stage in the development of a blood corpuscle.

HERMAPHRODITE. An individual possessing both ovary and testis.

HETEROPLASTIC. (*Exp.*) A graft or transplant made from the body of one individual to that of another belonging to the same species (Dürken, 1932). *Note:* Some authors use this term to mean transplantation to a host of a different species.

HETEROZYGOUS. (*Gen.*) Possessing unlike genes at the same locus of homologous chromosomes. *Syn.*, hybrid.

HIND-BRAIN. The more posterior of the three primary brain vesicles.

HIND-GUT. The more posterior region of the digestive tube.

HISTOGENESIS. The development of tissues.

HOLOBLASTIC. A type of cleavage in which the entire egg is divided.

HOMOLOGY. A type of resemblance between structures based on structural rather than functional identities. A very common error is to assume that homology is based solely on developmental identities.

HOMOPLASTIC. (*Exp.*) A graft or transplant made into the body of the same individual (Dürken, 1932). *Syn.*, autoplastic. *Note:* Some authors use the term when the graft is made to a different individual of the same species.

HOMOZYGOUS. (*Gen.*) Possessing identical genes at the same locus of homologous chromosomes.

HOMUNCULUS. An imaginary miniature human adult supposed to exist in the egg or sperm according to the theory of preformation.

HYALOPLASM. (*Cyt.*) The ground substance of cytoplasm.

HYPOCHORD. A temporary mesodermal rod lying under the notochord of the amphibian embryo. *Syn.*, subnotochordal rod.

HYPOMERE. That portion of the mesoderm farthest removed from the notochord and giving rise to the coelom. *Syn.*, lateral mesoderm.

HYPOPHYSIS. A solid or hollow structure arising from the stomodeum and attaching itself to the brain, where it gives rise to the anterior and intermediate parts of the pituitary gland. *Syn.*, Rathke's pouch.

IDIOSOME. (*Cyt.*) The clear (chromophobic) area associated with the Golgi bodies, usually surrounding the centrosomes. *Syn.*, idiozome.

IMPLANTATION. (1) The act of the mammalian embryo establishing itself in or on the surface of the uterine wall.

(2) (*Exp.*) The transplantation of a bit of tissue from one individual into a cavity in the body of another individual which serves as a nutrient chamber. *Syn.*, interplantation.

INCUBATION. The application of heat to the developing eggs, as in the brooding of the hen.

INDECIDUATE. A type of placentation in which there is no destruction of maternal tissue.

INDETERMINATE. Cleavage in which the early blastomeres have each the potentiality of producing a complete embryo if artificially separated. *Syn.*, regulation type.

INDUCTION. (*Exp. emb.*) An effect produced on one part of the developing embryo by another, as demonstrated by transplantation.

INFUNDIBULUM. That part of the floor of the diencephalon to which the hypophysis attaches itself. It gives rise to the nervous part of the pituitary gland.

INTERMEDIATE MESODERM. That part of the mesoderm from which the gonad and kidney arise. *Syn.*, mesomere.

INTERPHASE. The period in the life of the cell between mitotic divisions.

INTERRENAL. An endocrine gland arising from intermediate mesoderm. Becomes the cortex of the mammalian adrenal.

INTERSEGMENTAL. Passing between somites.

INTERSEX. (*Gen.*) An individual abnormal so far as its sexual characteristics are concerned.

INTERSTITIAL CELL. A cell found in the interstices between the seminiferous tubules of the testis. Supposed to have endocrine properties.

INTESTINAL LOOP. A loop of the intestine extending into the umbilical cord in mammals.

INTESTINAL PORTAL. The opening between the mid-gut and the fore-gut (anterior) or the mid-gut and the hind-gut (posterior).

INVAGINATION. The movement of one surface into the interior of a cavity, as in the gastrulation of the coeloblastula.

INVESTING BONES. Bones formed around and partially replacing others already in existence.

INVOLUTION. The movement of cells into the interior along a definite line as in the gastrulation of the frog's egg.

ISOLECITHAL. A type of egg characterized by an approximately equal distribution of the yolk. *Syn.*, homolecithal.

ISTHMUS. A connection, as in the yolk isthmus connecting the yolk in the center of the hen's egg to the nucleus of Pander.

KARYOKINESIS. The phenomena displayed by the nucleus during mitosis.

KARYOLYMPH. The ground substance of the nucleus. *Syn.*, nuclear sap.

KARYOPLASM. The substance of the nucleus. *Syn.*, nucleoplasm.

LABIO-SCROTAL SWELLINGS. The primordium of the labia majora (female) or part of the scrotum (male) in mammals.

LACUNA. A gap, e.g., that portion of the gastrocoel roof devoid of endoderm during the early period of gastrulation in amphioxus and the frog.

LAMINA TERMINALIS. A swelling on the floor of the embryonic brain marking the anterior end of the neural tube.

LANUGO. The fetal hair of mammals.

LARVA. A stage in development in which the individual obtains its food from external sources, has an appearance markedly different from that of the adult, but has not attained the power of reproduction.

LATEBRA. A central mass of white yolk in the yolk of the hen's egg.

LATERAL MESODERM. That part of the mesoderm which forms the lining of the coelom (and exocoel). *Syn.*, hypomere.

LIMITING SULCUS. A groove undercutting the body of the embryo from the remainder of the blastoderm in telolecithal eggs.

LINKAGE. (*Gen.*) The continued association of two or more hereditary characteristics due to the fact that the genes concerned are located in the same chromosome.

LIQUOR. A fluid, e.g., liquor folliculi — the fluid contents of the vesicular follicle of mammals.

MACROLECITHAL. A type of egg containing a large amount of yolk. This type of egg is always telolecithal. *Syn.*, megalecithal.

MACROMERE. A large blastomere, usually yolk-laden.

MARGIN OF OVERGROWTH. The rim of the germ wall.

MARGINAL BELT. A ring of blastomeres slightly above the equator of the amphibian blastula and intermediate in size between the micromeres and macromeres. Coincides with the area originally occupied by the gray crescent.

MATURATION. The act of becoming mature. Especially the period in which the meiotic divisions of the germ cells take place.

MEATUS VENOSUS. The channel formed by the confluence of the vitelline veins before entering the sinus venosus.

MEIOSIS. The process by which the number of chromosomes is reduced from diploid to haploid during maturation of the germ cells.

MELANIN. A black pigment formed in the cell.

MENSTRUATION. Hemorrhages characteristic of the primate estrous cycle.

MEROBLASTIC. A type of cleavage in which the egg is not completely divided.

MEROGONY. The development of an enucleate egg when fertilized by a sperm.

MESECTODERM. Term applied to the outer layer of a gastrula containing ectoderm, mesoderm, and notochord cells before these are separated from each other. *Syn.*, " primary ectoderm."

MESENCHYME. Loose aggregates of embryonic cells not organized in a layer, and densoid either from mesoderm, or, in some cases, the neural crest.

MESENDODERM. Term applied to the inner layer of a gastrula containing endoderm, notochord, and mesoderm cells before these are segregated from each other. *Syn.*, mesentoderm, " primary endoderm."

MESOCARDIUM. Part of the ventral mesentery persisting temporarily in the region of the heart.

MESOCOEL. Cavity of the mesencephalon. *Syn.*, iter, aqueduct.

MESODERM. The middle germ layer, exclusive of the notochord. *Syn.*, mesoblast.

MESOHEPAR. Part of the ventral mesentery persisting in the region of the liver, e.g., gastrohepatic omentum.

MESOMERE. (1) The intermediate region of the mesoderm. *Syn.*, intermediate mesoderm.

   (2) Sometimes used for blastomeres intermediate in size between macromeres and micromeres.

MESONEPHROS. Functional kidney of anamniota, an embryonic organ of amniota.

MESORCHIUM. A double fold of the peritoneum supporting the testis.

MESOVARIUM. A double fold of peritoneum supporting the ovary.

METABOLIC. Pertaining to metabolism, the chemical reactions taking place in protoplasm.

METABOLIC CELL. (*Cyt.*) A cell that is not dividing. *Syn.*, resting cell.

METAMORPHOSIS. A more or less sudden change in structure and form: (1) applied to the transformation of the larva into the adult; (2) applied to the transformation of the spermatid into the sperm, *syn.*, spermioteleosis.

METANEPHROS. The functional kidney of the amniota.

METAPHASE. (*Cyt.*) That phase of mitosis in which the attachment points of the chromosomes occupy positions in a plane at right angles to the long axis of the spindle.

METAPLASM. (*Cyt.*) The lifeless materials contained within the cytoplasm, e.g., yolk, pigment, etc.

METESTRUM. A period of the estrous cycle in which the destruction of tissue during the preceding period is repaired preparatory to the anestrum (Marshall).

MICROLECITHAL. A type of egg containing a small amount of yolk. *Syn.*, oligolecithal, meiolecithal.

MICROMERE. A small blastomere, usually near the animal pole.

MICROPYLE. An opening in the chorion (egg envelope) permitting the entrance of sperms.

MID-BRAIN. The middle vesicle of the three primary vesicles of the brain.

MID-GUT. Middle region of digestive tube.

MILK RIDGE. An elevation on the ventral surface of the mammalian embryo foreshadowing the mammary glands.

MITOCHONDRIA. (*Cyt.*) Small bodies in the cytoplasm, demonstrable with such vital dyes as Janus Green B and Janus Red, and apparently having the power of independent growth and division. *Syn.*, chondriosomes.

MITOSIS. That mode of cell division in which chromosomes appear and are divided longitudinally. *Syn.*, indirect division.

MORULA. A form of blastula in which no cavity exists.

MOSAIC. (*Exp.*) A term applied to an egg or embryo in which the prospective fate of the different regions is determined.

MÜLLERIAN DUCT. Oviduct.

MUTATION. (*Gen.*) A change in the composition or structure of a gene whereby it induces new characteristics in development. *Syn.*, point variation. *See* aberration.

MYELOCOEL. The cavity of the myelencephalon. *Syn.*, fourth ventricle.

MYOCARDIUM. The muscular layer of the heart.

MYOCOEL. A temporary cavity in a somite.

MYOTOME. That part of a somite which contributes to the development of muscles.

NEONYCHIUM. A horny pad filling the concavity of the claw in birds before hatching.

NEOTENY. The assumption of sexual maturity in a larval stage, e.g., the axolotl. *Syn.,* paedogenesis.

NEPHRIC. Having to do with the kidney.

NEPHROCOEL. A cavity of the nephrotome.

NEPHROGENOUS. Giving rise to kidney tissue.

NEPHRON. The functional unit of a kidney, consisting of a nephric tubule and its glomerulus.

NEPHROSTOME. An opening from the coelom into the nephric tubule.

NEPHROTOME. A metameric portion of the intermediate mesoderm corresponding to a somite of the axial mesoderm.

NEURAL. Having to do with the nervous system.

NEURAL CREST. A ridge of cells at the line of fusion of the neural folds forming a temporary connection between the neural tube and epidermis of the skin. Gives rise to the ganglia.

NEURENTERIC CANAL. A connection between the neural tube and digestive tube formed by the closure of the blastopore.

NEUROBLAST. Early embryonic cells of the nervous system.

NEUROCOEL. Cavity of the neural tube.

NEUROCRANIUM. That part of the cartilaginous cranium enclosing the brain and sense organs.

NEUROMERE. A pseudometameric division of the neural tube.

NEUROPORE. A terminal opening of the neural tube in early development.

NEURULA. An embryo at the time the neural plate is visible.

NEURULATION. A term applied to the period during which the neural tube is being formed.

NON-DISJUNCTION. (*Gen., Cyt.*) A variety of chromosomal aberration. The failure of chromatids derived from the dissimilar members of a synaptic pair to separate during the reduction (disjunction) division.

NOTOCHORD. An axial rod derived from the middle germ layer, characteristic of all chordates in some stage of development. *Syn.,* chorda dorsalis.

NUCLEI PULPOSI. The intervertebral discs which represent the remains of the notochord in higher vertebrates.

NUCLEOLUS. (*Cyt.*) A body in the nucleus. *Syn.,* plasmasome.

NUCLEUS. That part of the cell containing the chromatin.

OCCLUDE. To close, or fill, a cavity.

OLFACTORY. Pertaining to the nose or sense of smell. *Syn.,* nasal.

ONTOGENY. The life history of an individual organism.

OÖCYTE. A female germ cell during the period of maturation.

OÖGENESIS. The development of the germ cells of the female.

OÖGONIUM. The female germ cell after the development of the ovary and prior to maturation.

OÖTID. A generic term for the ovum and its polocytes. The cells produced by the meiotic divisions of the oöcyte.

OPERCULAR APERTURE. Opening of the opercular (peribranchial) cavity on the left side of a tadpole. *Syn.*, " spiracle."

OPERCULUM. A cover. Especially with reference to the covering of the internal gills.

OPTIC. Having to do with the eye or sense of sight. *Syn.*, ophthalmic.

ORAL. Having to do with the mouth.

ORGAN FIELD. (*Exp. emb.*) The region in which a specific part of the embryo will be formed.

ORGAN-FORMING AREAS. Regions of the embryo which in the course of normal development will give rise to the primordia of particular structures.

ORGAN-FORMING SUBSTANCES. (*Exp.*) Substances formed in the egg and segregated into different blastomeres, resulting in a mosaic stage of development.

ORGANIZER. (*Exp.*) A region characterized by self-differentiation and capable of inducing organization in neighboring regions, e.g., the dorsal lip of the blastopore in amphibia. *Syn.*, organizator.

ORGANOGENY. The development of the organs from their primordia.

ORONASAL GROOVE. A groove connecting the mouth with the nasal pits.

OSSIFICATION. The process of bone formation.

OSTEOBLAST. A cell concerned in bone formation.

OSTIUM TUBAE. The opening of the oviduct.

OTIC. Pertaining to the ear or sense of hearing. *Syn.*, auditory, acoustic.

OTOCYST. The cavity of the inner ear. *Syn.*, otic (auditory) vesicle.

OVIPAROUS. A term applied to those animals in which the new individual leaves the body of the mother as an egg, i.e., enclosed in egg envelopes.

OVIPOSITION. The act of discharging the eggs from the body. *See* spawning, laying, etc.

OVULATION. The discharge of the eggs from the ovary.

OVUM. The mature egg. In a strict sense the female germ cell after the meiotic divisions and before fertilization. This stage does not exist in vertebrates as such because the sperm enters the egg before the completion of the second meiotic division.

PARABIONTS. (*Exp.*) Embryos experimentally united side by side.

PARADIDYMIS. A group of mesonephric tubules forming a small body near the testis of the adult male mammal.

PARANUCLEUS. (*Cyt.*) A body found near the nucleus and composed of mitochondrial material. *Syn.*, nebenkern.

PARAPHYSIS. A dorsal evagination from the roof of the diencephalon anterior to the epiphysis. Primordium of the pineal eye of reptiles.

PARIETAL RECESS. A passage connecting the pericardial cavity with the abdominal cavity in the mammalian embryo.

PAROÖPHORON. A mass of tissue derived from a group of mesonephric tubules lying near the ovary and corresponding to the paradidymis of the male.

PARTHENOGENESIS. A method of sexual reproduction in which the egg develops without fertilization by a sperm.

PARTURITION. The act of giving birth.

PENETRATION PATH. The path followed by the sperm immediately following its entrance into the egg.

PERIBLAST. That part of the blastoderm in which the cells are not completely separated by a plasma membrane. In early cleavage there is both a marginal ring and a lower layer of periblast, the latter of which soon disappears.

PHALLUS. An elevation on the posterior ventral surface of the mammalian embryo which is the primordium of the penis (male) or labia minora (female).

PHENOTYPE. A group of individuals possessing similar hereditary characteristics. *Cf.* genotype.

PLACENTA. An extra-embryonic structure of mammals serving as an organ of interchange between fetus and mother.

PLACODE. An ectodermal plate-like thickening.

PLASMA MEMBRANE. (*Cyt.*) The outer membrane of the cytosome.

PLASMATROPHODERM. Outer syncytial layer of the trophoderm after implantation. *Syn.*, syncytiotrophoderm.

PLASTICITY. (*Exp.*) The ability to develop into parts of the body other than those formed in normal development.

PLASTID. (*Cyt.*) A body in the cytoplasm of plant cells having the power of independent growth and division.

POLAR. Pertaining to the animal pole of the egg.

POLAR FURROW. A groove at the animal pole of the egg resulting from the rounding up of the blastomeres at the four-cell stage.

POLARITY. The possession of unlike poles.

POLE. One extreme of an axial gradient in the egg. Especially the animal pole.

POLOCYTE. One of the small cells formed during the maturation of the egg, usually at the animal pole. *Syn.*, polar body.

POLYESTROUS. Mammals with several estrous cycles in one year.

POLYINVAGINATION. Method of segregating endoderm in the hen's egg according to Pasteels. Individual endoderm cells migrate beneath the surface of the blastodisc and spread out to form lower layer.

POLYSPERMY. The entrance of several sperms into the egg, as in the hen's egg.

POST-ANAL GUT. The digestive tube posterior to the point where the proctodeum joins the gut. *Syn.*, post-cloacal gut.

POSTERIOR TUBERCLE. A swelling on the ventral surface of the brain floor, located at the anterior end of the notochord and marking the line of separation between the prosencephalon and mesencephalon. *Syn.*, tuberculum posterius.

POSTNUCLEAR CUP. A cup-shaped structure covering the posterior surface of the nucleus in the head of the mammalian sperm.

PRECHORDAL BRAIN. That part of the brain anterior to the anterior end of the notochord. *Syn.*, archencephalon.

PRECHORDAL PLATE. A small area of endoderm invaginated before the notochord and hence lying in front of it after gastrulation.

PREFORMATION. The theory that the several parts of the adult are performed in the egg (or sperm). *Cf.* epigenesis.

PRE-ORAL GUT. The digestive tube anterior to the point where the stomodeum joins the gut. *Syn.*, Seessel's pouch.

PRIMITIVE STREAK. An axial area of the blastoderm or embryonic disc where ectoderm and endoderm are in close contact and from which the notochord and mesoderm originate. Homologous with the blastopore of anamniota.

PRIMORDIAL GERM CELLS. The first stage at which the germ cells are completely set apart from the soma cells. The stage in which the germ cells are first recognizable in vertebrate embryology.

PRIMORDIUM. The first distinguishable stage in the development of a new structure. *Syn.*, anlage.

PROAMNION. The region just anterior to the head fold of the chick embryo, containing no mesoderm. The head fold of the amnion develops in this region.

PROCTODEUM. An invagination on the ventral surface of the embryo just anterior to the tail which will unite with the hind-gut to form the cloaca.

PROESTRUM. The stage in the estrous cycle just prior to estrus.

PROGESTIN. A hormone formed by the corpus luteum in all vertebrates with a placenta.

PRONEPHROS. The first kidney formed by the embryo. Functional only in the larvae of anamniota.

PRONUCLEUS. The haploid nucleus of the egg or sperm as found in the fertilized egg prior to the first cleavage division.

PROPHASE. (*Cyt.*) The phase of mitosis in which the chromosomes become apparent.

PROSOCOEL. The cavities of the prosencephalon. *Syn.*, lateral ventricle.

PROTOPLASM. The material of which living things are formed. Sometimes contrasted with metaplasm.

RAMUS. A branch, e.g., of a spinal nerve.

RAUBER'S CELLS. The remains of the trophoblast at the point where it joins the embryonic knob.

RECAPITULATION. The theory that the stages of embryology recapitulate stages in the evolution of the systematic group to which the individual belongs.

RECESSIVE. (*Gen.*) A gene whose effects are not apparent in the presence of its allelomorph.

REDUCTION DIVISION. (*Cyt.*) The meiotic division in which the unlike chromatids of the tetrad are separated from each other. *Syn.*, disjunction division.

REGULATION EGG. (*Exp.*) A type of egg with cleavage in which each of the early blastomeres has the capacity of developing a complete embryo when separated.

RESORB. To re-absorb, or remove by phagocytosis.

RETICULUM. A network. (*Cyt.*) The chromatin network of the nucleus.

RHOMBOIDAL SINUS. The region contained within the widely open neural folds in the posterior region of the early chick embryo. *Syn.*, sinus rhomboidialis.

SACCULE. That portion of the inner ear which gives rise to the cochlea. *Syn.*, sacculus.

SCLEROTOME. That part of a mesodermal somite which contributes to the formation of the skeleton.

SECRETORY TUBULE. The part of the nephric tubule actually concerned in removing wastes from the blood.

SENSE PLATE. A thickening of the ectoderm from which the primordia of the nose, lens, and inner ear originate.

SEPTUM. A partition wall, e.g., septum transversum, a wall of mesoderm separating parts of the coelom.

SINUS TERMINALIS. The circular blood vessels marking the limit of the area vasculosa of the yolk sac.

SITUS INVERSUS. A reversal of left-right symmetry.

SOLE PLATE. A mass of the stratum corneum lying beneath the nail.

SOMATIC. (1) Pertaining to the body; contrast germinal.
   (2) Pertaining to the body wall; contrast splanchnic.

SOMATIC MESODERM. The outer layer of lateral mesoderm.

SOMATOPLEURE. The somatic mesoderm plus the ectoderm immediately adjacent to it.

SOMITE. A metameric division of the axial mesoderm.

SPAWNING. The act of discharging the eggs of anamniota.

SPERM. The mature male germ cell. *Syn.*, spermatozoön.

SPERMATID. The male germ cell after the completion of the meiotic divisions but before metamorphosis.

SPERMATOCYTE. The male germ cell during the meiotic divisions.

SPERMATOGENESIS. The development of the male germ cells.

SPERMATOGONIUM. The male germ cell in the testis before the meiotic divisions.

SPINA BIFIDA. An abnormality in development in which the vertebral column is cleft at its posterior end.

SPINDLE. A mass of material in the form of a double cone lying between the centrosomes during mitosis, and involved in the mechanism of separating the chromatids.

SPLANCHNIC. Pertaining to the viscera. Contrast somatic (2).

SPLANCHNIC MESODERM. The inner layer of lateral mesoderm.

SPLANCHNOCRANIUM. That part of the cartilaginous skull derived from the visceral arches.

SPLANCHNOPLEURE. The splanchnic mesoderm plus the endoderm immediately adjacent to it.

SPONGIOBLAST. An epithelial cell of the neural tube which will give rise to supporting elements of the nervous system.

STEM CELL. A blastomere which divides into a soma cell and another stem cell. Eventually one of the stem cells divides to form two primordial germ cells.

STOMODEUM. An ectodermal invagination on the ventral surface of the head which unites with the fore-gut to form the mouth.

STROMA. Connective tissue or supporting framework of an organ.

SUBSTITUTION BONES. Derm bones which replace cartilage bones.

SUCKER. Adhesive gland characteristic of anuran larvae when first hatched. *Syn.*, cement organ, oral gland.

SUPRARENAL. A gland formed from ganglion cells which becomes the medulla of the mammalian adrenal.

SUSTENTACULAR CELL. A nourishing cell, e.g., follicle cell of ovary or Sertoli cell of testis.

SYNAPSIS. (*Cyt.*) The union of the paternal and maternal homologous chromosomes in the prophase of the first meiotic division. *Syn.*, " pseudo-reduction."

SYNCYTIUM. A multinucleate mass of protoplasm (Haeckel).

SYNGAMY. The union of two gametes. *Syn.*, fertilization, zygotogenesis.

TELOBIONTS. (*Exp.*) Amphibian embryos experimentally fused head to tail.

TELOLECITHAL. Type of egg in which the yolk is accumulated in the vegetal hemisphere.

TELOPHASE. (*Cyt.*) The concluding phase of mitosis, in which the daughter chromosomes return to the reticular condition and the cytosome is divided.

TERATOLOGY. The study of abnormalities in development.

TETRAD. (*Cyt.*) A compound chromosome composed of four chromatids arising by the splitting of the two synaptic mates in the prophase of the first meiotic division.

THIGMOTAXIS. Movement in response to a tactile stimulus.

THYROGLOSSAL DUCT. A temporary connection between the thyroid gland and the pharynx near the base of the tongue.

TORSION. The twisting of the chick embryo so that it lies on its left side.

TRACHEAL GROOVE. A depression on the floor of the pharynx which is the primordium of the trachea and lungs.

TRANSPLANTATION. (*Exp.*) The grafting of part of an embryo into the body of another.

TROPHOBLAST. The outer layer of the mammalian blastocyst. It gives rise to the chorion.

TUBERCULUM POSTERIUS. A projection on the floor of the brain marking the posterior boundary of the diencephalon.

UMBILICAL. Having to do with the navel. Hence used in reference to the cord connecting the fetus with the placenta and any structures contained in the cord.

UNGUIS. A claw.

URACHUS. The canal connecting the allantois and urinary bladder in mammalian embryos.

UROGENITAL. Pertaining to both excretory and reproductive functions. *Syn.,* urino-genital.

UTRICLE. A bladder-like structure, e.g., utricle of the ear; prostatic utricle. *Syn.,* utriculus.

VEGETAL (POLE OR HEMISPHERE). At the extremity of the polar axis opposite the animal pole. *Syn.,* vegetative, abapical, antipolar.

VELAR PLATE. An extension of the pharyngeal floor extending over the visceral clefts and aiding in retaining solid particles while permitting the free passage of water.

VILLUS. A projection; e.g., chorionic villi.

VISCERAL. Pertaining to the viscera.

VISCERAL CLEFTS. Openings connecting the pharynx with the exterior. *Syn.,* pharyngeal, branchial (in part), gill clefts.

VISCERAL GROOVES. Ectodermal furrows which contribute to the formation of the visceral clefts if completed.

VISCERAL POUCHES. Endodermal pockets which contribute to the formation of the visceral clefts if completed.

VITELLINE. Pertaining to the yolk; e.g., vitelline vein carrying blood from the area vasculosa of the yolk sac.

VIVIPAROUS. A term applied to those animals which bring forth the young in an advanced stage of development.

WOLFFIAN BODY. Term applied to mesonephros.

WOLFFIAN DUCT. Term applied to mesonephric duct.

X-CHROMOSOME. (*Cyt.*) One of the paired sex chromosomes in most vertebrates.

XENOPLASTIC. (*Exp.*) A form of transplantation in which the host belongs to a different species (Dürken, 1932).

Y-CHROMOSOME. (*Cyt.*) A chromosome pairing with the X-chromosome in the male of most vertebrates.

YOLK. A form of metaplasm found in the egg and used for food by the early embryo. *Syn.,* deutoplasm.

YOLK NUCLEUS COMPLEX. (*Cyt.*) The idiosome and associated mitochondria in the oöcyte.

YOLK PLUG. A mass of large yolk-laden cells protruding through the blastopore of the amphibian egg.

YOLK SAC. An extra-embryonic sac of splanchnopleure surrounding the yolk.

YOLK SAC PLACENTA. A form of hemiplacenta in which the blood vessels are derived from the area vasculosa of the yolk sac.

YOLK SAC UMBILICUS. The region where the yolk which is not surrounded by the yolk sac until the development of the albumen sac.

ZONA PELLUCIDA. A thick capsule with radial striations enclosing the human ovum. There is some uncertainty as to whether it is formed by the egg or by follicle cells.

ZONE OF JUNCTION. The region of the germ wall of the chick blastoderm immediately internal to the margin of overgrowth. Here the cells are not sharply separated from the underlying yolk.

ZYGOTE. The cell formed by the union of two gametes. *Syn.*, fertilized egg.

INDEX

References to figures have an asterisk (*) prefixed to the page number. Compound terms are indexed under the first word, e.g., Dorsal aorta *not* Aorta, dorsal. Synonyms are distinguished by being set in italics and referred to the terms employed by the author. *See also* the Glossary.

A

Abapical, see Vegetal
Abbé, 321
Abdominal cavity, *158
Abducens nerve, *226, 227
Aberration, see Chromosomal aberration
Accessory nerve, see Spinal accessory
Acoustic, *see also* Auditory, Otic
  ganglion, 240, *300
  nerve, *226, 228, 241, *282
Acousticofacial ganglion, 228, 232, 234
Acrosome, 26, *27, 47
  bead, *41
Adamstone, 28, 269
Adnexa, see Extra-embryonic structures
Adrenal gland, *168, 171, *172, *174, 177, 179, 267
Adrenalin, see Epinephrin
Afferent branchial artery, *151, *192, *277
  neuron, *218
Affixing sections, 316
After-birth, 134
Agglutination, 46
Air chamber, *123
  sac, 154
Alar plate, 219, *220
Albumen, *32, *33, *123
  sac, *123, 126
Alimentary canal, see Digestive tube
Allantoic artery, *186, 187
  blood vessels, 125
  placenta, 129
  stalk, *120, *140, *148
  vein, *188, *297
Allantois, *122, 125, 129, 142, 165, *166

in chick, 18, *123, *126, *145, 147, *295, *297
in man, 20, *100, *120, 127, *133, *134, *135, *166, *179
in pig, *130, *305
Allele, 65, 68
Ambystoma, 225
Amitosis, 53
Amniocardiac vesicle, 122, 159, *285, *287
Amnion, *98, *120, *122, *123
in chick, 17, 122, *123, *126, 146, *291 *ff*
in man, 20, *98, *100, 124, *133, *135
in marsupials, 129
in rat, *121
Amniotic cavity, *98, 99
  fluid, 121
  folds, 101, *102, 124, *125
  raphe, 121, 122, 124, *294, *297
Amphioxus, life history, 8, *10
Amplexus, 50
Ampulla, 241
Anaphase, *54, *58, *59
Androgenesis, 248
Anestrum, 128
Animal pole, 30
Anomaly, 265
Anterior cardinal vein, 184, *189, *278
  in chick, *194, *293, *296
  in pig, *301, *302, *307
caval vein, see Precaval vein
  chamber (of eye), *239, *240
  intestinal portal, 109, 110, *285, *288
  limb bud, *294, *298, *302, *303
  mesenteric artery, *299
  neuropore, *285, *288
vena cava, see Precaval vein

353